My so
Chrismas '202..
love
Janet
x

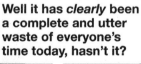

TOMMY 'BANANA' JOHNSON - HE'S GOT A BIG BANANA! Dr Seuss edition

Young Tommy Johnson was an ordinary sort
Who had never excelled in education or sport
But he had a thing which made every day fun
A banana so large it could blot out the sun

He set off for the park where the folk rubbed their eyes
When they saw his banana of considerable size
And met there a man who looked up to the sky
"Why, it's raining," he cried, *"and my paint isn't dry!"*

Tommy knew then that today was the day
He could show the whole world that his fruit was the way
"Fret not," assured Tommy, *"for things aren't so dire
We can use my banana as a giant hair dryer!"*

The man took one glance at Tommy's big herb
And uttered some words which were sure to disturb
Young Tommy skulked off, his banana in tow
Feeling sure that that his fruit could yet ease the world's woe

He took his banana then down to the heath
Where he there met a man in an advanced state of grief
For he'd lost his poor dog, a pet faithful and true
And Tommy knew then just what he had to do

"Don't worry," said Tommy, *"your dog shall be found
A telescope banana will locate the hound!"*
But the words the man said cannot here be repeated
And Tommy once more took his banana, defeated

He wandered the precincts, feeling quite raw
But it seemed that his antics had attracted the law
For along came a constable, tall and astute
Who knew just what to do with the troublesome fruit

Up into Tommy the giant herb went
'Til his ends were quite straight but his middle was bent
And the folk gathered round at the sight and gave thanks
That no more would be heard of his banana-based pranks

TOOT! TOOT! All Aboard! It's

Viz

THE GUARD'S PARCEL

A Flyblown Bundle of Foulage from Issues 312~321

First Class Tickets
Graham Dury, Simon Thorp, Alex Morris

Off-Peak Day Rovers

Adrian Bamforth, Mark Bates, Christian Boston, Peter Brooker, Kevin Caswell-Jones, Simon Ecob, Tom Ellen, Barney Farmer, Lee Healey, Davey Jones, Marc Jones, Christian Marshall, Luke McGarry, Richard Milne, Paul Palmer, Tom Paterson, Paul Rainey, Tom Richmond, Paul Roberts, Joe Shooman, Paul Solomons, Kirsty Stebbings, Cat Sullivan, Neil Tollfree, Nick Tolson, Joe Wade, Stevie White and Emma M Wilson.

**Hiding in the bogs while
the Inspector comes round**

David Saunders and Lee Boyman

Published by Diamond Publishing Ltd,
Part of the Metropolis Group,
4th Floor, Harmsworth House,
13 – 15 Bouverie Street,
London, EC4Y 8DP

ISBN 978-1-9164219-5-0
First Printing Summer 2024

Subscribe online at www.viz.co.uk
Find us at facebook.com/vizcomic and twitter.com/vizcomic

the REAL ALE TWATS

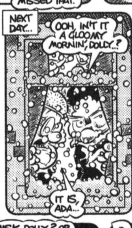

5

BIGSBY
THE BIGGEST DOG IN THE WORLD

After eating an experimental growth powder invented by his uncle Jack, Billy Bobcut's dog Bigsby grew to gigantic proportions… but he was the same gentle, loveable dog that he ever was…

Come on, Bigsby… let's go for a walk in the woods.

WOOF!

Hello, Billy… hello, Bigsby…

Hello, Postie.

WOOF!

Yes, Bigsby, don't worry… I've got you a dog biscuit as usual…

Ha! He really looks forward to that, don't you, boy?

WOOF!

CRUNCH!

There you go…

Anyway… I'd best be off. Have fun.

Bye, Postie… …come on, Bigsby…

YANK!

Woah!

Aw, no… he's doing a poo…

Bigsby! You could have waited until we got to the woods to do that…

Crumbs!…

I don't think anyone saw us…

…nobody will know it was you…Come on, boy, let's go. Quick!

Hey! Billy!…

PC Todd!… What!?!… I… er…

I hope you're not going to leave that outsized chod there.

It's an offence not to clean up after your dog.

Yes, I know… but…

You can't go leaving foulage all round the village…

…What if somebody were to step in it?… some little kiddie…

Yes… …get any of it in their eyes and they'd go blind.

I know, but… I…

Get it cleaned up, Billy… I'll slap a £200 fine on you if it's still there when I get back.

Yes, PC Todd.

Excuse me… you haven't got a doggy poop bag I could have, have you?

Of course, Billy…

…mind, I don't think you'll get it in one of these… it's a big old barker's egg, that…

…and even if you had a poop bag big enough, it'd take twenty people to lift it…

…there must be the best part of a ton of hound rope there.

You're right. I'd better call my Uncle Jack.

6

Billy's Uncle Jack was a brilliant inventor who, as luck would have it, was working on a machine to solve the very problem that Jack faced…

DRING! DRING! DRING! DRING!

Hello?… Yes, Billy… yes…

…Yes… I foresaw something like this happening… I'll be there in 5 minutes.

5 mins later…

Do hurry up, Uncle Jack… PC Todd will be coming back any minute…

CHUGGA! CHUGGA! CHUGGA!

Hello, Billy

MegaPoopScoop 3000

Uncle Jack!

Gosh! What a fantastic machine!

How does it work?

Yes, Billy… And it'll soon have Bigsby's copper bolt bagged up and safe in no time…

Well… I've taped several large bin bags together to make the poop bag, which fits onto these mechanical arms…

Gosh!

CHUGGA! CHUGGA!

…The arms lift and then drop, covering the enormous chod…

CHUGGA!, CHUGGA!

…then, when covered, the arms roll the log over to make sure it is completely enveloped in the bag…

…after which they tie a knot in the top… and it's job done, Billy.

Yes, but… we can't just leave it here,… I'll get a £200 fine.

Don't worry…

…we'll do what everyone does.

SPRANG!

FLING!

WOW! That's fantastic! Thanks, Uncle Jack…

…and I think you need to say thank you, too, Bigsby…

Bigsby!?!… Bigsby! Where are you, boy…?

Look!

Bigsby!… **NO!**

FSQUISHHHHHH!

AAARRRGH! He's got the squits!

Next issue: Uncle Jack invents the *DiarrhoeaGone 3000*, a machine capable of mopping up 200 gallons of bright orange fizzy dog-gravy, putting it into a bag and pushing it into somebody's hedge.

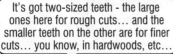

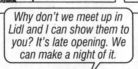

RAFFLES the GENTLEMAN THUG

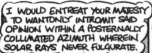

LETTERBOCKS

letters@viz.co.uk

IN the 70s in Nottingham, my older brother played in a kids' football team run by my dad, and one of the defenders was a young Viv Anderson. I was too young to sign on for the team, but I used to train with them every Wednesday at Clifton Playing Fields. One week as we played, I found myself with the ball on goal with only Anderson to beat. I don't know how I did it to this day, but I did a little double-flick with the ball, before tapping it through the future England international's legs, and rounding him, leaving him rooted to the spot. It was poetry in motion. There isn't any kind of punchline to this story, I just want as many people as possible to know about it. My only regret is not writing in to you years ago when your circulation was much higher.

Graham Drurige, Clifton

HOW come a butterfly can find another little butterfly to mate with in in a two-acre field of wild flowers, but it can't see me bearing down on it with a lawnmower? Selective vision if you ask me.

D Williams, Donegal

GIVEN that 99.9% of us are incapable of making a record of any description, I think it is grossly unfair that artistes who have achieved a solitary success on the hit parade are insultingly referred to as 'One-Hit Wonders'. Let me assure your reade rs that, had I written *Kung Fu Fighting*, I would spend every waking hour waving my cock around and referring to everyone I met as 'no-hit cunts'.

Kevin Caswell-Jones, Gresford

HAVING seen so many magnificent, fine and delicate sculptures created throughout the ages, I can only presume that carving in marble is a piece of piss. I might give it a go sometime.

Belle End, Launceston

IT wasn't until I dislocated my ring finger at work that I discovered how integral it is in wiping my arse. Two fingers just don't cut it.

Keith Jenkins, Kings Langley

THE bible refers to The Land Of Milk and Honey like it is paradise. But I can't think of one decent meal you could knock up with just those two ingredients, and I'm pretty sure anyone would quickly get fed-up of drinking hot milk and honey. Besides, I'm lactose intolerant so it would be more The Land Of Screaming Shits and Honey for me.

K, Oboe, Bury St. Edmunds

IF planes used the existing network of bus routes and bus stops, we would have a much faster public transport system. I for one look forward to hopping onto the number 10 Easyjet to Fawdon, cutting the current half-hour journey to about 25 seconds.

Col P Fawcett, Durham

THE very notion of electric cars, bikes and buses is not only ridiculous but potentially lethal if the vehicles are operated in wet weather or drive through a large puddle. You might as well drop a toaster into your bath as risk your life in one of these deathtraps.

T.O'Neill, Glasgow

ABBA'S hit song *Waterloo* begins with the lyric "My! My! At Waterloo, Napoleon did surrender." But any student of European history could tell you that Napoleon didn't surrender until some 5 weeks later, in Rochefort, about 400 miles away on the west coast of France. So come on, ABBA. How about handing back that Eurovision trophy from 1974?

Steve Kimberley, Bideford

I THINK that a box of Weetabix should feature a picture of a bowl of the breakfast cereal next to a slumped, knocked-over bag of granulated sugar containing a claggy spoon used moments before for stirring coffee. There may be people who cover their Weetabixes in strawberries, grapes and locally-sourced honey, but I've never met them.

Rob Young, Chingford

I HATE the Zoom meeting-induced phrase 'comfort break'. Let me tell you, there is absolutely nothing 'comfortable' about being given 5 minutes to spray the bog pan with diarrhoea *and* make a cup of tea.

Ben M, Rochester

I WONDER if COP26 have considered that if we all just stayed indoors for 2 hours every day and wanked instead of commuting, our carbon output would dramatically reduce.

Branwell Govier, Cambs

THE uvula and the vulva are poles apart in both location and function, so why are they named so similarly? If my wife is ever admitted to hospital with some throat condition, I don't want some junior doctor with bad hearing or a poor grasp of Latin fiddling about with her nether regions. Not with her loose morals anyway.

D Williams, Donegal

THEY say spirits and poltergeists haunt places where they were deeply unhappy. If this is the case. After working for years in a shitty hotel as a lift operator, I'm going to come back and fart my head off.

Les Lloyd, email

HOW do I go about getting a major international airport named after me in the next twelve months? It's for a bet.

Dominic Twose, L'ton Spa

* That's a tricky one, Mr Twose, but let's see if we can help. Are there any Viz-reading governments who are in the process of building a major interantional airport somewhere and haven't got a name for it yet? If so, perhaps you would consider calling it Twose International Airport, after the above-named Viz reader? But it has to be in the next twelve months. If it's any longer than that, it's no good to us and you can fuck off.

TRAFFIC lights are a load of bollocks. If you have the common sense to pass your driving test, then you have the common sense to know when to stop and when to go. It's just another example of how our lives are being controlled by ruthless machines. It's like *The Terminator* all over again.

Terry Farricker, Blackpool

IF airlines were serious about reducing their carbon footprint, they wouldn't waste fuel flying all the way up to 36,000ft, only to come down to ground level again later. Why don't they pick a height that requires less fuel to get to, like 100ft, and fly everywhere like that?

Joe Dzwonczyk, Avoch

The *Fantastic* Mr. Laurence Fox

LOOK AT THAT SHEEP, DOING WHAT IT'S TOLD BY SOME SHILL OF A SHEPHERD. PROBABLY BEEN IN THE SHEEP DIP LIKE ALL THE OTHERS. "FOR ITS OWN GOOD AND THAT OF THE FLOCK". FLOCK IMMUNITY... NOT EVEN WORTH EATING.

...OF COURSE I'D BE CANCELLED IF I TRIED TO EAT IT. THE WOKE BRIGADE ARE COMING FOR US CARNIVORES NEXT, MARK MY WORDS. WE'LL ALL BE LINED UP AND FORCED TO EAT TOFU AND CHANGE OUR PRONOUNS AT GUNPOINT. ANYONE WHO FAILS TO COME OUT AS NON-BINARY HAS TO LEARN THE KORAN IN ITS ENTIRETY ...OR SOMETHING.

NOT *YOU* GUYS, YOU STAND WITH *ME!* YOU'RE AS MUCH A PART OF THE COUNTRYSIDE AS THE MIGHTY ENGLISH OAK! NOT LIKE THE *SOCIAL JUSTICE WARRIORS*, TRYING TO LOCK US DOWN IN OUR BURROWS CONSTANTLY, WELL OVER MY DEAD BODY...

ANYWAY, YOU CAN'T EVEN RIP ME TO SHREDS ANY MORE, NO... THE WOKERATI OUTLAWED THAT YEARS AGO...

...BUT YOU GO FOR IT... DON'T LET THE *BLEEDING HEART METROPOLITAN ELITE* TELL YOU WHAT TO DO.

OKAY EVERYBODY... TALLY HO!

...JUST LET ME TWEET THAT.

I STAYED up late last month to see that International Space Station fly over our house. Quite apart from the disappointment of just seeing a white dot cross the sky, I was very concerned at the speed they appeared to be doing. I don't care how much NASA has spent at Halfords on spoilers and go-faster stripes, we've got speed humps and a 20mph limit on our estate, and I reckon they must have been doing at least 17000mph. I'll be watching for them again next month and hope to see the police in pursuit.

Col P Fawcett, Durham

I HAVE recently purchased two cat litter trays for my girlfriend's cat, and they closely resemble the two telepods used by Jeff Goldblum in *The Fly*. Sadly, neither the cat nor her plentiful shits have so far managed to complete the teleportation process, thus proving that the laws of physics, for now, remain firmly intact.

P Brooker, Chiswick

I FOLLOWED the instructions on this deodorant and just ended up with a sticky mess under my arm.

Alizundy, Brisbane

I'VE just returned from a peaceable walk by the sea. Everything was so perfect that it could have been a promotional movie for idyllic walks by seas. But then I came across a pair of discarded, recently shitted pants. I was just wondering if any of your readers can imagine my dismay.

T Waterman, Brighton

✻ Well, readers, can YOU imagine T Waterman's dismay at his perfect beach walk being ruined by finding a discarded pair of shitted pants? Can you envisage the disillusion he felt as his inner calm was torn away and replaced with anguish when the shitted pants came into view? Or is that the kind of raw emotion that defies empathy, and simply cannot be conceptualised by anyone who has not experienced it? Write in and let us know.

I CAN'T help but think that if Stone Age people had pulled their fingers out and invented things instead of faffing about with rocks and mud for 2.5 million years, then we wouldn't find ourselves hurtling towards the environmental catastrophe that we now do. More likely we would already be living on Mars wearing silver suits.

Tim Buktu, Timbuktu

WHILE watching a football match recently, I was really impressed by the actions of one quick-thinking fan, immediately standing up after his team conceded a goal and sticking two fingers up at the scorer. This simple but effective gesture must surely have taken the shine off the striker's achievements somewhat and lifted the spirits of his own team. Such commendable behaviour will have cemented that supporter's place in his club's history.

D Williams, Donegal

I'M not the sort of person to dwell on the past or to over-analyse popular culture, but when The Osmonds sang *Crazy Horses* in 1972, they should have put together some sort of horse-based dance rather that doing that twatty wobbly legs shite. I mean if a horse actually walked like that, a vet would have to shoot it.

Eugene Ruane, Liverpool

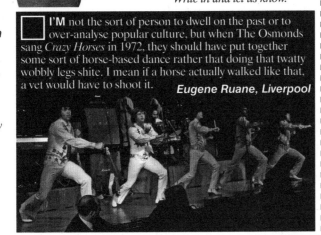

A FRIEND of mine is the Vice Chancellor at a leading UK University, and last night he invited four of the world's most eminent climate scientists round to his house to discuss the outcome of the recent COP26 meeting in Glasgow. Towards the end of the evening, he asked them if they would help shift a really heavy table from one of the upstairs rooms to his kitchen, which they duly did. Have any other readers had any internationally renowned experts in their scientific field do a spot of furniture removals for them?

Hector Barnfeather, Bristol

✻ Well, readers, have any renowned eggheads moved any furniture for you? Perhaps physician and Chief Government Scientific advisor Sir Patrick Valance has helped you carry a bed upstairs. Maybe Nobel Prize-winning stem cell researcher Shinya Yamanaka took some old units to the tip for you when you had a new kitchen fitted. Or perhaps mathematician and director of UCL's Clinical Operational Research Unit Professor Christina Pagel helped you carry an old wardrobe out of your house and dump it in the back lane. Write in and let us know.

TO remember the planets of the Solar System I use the mnemonic *"After Dinner I Did A Great Big Shit."* It's very easy to remember, but unfortunately none of the initial letters of the words correspond to the names of a planet except 'S', and I can never remember the name of the planet that begins with that one.

J Brown, Edinburgh

WHATEVER happened to ferrets? Back in the 80's they were right hard little bastards, living in trousers, stinking out repurposed rabbit hutches and biting Richard Whiteley on the finger. Nowadays, all they do is prance about on TikTok videos with people who dress them up and try desperately to be alternative. It's a hell of a fall from grace if you ask me. Come on ferrets. Get your acts together.

Joe Hartshorn, Grassmoor

SELF-ABUSE

Man suffered years of torment at his own hands

It's NOT good to stalk: Pebbles followed himself for four years.

A LEEDS man who has confessed to stalking himself for 4 years has been warned by a judge to expect a custodial sentence.

52-year-old council roadsweeper Mick Pebbles was enjoying a quiet life when he began to receive threatening letters from himself through the post.

"I came home from the pub one afternoon and there were all these letters addressed to me lying on the doormat," he told the *Kippax Rectal Examiner*. "They were vile and threatening, saying they knew where I lived, and what time I went to bed."

"And the fact they were written in my own handwriting left me terrified."

officer

Pebbles contacted police with his concerns, but the officer he spoke to was unsympathetic and laughed him out of the station.

He now believes that the police's lack of action only served to embolden himself to carry on. The next day, Pebbles awoke after a heavy drinking session to find an envelope on his bedside table. When he opened it, he was shocked to the core at what he saw.

"There were photos of me in various states of undress," he told the paper. "I felt sickened when I saw the pictures as I knew they could only have been taken inside my bathroom by me."

Things escalated further in the following months, with a series of late night phone calls to Pebbles's landline. "I recognised the number

straight away as it was my own mobile. I ran upstairs to get my phone but it was too late. I'd already hung up," he said.

And Pebbles's behaviour wasn't confined to menacing letters and telephone calls. He also said that he spotted himself following him home after a particularly long drinking session at the pub.

"I was walking home one night from my local flat-roofer when I spotted myself following me in a bus shelter window," he said. "I quickened my pace, but when I looked in the butcher's shop window up the road, I was still there."

Pebbles ran into a local police station, but was once again given short shrift by the officers on duty. "They told me to fuck off," he explained.

station

With the police showing no interest in his plight, Pebbles' was stalked by himself for the next 4 years – a period he describes as a nightmare. And he believes it was the pressure and distress caused by stalking himself which resulted in him turning to drink and occasionally breaking into his neighbour's bedroom.

Eventually Pebbles decided it was time to take matters into his own hands and confront his tormentor. "I waited outside my house after I'd had a few drinks and followed myself when I left," he said. "And I couldn't believe it when I saw myself nipping through the downstairs window

of my neighbour's ground floor flat. I followed myself in but I somehow gave myself the slip."

camera action

At that point, Pebbles believes that he must have tumbled into his neighbour's laundry basket and fallen asleep, because the next thing he knew he was being woken by his furious neighbour and two police officers.

"I had a pair of her knickers on my head and there were police sirens outside," he said. "I tried telling the coppers that they'd got the wrong me, but they didn't want to know."

Pebbles was charged with breaking and entering and was taken to the local police station. He was also charged with breaching a previous restraining order, an offence carrying a custodial sentence.

"In 2018, I performed a citizen's arrest on myself after I caught me fitting a hidden camera in my neighbour's bathroom," he said. "I thought I would get a medal for being a good citizen, but that's not how the law works, apparently."

"Once again it's me getting into trouble while I get away Scot free," he added.

ONE MORNING... OCH! THARE WE GANG. THAT SHUID BE ENOUGH.

PFFFFST! PFFFFST!

JINGS, SON... WHIT OAN EARTH URR YE UP TAE?

I'M JUIST SPRAYING A WEE BIT O' DEODORANT UNDER MAH ARMS, MA...

A WEE BIT!?!...

PFFFFST!

...THARE MIST BE FUFTY TINS O' TH' STUFF 'ERE.

HOW COME YIR PUTTING SAE MUCH OAN?

I'VE GIT AULD DOCTOR MCTAVISH COMIN' ROUND THIS AFTAE...

HE'S GOIN' TAE EXAMINE ME AN' GIMME A MEDICAL NOTE TAE SAY THAT AH CANNAE SWEAT...

...YOU KNOW... JUIST IN CASE AH'M NEEDIN' IT.

AYE, BUT FUFTY TINS!?...

...WID IT NAE BE CHEAPER TAE SETTLE OOT O' COURT?

SO...

RICHT. NOO FUR A RELAXING READ. NOTHIN' TAE GIT THE AULD METABOLISM GAUN.

SQUIRT!

BANG! BANG!

SQUEAL!

SQUIRT!

SQUIRT!

OCH! FUR FUCK'S SAKE!

LOOK AT ME. I'M DROOKIT, THANKS TAE YE TWA BUGGERS! YE SHOULD NAE BE PLAYIN' WI' THEY BLUIDY HINGS IN TH' HOOSE...

...GANG OOTDOORS WI' 'EM.

SORRY, GREAT UNCLE ANDY.

NOO AH'VE GIT TAE PAT ANITHER CLEAN SHIRT OAN.

SO...

THARE WE GO... RIGHT... NOO JIST RELAX.

I'LL HAE A WEE DRAM WHILE AH WAIT FUR AULD MCTAVISH... KEEP ME NICE AN' CALM.

YOU... FETCH ME A WHISKY.

VERY GUID, YIR HIGHNESS.

THARE WE GANG, YER HIGHNESS

STOATIN!

COONCIL JUICE, YER HIGHNESS?

AYE. JUIST A SPLASH!

CRIVVENS!

AAAACH! MAH HERT!

LOOK WHIT YE'V DANE, YE GLAIKIT AULD GOWK!

GNNNNN!

CUID YE NAE HAULD YER HORSES TAE HAE YER HERT ATTACK 'TIL YOU'D SERVED MAH DRAM?

D' YE THINK AH'M MADE O' CLEAN SHIRTS?

HNNNNNG!

SHORTLY...

RICHT. LET'S SEE IF AH KIN KEEP THIS YIN DRY...

AULD DOC MCTAVISH WULL BE 'ERE ANY MINUTE...

AN' AH NEED TAE BE AS DRY AS A BANE WHEN...

14

Take a Shit

NO COUNT

A LEICESTER fun-seeker has declared WAR on the British countryside following a *Holiday From Hell* in the Yorkshire Dales. And now former key-cutter Dougie Doig, 68, has started an online petition calling for the countryside - the large, irregular green areas between towns and cities - to be *cancelled!*

In July, Doig - a familiar face to thousands after his 29-year stint behind the counter of Mr Minit in the Haymarket bus station precinct - set out with his wife Eileen to spend a week on a farm campsite near Settle. It was to be the couple's first Great British holiday this century.

"It was a huge change for us," says Dougie, 68. "We've been to Spain every year since 1983, barring one odd fortnight in Kosovo back in the late nineties. But given the current cost of living crisis, we decided to tighten our belts and stay in Britain this year."

"We also felt strongly that it was our patriotic duty, what with everything that's going on."

COW'S ABOUT THAT?

The couple embarked on what they hoped would be a dream escape to the glorious Yorkshire countryside. But their relaxing sunshine break in the 'Herriot Country' made famous in All Creatures Great and Small turned into a nightmare within seconds of them parking up in a farmer's field near Skipton.

"We had no idea what to expect," says Dougie, still 68. "But one thing we definitely didn't expect was for

Where there's muck... The Doig's British holiday was a nightmare from the start.

As told to *Vaginia Discharge*

Eileen to be caked head-to-toe in faeces before we'd so much as got the tent up."

Doig's wife of 50 years shudders at the memory. "Dougie's mobility cart was on the roof-rack of the Berlingo, and I shifted my footing to get a better grip on the back axle to get it down," she explains. "But I suddenly became aware that my right foot was cold."

Eileen looked down to see her sandalled foot immersed to the ankle in a dinner-plate-sized mound of soft excrement. Horrified, she lost her grip on the mobility scooter, fell over backwards and rolled sideways down a slope towards a brook, a course which took her across as many as two-dozen similar stools. "You just don't get that in Benidorm," she insists.

Dougie immediately identified the likely culprits. "It was the cows, I've no doubt on that score," he says firmly. "They were an obvious presence in that field, standing around as if butter wouldn't melt."

"One literally raised its tail and patted while looking me dead in the eye," he says, shuddering at the

Staycation not a patch on sunny Spain, say Midlands couple

Unhappy trails: Dougie and Eileen Doig hoped for a dream escape in Yorkshire.

memory. "I'll never forget that sound, or that awful, arrogant gaze."

But when he reported the incident at a nearby farmhouse, the farmer simply didn't want to know. "He completely brushed me off," he says. "It's apparently 'anything goes' toilet-wise in the countryside."

After working out they had initially parked up in the wrong field, the couple eventually pitched their tent in an adjacent meadow reserved for camping, and after freshening up with a couple of wet wipes, they headed out to enjoy the local Yorkshire nightlife.

"The plan was to go in a few bars along the strip, have some cheap cocktails, then choose a restaurant for a happy holiday meal like we do in Spain," says Eileen. "But there was none of that. We walked miles, right up onto the tops, until it was almost dark. But there was nothing."

After several hours of searching for a Taverna along the rock-strewn

> *It was the cows, I've no doubt on that score ... it's apparently 'anything goes' toilet-wise in the countryside.*

path, the battery on Dougie's scooter eventually went flat, and 71-year-old Eileen was forced to drag him back to the tent. "His best jacket and shirt were hanging off him in shreds by the time we crawled through the flap," she recalls.

ICE SCREAM

It was a bad start to their holiday to say the least, but undeterred, the couple decided to explore the locality the following morning in search of memorable experiences.

"We love just wandering in Spain, and you usually come across a vineyard doing wine tastings, or a restaurant with a flamenco dancer on, so we were looking forward to something similar," says Dougie.

"Eileen's feet were still bleeding from the night before and she'd sprained her ankle on some scree, so we couldn't go too fast, but we were on holiday. We were in no hurry."

With hindsight, the couple wish they had simply stayed in their tent. Because rather than gently strolling around souvenir shops or relaxing in tavernas, the day saw a terrified Doug and Eileen fighting for their lives.

"There's a nice wooded bit of the complex we stay at in Benidorm, and they have benches and little refreshments carts," says Dougie. "So when we came across a wood near the campsite, we thought we'd pop in for a refreshing ice cream."

But their experience in the British woodland was a world away from their usual picturesque Spanish walks. Their path very quickly disappeared and the couple soon found themselves battling their way through dense undergrowth. "It was one obstacle after another," says Eileen, flinching at the memory. "Streams, gullies, mud, exposed roots, you name it."

"It's about as far from the typical modern Spanish resort accessibility experience as I ever hope to be."

Eileen is adamant that the dense and tangled historic forest could only have been laid out to deliberately hinder passage by mobility cart. "At one point I was up to my waist and sinking in a mire with the cart held above my head," she recalls.

"I should point out that I wasn't in it at the time," says the hugely overweight Dougie. "I was hanging back, waiting for Eileen to return and carry me over. Luckily for her, I spotted she was going under in the filth and managed to pull her out with a rotten log."

"Holidays are meant to be fun, but this was no fun at all. We could have been in one of the Vietnam films," he vouchsafes, once again shaking his head sadly at the memory.

Scared and hungry, the couple wandered the woodland, an area around the size of four football pitches, until once again Dougie's

Camping carry on: The Doig's UK campsite was a million miles from their Spanish holiday experiences.

battery went flat. By late afternoon, the couple had found their way out of the wood, and an exhausted Eileen managed to drag her scooter-bound husband onto the road back to the campsite.

"Six hours we were stuck in there," says a furious Dougie. "Why they don't have rocks painted white lining the paths like they do in the Hotel Mirador gardens I'll never know."

INHUMAN REMAINS

Although in low spirits, the seasoned holidaymakers were determined to make the best of their staycation and decided to set out the next morning to look at the local Roman ruins.

"Me and Eileen are very interested in history, especially all the Roman and Greek stuff," says Dougie. "The hotel in Spain where we go runs a coach trip to an ampy-theatre, and we love to wander round and imagine all the gladiators and Christians and lions and stuff, like in the films."

"We decided we'd see what ancient Roman relics the Settle and Skipton area had to offer. We hadn't read

about any ampy-theatres locally, but we were sure there was bound to be some old columns, a broken statue or a Hadrian's wall or something," says Dougie.

The couple set off across the countryside in search of the ancient past, but hit their first snag when they encountered a stile in the far corner of the field where they had had their run-in with the cows when they arrived.

"I don't know how they think a mobility scooter can get over a stile," fumes Dougie. "The ampy-theatre in Spain has got ramps all over the place, even into the gift shop. But here there was nothing!"

Eileen eventually found an area where the dry stone wall had partially collapsed, and by moving several of the remaining stones, was able to make a passage large enough for Dougie's scooter to squeeze through.

"We got through the wall eventually," says Dougie. "But my Eileen shouldn't have had to shift half a ton of rock to do it. She's seventy-one."

The couple spent several hours wandering the fields in search of Roman remains, but by late afternoon, Dougie's battery had gone flat again, and he decided it would be best if they abandoned their search and returned to the campsite.

"To say I was disappointed as Eileen pushed me back across the fields would be an understatement," says Dougie. "When we've been on

holiday before, you can't move for Roman history, but over here in the UK there's bugger all."

PAT ON THE BACK

But Dougie's disappointment soon turned to horror as the couple approached the cowfield near the campsite. "I'd got off my scooter to make it a bit easier for Eileen to get it over the bit of wall," he says. "But she trod in another cow dirt and lost her footing."

For a second time, Eileen found herself rolling down the slope through cow faeces towards the brook, eventually coming to rest spreadeagled against a barbed wire fence.

"That was the final straw, for me," says Dougie. "We'd both had a bellyful by now, especially Eileen. Much more cow tuppence went in her mouth that second time, and she was probably going to need a tetanus from the barbed wire."

The couple returned to their home in Leicester the following morning, where they have since fought a losing battle to put the ordeal behind them.

"It's been tough. We aren't who we were," says Dougie. "Eileen's back has never been the same. And all I see when I close my eyes is that cow looking straight at me while it did its numbers."

> "Holidays are meant to be fun, but this was no fun at all. We could have been in one of the Vietnam films"

The couple now hope their online petition to cancel the British countryside will attract the 100,000 signatures it requires to be debated in the House of Commons, although to date it has only been signed four times by Dougie and Eileen using two different email addresses. Nevertheless, Dougie remains optimistic.

"For various reasons, more people will have had holidays in Britain this year than for ages," he says. "And they'll all have been rubbish compared to Spain, so I'm expecting a deluge of support once they hear about my campaign."

With a bit of luck, he hopes that by this time next year the countryside will have been cancelled. "I'm not exactly sure what being cancelled actually entails. But it sounds terrible and our countryside definitely deserves it," he says.

"Next year we're off to sunny Spain. Eh viva Espanya."

Stile it out: Dougie found traditional footpaths impossible to navigate on his mobility scooter.

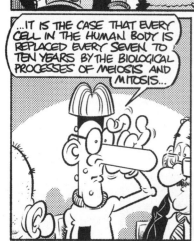

ROYAL PURRS

Queen bequeathes fortune to moggy

HER MAJESTY the Queen is one of the richest women on the planet, with the monarchy owning assets of almost £56 billion worldwide, along with a personal fortune of £500 million. But Royal watchers were surprised yesterday after her Majesty the Queen announced that this wealth would not be passed down to the next in line to the throne as she is leaving the lot... *to a cat!*

Being named as the sole benefactor in the sovereign's last will and testament means that the 6-year-old tabby, Mr Tibbles, will become the richest animal on the planet when the Queen passes on. And, in addition to the money and income from the Royal Estates, the well-heeled feline will be the proud owner of hundreds of priceless paintings, art treasures and Fabergé eggs. It will also be the owner of the Crown Jewels, which have been passed down from monarch to monarch since the restoration of Charles II in 1661.

hairball

Her majesty has, for many years, threatened her family that she will *"leave it all to the cat"* unless they improved their behaviour. But Royals treated

LAST WILL AND TESTAMA'AMT: *Lucky Tibbles (above) set to become richest animal on the planet after Queen (top left) passes on.*

her threat as a joke, not least because Britain's longest serving monarch doesn't own a cat.

But last month a stray tabby, who'd entered the gardens at Buckingham Palace by climbing a tree, made its way inside the building and settled in her majesty's apartment. According to a palace insider, the Queen was delighted when she saw the flea-bitten moggy, and immediately gave it a bit of roast swan and a saucer of milk.

"Her majesty absolutely fell in love with the thing. They became somewhat inseparable," the insider said.

Over the following weeks, palace staff reported numerous instances of the Queen bonding with her new favourite pet, including:

- *Going on "midnight adventures" in the palace garden with Mr Tibbles in her dressing gown.*

- *Kicking the corgis off her bed and coaxing Mr Tibbles up there with packs of Dreamies.*

- *Dropping ping-pong balls off the balcony for Mr Tibbles to chase.*

"The next thing we knew, she had gone to WHSmith just off the Mall and bought one of those do-it-yourself wills," the insider continued. "She filled it in and left everything to Mr Tibbles. The lot."

worms

Constitutional experts believe that although the will was signed without a solicitor present, the document is nevertheless legally binding. "Any monarch's will that is signed in the presence of a witness will supersede any other that precedes it," said *Majesty Magazine* editor Ingrid Fartsucker. "The fact that the witness in this case was one of the Royal corgis is neither here nor there," she added.

But although the cat will cop for the lot, the line of succession will not be altered. "Charles, Prince of Wales will still succeed his mother and be crowned His Royal Highness King Charles III of the United Kingdom and head of the Commonwealth," said Fartsucker. "It's just that unlike every monarch before him, he won't have a pot to piss in."

Drunken bakers

I set out drinking to forget, and –

Heh heh.

I know this one.

Know what one?

Heh, I go *forget what?*

And *you* go, ha ha –

I forgot!

Ha ha ha.

Ha ha ha haah!

What the fuck're you on about?

I ain't bloody joking.

I was *going* to say, it worked.

I did.

You did what?

Forgot.

What y'fuckin' moaning for then?

It don't last. You start remembering.

Cough!

The stuff you forgot?

No, the fuckin' phonebook.

I don't suppose you remember what these were, do you?

One time, two or three drinks and all of the bad shit was behind you.

Ashes to ashes...

Then it's four or five, six or seven, eight or nine...

Aaah, what *you* got to forget any road?

Better times. My little girl.

Oh *that*. Mind you, she won't be little no more.

Grown woman. Maybe has little 'uns of her own.

Your grandkids, as they'd be...

I see why you'd want to forget that.

Aye.

Try a large one.

That's the way.

Down the old hatch.

You forgot it all yet?

No...

Don't worry.

We can open another bottle, if needs be.

Forgot?

Forgot what?

ROGER MELLIE
THE MAN ON THE TELLY

5:00 pm...

OH, HI, TOM!

HI, ROGER. HOW'S THE FIRST DAY GONE?

IT'S A PAIN IN THE ARSE, TOM. WHY CAN'T PEOPLE TAKE THEIR LITTER HOME? AND WHAT IS IT WITH LORRY DRIVERS PISSING INTO POP BOTTLES WHILE THEY'RE DRIVING?

CAN'T THEY JUST PULL OVER AND PISS OUT THE WINDOW LIKE EVERYONE ELSE?... FUCKING ANIMALS

ANYWAY, FUCK IT

THAT'S ME DONE FOR THE DAY

WELL, FIRST DAY OVER, EH, ROGER?.. 8 HOURS DOWN, 192 TO GO. HEH! HEH!

199 TOM... DIDN'T START 'TIL AN HOUR AGO...SLEPT IN A BIT

FOR GOD'S SAKE, ROGER. I HOPE YOU'VE LEARNED YOUR LESSON FROM THIS

OH, I HAVE, TOM...I HAVE!

SORRY... WHAT AM I DOING IT FOR AGAIN? WAS IT THE SHOPLIFTING?

DRIVING OVER THE LIMIT, ROGER. THE SHOPLIFTING WAS A £500 FINE

THAT WAS IT, TOM... WELL I HAVE LEARNT MY LESSON. I CERTAINLY WON'T BE DOING THAT AGAIN!

I'M GLAD TO HEAR IT, ROGER

TOOK THE WHOLE FRONT OF MY CAR OFF GOING THROUGH THAT CHURCHYARD WALL. AND THEM FUCKING HEADSTONES WRECKED MY FUCKING ALLOYS

CLACK!

I MEAN, WHO PUTS A FUCKING CHURCH AT THE BOTTOM OF A HILL?... I'M ONLY SURPRISED IT'S NOT HAPPENED BEFORE, TOM

THEY WANT TO GET SOME BIG CHEVRONS ON THE FUCKER

ANYWAY, THE MONEY I GET FROM THIS SHOULD BUY ME A NICE NEW MOTOR

WHAT DO YOU MEAN, "MONEY YOU GET FROM THIS"...?

WELL, MY GOING RATE FOR AN APPEARANCE IS £350 AN HOUR... 200 HOURS AT 350 AN HOUR. THAT'S SEVENTY BIG ONES, TOM... PLUS EXIES, OBVIOUSLY...

...GOT TO GET A TAXI HERE EVERY DAY SINCE THEY TOOK MY FUCKING LICENCE AWAY

ROGER...YOU DON'T GET PAID FOR THIS. IT'S A PUNISHMENT! IT'S YOU WHO IS PAYING YOUR DEBT TO SOCIETY!

WHAT!?!

ARE YOU TAKING THE PISS, TOM!?! I'M A PROFESSIONAL!... I DON'T DO ANYTHING FOR NOTHING. EVEN MY CHARITY WORK GIVES ME EXPENSES...

...GOOD 'UNS TOO, TOM

WE'VE GOT TO MONETISE THIS SOMEHOW, TOM. GET YOUR THINKING CAP ON

WHAT!? NO. THIS IS A PUNISHMENT, NOT A BUSINESS OPPORTUNITY, ROGER!

BOLLOCKS!

EVERYTHING'S A BUSINESS OPPORTUNITY, TOM

SIX WEEKS LATER...

HOW MUCH FOR A 'PRISONER ROGER' MUG?

£15, OR TWO FOR £25

ROGER MELLIE COMMUNITY SERVICE STATION

T-SHIRTS: £30
MUGS: £15
BOOK

HELP
ROGER PAY HIS DEBT TO SOCIETY

GENUINE LITTER HAND PICKED BY TV'S ROGER MELLIE £5 per BAG

I'LL HAVE TWO, PLEASE

SAY CHEESE ROGER

CHEEEEEESE!

CHAT W/ ROGER
5 mins £20
10 mins £35
SELFIES £15 per person

20

BIRD FANCIERS DESCEND ON CUMBRIAN VILLAGE

HUNDREDS of birdwatchers yesterday descended upon the Cumbrian village of Butterthwaite following the sighting of a rare red-necked grebe.

IN A FLAP: *Keen birder Crispin spotted rare grebe (left) on reference book page.*

By mid-morning, around 500 bird enthusiasts – or 'twitchers' – had gathered on the village green as word spread that the elusive creature had been spotted on page 235 of The Usborne Book of Birds.

The rare avian was first sighted yesterday morning by 62-year-old retired GP Crispin O'Toole as he was flicking through the book in a neighbour's front room. As he turned the page, the keen birder immediately recognised the animal as a rare red-necked grebe.

tremendously

"It was a tremendously exciting moment," O'Toole told reporters. "The red-necked grebe has only been spotted in Britain a handful of times, so I couldn't believe it when I saw it on the page in front of me."

"And to make things even more exciting, there were pictures of a pair of them, a male and female."

As lunchtime approached, a queue of almost a thousand ornithologists snaked down the lane leading to the house in which the book was found, all hoping to catch a glimpse of the picture of the migratory aquatic avians.

"I can't tell you how excited I am," said keen birder Jerry Cashew, who travelled from Cornwall to see the illustration. "It's every twitcher's dream to see a red-necked grebe, so to find a breeding pair in this book is a real event."

The owner of the book, Ethel Osset, admitted to feeling a little overwhelmed by all the attention.

"It belonged to my late husband, and since he died I've been meaning to have a clearout," she told the *Cumbrian Sausage and Herald*. "I knew Dr O'Toole was a keen birdwatcher, so I asked if he'd like it before I put it in the charity bag."

"He was flicking through it, and then his jaw just dropped. He laid the book down open at that page and backed away from it very slowly," she said.

Dr O'Toole took a couple of photographs of the page and posted them up on the British Ornithological Society website, and news of the sighting quickly went viral.

"Half an hour later I'm besieged by all these middle aged bearded men with binoculars and cameras," said Mrs Osset. "They all seem nice enough, though."

twitchers

The twitchers quickly set up a hide in Mrs Osset's hallway, about ten yards from the kitchen where the book lay nestled on the table, and took turns to crouch inside, taking pictures of the page with the rare grebes on it.

"There was a nasty moment about an hour ago when a draught blew the book shut," said Dr O'Toole. "The disappointment in the queue was enormous, with everyone thinking they'd missed their once-in-a-lifetime chance to see this exceptionally rare bird."

"Luckily, I went through the index and managed to get it open at the right page again."

This is the second time that Mrs Osset's home has been the centre of attention. In 2006, around 350 trainspotters gathered in her garden to look at a photograph of a decommissioned DP1 Prototype Deltic diesel locomotive in a 1972 copy of The Boy's Book of Trains which had belonged to her son.

BO-HEAT-MIAN RHAPSODY!
Rocker May to turn iconic guitar back into fireplace

BURNIN' THROUGH THE NIGHT: *May plans on beating Cost of Living crisis by turning 'Red Special' guitar back into fireplace.*

QUEEN GUITARIST Brian May famously built his trademark guitar using the timbers taken from an old mantelpiece. But after playing it in countless concerts, May now plans to turn the instrument, nicknamed the 'Red Special' back into a working fireplace in an attempt to save on heating bills.

The one-of-a-kind instrument, constructed with the help of his father in 1964, is one of rock and roll's most famous guitars and has been a mainstay of the trademark Queen sound for more than fifty years. Like BB King's 'Lucille', Willie Nelson's 'Trigger' or Mark King off of Level 42's bass with all them lights on the neck, it's hard to imagine Brian May without his trademark 'axe'.

THE HOTTEST ROCK EXCLUSIVES ARE IN YOUR #1 Viz

"Since playing with Queen, I've made loads of cash and can afford whatever guitar I want," the *Seven Seas of Rhye* rocker told *NME* journalists. "But like everyone else I'm feeling the pinch from the current cost of living crisis."

"Converting 'the Old Lady' - another name for my well-known guitar - back into a fireplace was a no-brainer," the poodle-haired *Bohemian Rhapsody* axeman continued. "We're all in the same boat during this period of rising energy prices, albeit my boat is larger than most, and I thought it prudent to try and find ways to save money on my heating bills."

mercury

Since 'the Fireplace' - yet another name for the iconic, hand-built instrument - was fashioned from mantelpiece wood originally, May is confident that converting it back into a fully-functioning feature fireplace should be little trouble.

"There's a bit above the bridge of the guitar where I'm planning on chiselling out a hole and installing a tiny fire grate and hearth," the *Keep Yourself Alive* guitarist explained.

"I'm also planning on fitting a little shelf above the top string that I could rest my arm on between songs, or stack my collection of sixpence plectrums in a pile," star-gazer May continued.

"If I adjust my playing style a little, I don't reckon my hand will get too hot while I'm performing on stage. And if Roger gets a little chilly during a drum solo, I could just turn to face him so that he got the benefit, too."

west

However, multi-millionaire May acknowledged that having a roaring open fire slung over his shoulder during live performances might be potentially dangerous. "I'd be lying if I said that I wasn't a little concerned about stray embers or pops and spits coming from the fire and catching my hair alight," the *We Will Rock You* string bender revealed, "With all the dry weather we've been having recently, my hair is tinder-dry and that, combined with the hairspray on my barnet, is an accident waiting to happen."

TINDER-DRY STARS

IT IS NOT only Brian May who risks going up like a rocket. The recent bout of unseasonably dry weather has led to many of Britain's celebrities becoming tinder dry, and the risk of a celebrity fire is now more real than it's ever been. The Fire Service has asked people to exercise particular caution around stars to avoid fires. But what could the household names do to prevent themselves going up in smoke? We asked the – presumably, late – firefighter **RED ADAIR** to assess the danger to four VIPs, and suggest what precautions they could take to stop themselves going up in smoke.

Daniel Craig
BOND ACTOR

"This spell of dry weather presents a particular danger for those celebrities with smouldering good looks, and 007 actor Craig falls into that category. The heat generated by his rugged handsomeness is always there, just under the surface, and most of the year it won't be a problem. But the recent heatwaves have left Craig parched, and he could burst into flames any minute. He shouldn't go anywhere, be it a red carpet film premiere, glittering awards ceremony or swanky restaurant without carrying two buckets of water with him.

These could be used to damp himself down if he finds himself become even more dishy."

Syd Little
FORMER DOUBLE ACT STRAIGHT MAN

"Many heath and moorland fires are caused by the sun's rays being concentrated through discarded bottles or bits of broken glass. And sitting on a tinder-dry face, Little's bottle-bottom specs are an accident waiting to happen. Just one ray of sunlight going through those inch-thick lenses could set light to an eyelash. Before you know it, his eyebrows are on fire and the flames would quickly spread to the rest of his body. In the interests of safety, Little should remove his specs immediately and not put them back on until we have had a significant period of rainfall."

Naomi Campbell
FASHION MODEL

"According to *Elle* magazine, fashion diva Naomi loves the odd cigarette. But after the summer we have had, she is quite literally playing with fire. Lighting her coffin nail, smoking it, and even stubbing out the dog end are flash points that could easily lead to the model's combustion. And a Naomi fire would not be easy to put out, as the notoriously picky model would demand that the firefighters wear couture safety equipment and and use diamond-studded hoses to put her out. It goes without saying that Campbell would do well to stop smoking until we have had sufficient rain to enable her to be able to start lighting up again in safety."

Jeremy Clarkson
PETROL HEAD MOTOR GOBSHITE

"Clarkson's home village of Chipping Norton has had some of the fiercest heat in the UK, so the former *Top Gear* presenter will be more desiccated than most stars. And his love of outdoor barbecuing puts him at enormous risk of conflagration. A stray spark a or a floating charcoal ember could quickly turn 6'5" Jezza into a towering inferno. And with his bulk, the flames could rage for days, setting light to other celebrities in the Chipping Norton glitterati. If he must cookout this summer, he should borrow a fireproof suit from fellow *Top Gear* presenter The Stig and wear it when at the grill."

24

THE Male Online

Beryl?

SLAM

You will not *believe* what I just saw in the covered market!

Was it a foreigner?

Worse!

A communist!!

Strolling around, *bold as brass*, fingering the goods!

In wartime!!

How'd you know he was a communist?

She, Beryl, she, a she.

It was a bloody woman!

I shouldn't be surprised, her sort are all over the internets.

Ex-Corbyn groupies.

He was the gateway drug.

BIP BIP BIP

Now they gleefully *parade their wares* as sex-bait for Putinism!

Who are you calling?

Police. Karl Marx splashed all over her chest!

I could barely believe what I was seeing.

Propagandised cleavage!

It's erotic brainwashing.

Like that dog salivating on the bell. Pavlova.

Stop telling me all your operators are busy!

While I listen to this infernal machine a fifth column tightens its Iron Curtain over Fulchester!

There should be a number certain trusted citizens can ring when we spot one.

Straight through to MI5.

Or a website where we can file reports, name names, time, place, trajectory...

Organise ourselves into patrols...

Thing is, I'm kicking myself for not making a citizen's arrest.

I so wanted to *pinch* her.

Too crowded in the market. I couldn't risk a scene...

So I tailed her.

Then out and around town...

But still too many people – it can get *messy* if women resist.

How long did you stalk this poor lass?

Not long. An hour?

To her car. I have the registration.

I'm popping to the police station to report in person.

I wouldn't.

The only thing necessary for the triumph of evil is people like *you*, Beryl.

I should ask them to extend me the use of a police radio, ready for next time...

FULCHESTER POLICE

Police

And a taser.

That's him!

BUZZZZ

POLICE

That's the perv!

CURE BLIMEY!

AN UNEMPLOYED Garforth man has boldly declared his intention to bring an end to the Covid-19 pandemic once and for all.

But 61-year-old **MICK TREADMILL** isn't a scientist or a doctor... he's a bona fide **MIRACLE WORKER**, a gifted individual blessed with the ability to cure the sick using *only the power of his mind!*

I BELIEVE IN MIRACLES: *'Miracle' Mick Treadmill is offering the UK government his supernatural healing services in the fight against Covid.*

"It's true," chuckles the 24-stone bachelor. "I didn't ask for this gift, I was just born with it. Like Spiderman's uncle said, with great power comes great responsibility. And if I don't use my extraordinary powers for the greater good, then what sort of energy-harnessing demigod am I?"

The terminally jobless father-of-eight – self-dubbed 'Miracle Mick' – is a practitioner of 'Cosmic Ordering': the science of channelling positive thoughts to cure physical ailments. Until now, Mick has only used his supernatural skills to combat sickness within his own circle of friends and family. But the big-boned shaman says he can no longer watch from the sidelines as the so-called 'experts' continue to allow the Coronavirus to run rampant throughout our green and pleasant land.

"I'm offering the government my otherworldly healing powers to finally defeat this deadly virus", Mick told the *Garforth Prolapse and Adhesion*. "And I won't ask for a single penny in return."

All selfless Mick desires is for HMRC to overlook a series of minor debts he has erroneously occurred over the past forty years. "Due to a few hundred misunderstandings with the self-employment regulations, I'm being hounded by the taxman for the thick end of twelve grand," Mick sighs. "I'm on the bones of my arse, so if Rishi Sunak can see his way clear to wiping my slate clean, I'll get straight to work curing every Covid patient from Land's End to John O' Groats."

Speaking to the paper, witchdoctor Mick explains how he came to discover his extraordinary powers – and the often-adverse effect they have had on his career, his finances ... *and his sex life!*

Going Against the Migraine

Mick's remarkable healing abilities were first revealed to him in 2012, towards the end of his troubled third marriage.

❝ Ten years back, I was still with my third missus, Carole. We were going through a bit of a rocky patch at the time, due mainly to Carole's chronic illness. She suffered from abrupt and inexplicable migraines. Throughout most of our marriage, the minute I suggested a spot of 'the other' she would suddenly be wracked with a splitting headache that meant intercourse simply wasn't possible.

As the years went by, we tried every pill and potion on the market, but Carole still complained of a bastard behind the eyes every time I tried to get my leg over, and it was driving us – me in particular – to our wits' end.

One night, I made my usual advances and as usual Carole winced in agony and retired to bed, massaging her temples. Normally, I would have just nipped out to the shed for a five knuckle shuffle, but that night something was different. I was consumed with worry for my poor sickly missus, and I wondered if there was something – anything – I could do to help her.

At the time, I was reading the autobiography of Noel Edmonds. Noel's always been a hero of mine and in his book, he outlines his commitment to the science of 'cosmic ordering'. Put simply, harnessing positive mental energy can ward off physical illness. Cancer sufferers, for instance, are only 'ill' because of their whiny, negative attitudes. If they could simply perk up and be a bit more 'glass-half-full,' their so-called 'cancer' would instantly disappear.

Inspired, I sat in my shed, I focused all my mental energy on curing Carole's noggin-based woes. I squeezed my eyes shut and thought about how long it had been since she let me on the nest as I chanted the words 'CURE CAROLE' over and over again.

When I opened my eyes, the energy in the shed felt different. I knew instantly that I had tapped into the electromagnetic fields surrounding Carole's bonce and healed her chronic migraine.

I rushed back into the house, and lo and behold, there was my beloved Carole – out of bed, dressed to the nines, and halfway out the front door!

I gasped in amazement as she span around, her eyes wide with shock at her miraculous recovery. Her migraine had completely gone, and thinking I was going to be a few hours in the shed, she had decided to have a night out with the girls.

I was dumbfounded. With just the power of my own affirmative thought, I had relieved my wife from a lifetime of suffering! *Or so I assumed.*

Unfortunately, the very next evening, Carole's headache returned in full force, just as I playfully goosed her arse while she was washing the pots. As she retired to bed in agony, I went back to the shed and repeated my cosmic incantations. Once again, it worked like magic, and the very next morning, Carole was well enough to go and meet her sister for lunch.

Over the next few months, it was the same story: Carole's migraine would take hold just as we were on the cusp of intercourse. I would perform my positive thinking ritual, and hey presto: the migraine would evaporate, albeit at the exact moment when intercourse was no longer feasible.

My nuts were still like two tins of Fussell's milk, but I was on cloud nine. I had discovered that I possessed the incredible ability to heal the sick... *using only the power of my mind!* ❞

> ## The minute I suggested a spot of 'the other' she would suddenly be wracked with a splitting headache

> ## My nuts were still like two tins of Fussell's milk, but I was on cloud nine.

"I've healed more sick than you've had hot dinners," says miracle worker Mick

Date With Destiny

Carole eventually filed for divorce from Mick after a misunderstanding involving his newfound cosmic ordering powers.

It all started when I was doing some faith healing on the woman from the chippy who had complained of recurrent pain in her buttocks and breasts. I had offered to try a spiritualist technique known as the 'laying on of hands' and I was midway through curing her ailments when the belt on my trousers went, along with the elastic on my pants, and they both fell down. To cut a long story short, Carole walked in, put two and two together, made five, and I was back in the divorce court.

Living out of a suitcase in a bedsit meant I was a single man again and ready to play the field. At the time, I was working as a lavatory technician at a local stationery firm, and the receptionist, Jeanette, was a right tasty piece. As a married man, I had previously restricted my interactions with her to flirtatious glances, or secretly filming her when she was in the toilet. But now I was officially back on the market, I decided to start laying the 'Miracle Mick' charm on extra-thick.

Every morning as I arrived at the office, I'd stop and chat with Jeanette, who lapped up my witty conversation. I knew our exchanges were the highlight of her morning, so I would always wait patiently to speak to her if she happened to be on the phone or have her earbuds in or be looking for something under her desk as I passed.

The chemistry between us was at boiling point and one morning I plucked up the courage to ask her out on a date. She blushed a delightful shade of pink, and told me she would love to, but unfortunately she had a severe stomach bug and would be staying in that night. I nodded sympathetically, and told her to get well soon. But as I walked away, I was grinning like a Cheshire Cat – *because I had the power to get her well sooner than she might think!*

Back at my bedsit that evening, I placed my fingers on my temples, shut my eyes and concentrated all my positive energy on healing Jeanette's dicky tummy. I meditated, hummed and chanted until I felt dizzy – and as I opened my eyes, I knew the cosmic balance had been restored and Jeanette was cured.

Excited at the prospect of asking her out again the next day, I nipped to the shops for a few celebratory cans of white cider. But as I stepped out of Booze-R-Us, I couldn't believe my eyes... A bus was passing right in front of me, and there on the top deck was Jeanette – *fit as a fiddle and laughing away with some pals!*

I couldn't help chuckling to myself. She would never know it was me who was responsible for her miraculous

> ## I was midway through curing her ailments when the belt on my trousers went

recovery that night. But as a faith healer, I don't do this for thanks – I do it to make the world a better place and, ideally, for the occasional knee trembler.

With that in mind, I decided to try my luck with the lovely Jeanette a second time the next day. But before I could speak to her, I was called into my supervisor's office. Apparently they had found some clearly doctored CCTV footage of the petty cash box accidentally falling into my rucksack on three or four occasions and I was being given the heave-ho as a result.

I never saw Jeanette again – but I sleep soundly to this day, knowing her stomach will forever be bug-free because of me.

Fakes and Ladders

Mick was gradually making the world a healthier place, but tragically, he had to put the brakes on his miracle working after an accident left him incapacitated.

I tweaked a muscle in my back whilst restoring sight to a blind man, and it rendered me unable to work. I've always been a career-driven go-getter – despite what my ex-wives might tell you – so having to claim benefits and spend all day lying on the couch watching *Homes Under The Hammer* was a living nightmare.

The quacks couldn't find anything wrong with me, but even standing up to get a can from the fridge left me in excruciating agony, so I had no choice but to accept the nash's generous cheques while I recuperated.

Then one day it hit me. I had the power to miraculously heal others... *but could I miraculously heal myself?*

Switching off *Police! Camera! Action!*, I drained my can and focused all my cosmic energies on fixing my bad back. I took a deep breath, summoned as much positive thought as I could physically muster and directed it straight at my own agony-stricken spine.

The result was instant. I felt a warm, tingly electricity fill my entire body, and as I sprang up from the sofa and began cartwheeling across the floor of my bedsit, I knew one thing for sure. *I was cured!*

Bursting with energy, I sprinted out the front door, heading straight the dole office. Now I was now technically eligible to work again, I aimed to hand back my latest benefits cheque and take the first job they could find me!

But on the way, I spotted an elderly neighbour setting up a wobbly-looking ladder in order to clean his windows. Full of joie de vivre, I couldn't resist helping, so I told him to sit tight as I scampered up the ladder and began soaping the grimy glass for him.

Unfortunately, it was at this *precise* moment that my dole officer, Mr Didcott, happened to walk past. Didcott knew me as the enfeebled wretch who wobbled into his office every fortnight to collect my disability benefit, so he was understandably surprised to see me up a 30ft ladder, washing windows.

I tried to explain that I was a spiritual healer and I had just self-cured my own fucked back. But he wouldn't listen to reason. He claimed he'd been building up a sizeable cache of 'evidence' that 'proved' I'd been performing cash-in-hand odd jobs for four decades, whilst also signing on, claiming disability and working as a freelance lavatory technician.

It was, quite honestly, the most preposterous thing I'd ever heard.

So, here I am today, twelve large in the hole and with eight lots of overdue child support to boot. That's why I'm reaching out to Her Majesty's government in the hope of brokering a deal."

And a tearful Mick had a final message for Chancellor Sunak: "Rishi – if you can drop me an email by Monday morning to confirm I owe you fuck all, I'll have every Covid ward in the country empty by lunchtime. And *that's* a Miracle Mick promise."

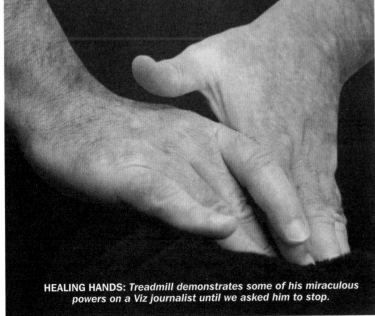

HEALING HANDS: *Treadmill demonstrates some of his miraculous powers on a Viz journalist until we asked him to stop.*

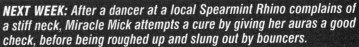

NEXT WEEK: *After a dancer at a local Spearmint Rhino complains of a stiff neck, Miracle Mick attempts a cure by giving her auras a good check, before being roughed up and slung out by bouncers.*

SELF-ABUSE SHENANIGANS WITH JOHN HARVEY KELLOGG

DJ '22

BATTLE CREEK, MICHIGAN — 1895.

MERCY ME! THIS NEW BREAKFAST CEREAL YOU'VE INVENTED IS A HUGE SUCCESS, JOHN HARVEY!

FOLKS JUST CAN'T GET ENOUGH OF YOUR "CORN FLAKES!"

THEY'RE CAUSING A GREAT DEAL OF EXCITEMENT!

EXCITEMENT? MY CORN FLAKES DO NOT "EXCITE" PEOPLE, WIFE!

EXCITEMENT IS A SNARE USED BY SATAN TO MAKE US SLAVES OF SEXUAL DESIRE AND DEFILE OUR GENITALS WITH ACTS OF SELF-POLLUTION!

MY SIMPLE AND NUTRITIOUS CEREAL WILL KEEP AMERICAN CITIZENS HEALTHY IN BODY AND MIND, AND HELP THEM RESIST THE TEMPTATION TO FIDDLE WITH THEIR PRIVATE PARTS!

YES DEAR. SORRY, DEAR.

NOW THEN! OUR LOCAL CHURCH'S ANTI-MASTURBATION LEAGUE WILL BE ARRIVING SHORTLY.

I'M GOING TO GIVE THEM A TOUR OF THE CORN FLAKES FACTORY I'VE SET UP IN THE BARN.

YES SIRREE, THE LOCAL CHURCH GROUP WILL BE MIGHTY IMPRESSED BY THE DECENT AND GOD-FEARING WAY I RUN MY BUSINESS!

JUMPIN' JEHOSEPHAT! A BIG SNAKE!

WHAT IN TARNATION IS A SNAKE DOING IN MY CORN FLAKES FACTORY!?

THIS HERE IS PERCY MY PET BELL-HEADED PYTHON, MR KELLOGG. HE KEEPS DOWN THE RODENT POPULATION.

THOSE DARN MICE ARE ALWAYS GETTIN' INTO THE CORN SACKS.

GIT THAT CONSARNED REPTILE OUTTA MY BARN!

THE BIBLE TELLS US THAT SNAKES ARE AGENTS OF SATAN, ALWAYS TEMPTING FOLKS TO SUCCUMB TO THEIR CARNAL URGES!

YOU'VE SCARED PERCY AWAY WITH YOUR SHOUTING, MR KELLOGG! HE'S GONE INTO HIDING!

SLITHER

OLD MR JENKINS THE PACKAGING DESIGNER IS ON THE PHONE FOR YOU, SIR...

HE WANTS TO KNOW IF YOU'VE CHOSEN A DESIGN FOR A MASCOT ON YOUR CORN FLAKES BOX.

AH YES...

HELLO? YES, I'VE DECIDED ON THE PICTURE OF A LARGE COCKEREL.

IT REALLY CONVEYS THE HEALTHY, EARLY MORNING BREAKFASTINESS OF MY CEREAL!

CAN YOU SPEAK UP A BIT, MR KELLOGG?

DESIGN STUDIO

MY HEARING'S NOT WHAT IT WAS.

A BIG COCK, MR JENKINS!

I WANT A PICTURE OF A BIG COCK ON THE CORN FLAKES BOX!

TSK! THAT MAN'S DEAFNESS IS GETTING WORSE...

DOUBTLESS CAUSED BY A LIFETIME'S INDULGENCE IN THE SINFUL PRACTICE OF TOUCHING HIMSELF DOWN BELOW!

LAN' SAKES!

THAT DARNED SNAKE HAS GONE UP MY TROUSER LEG!

HELP! GET IT OUT!

OL' PERCY GOES FOR WARM AND DARK PLACES...

HMM, I RECKON WE'LL HAVE TO PULL HIM OUT THROUGH YOUR FLIES...

JUST HOLD STEADY WHILE I UNZIP YOUR PANTS...

MR KELLOGG, HERE'S THE DESIGN FOR THE CORN FLAKES BOX WHICH YOU WANTED. WHERE SHALL I PUT IT?

JUST LEAVE IT OUTSIDE AND HELP ME GET THIS GOSH-DARN SNAKE OUT OF MY TROUSERS!

AND QUICKLY! THE CHURCH GROUP WILL ARRIVE ANY MOMENT!

MEANWHILE
SEVENTH DAY ADVENTISTS ANTI-MASTURBATION LEAGUE

AH, HERE WE ARE! I'M LOOKING FORWARD TO THIS TOUR OF MR KELLOGG'S CORN FLAKES FACTORY!

JOHN HARVEY HAS BEEN AN UPRIGHT MEMBER OF OUR CHURCH FOR MANY YEARS.

WE CAN BE SURE THAT HE CONDUCTS HIS BUSINESS WITH THE UTMOST DECENCY AND PROPRIETY.

HEAVE! YOU GOTTA PULL PERCY HARDER THAN THAT!

FASTER! FASTER!

KELLOGG'S CORN FLAKES

SEVENTH DAY ADVENTISTS ANTI-MASTURBATION LEAGUE

TUG! JERK! YANK!

Our Town Council's a Fucking ZOO!

THE TOWN of Wangcombe-on-Sea had the strangest local authority ever. For following a mix-up in the ballot papers on polling day, all the exotic animals in the local zoo were elected to sit on the municipal council...

Local youngsters Tommy and Tina Taylor were on their way to the town hall...

Hurry up, sis! There's a Parks and Planning meeting today. We don't want to miss it!

No! With all the wild creatures on the committee, it'll be an absolute shit-show! Ho! Ho!

...and the kids weren't disappointed!

Please Do Not Feed the Councillors.

Ha! Ha! Ha!

Ha! Ha! Ha!

Shortly...

That was super! Did you see when the Lord Mayor threw his shit at the alderman giraffe?

Yes. We're so lucky to have a Town Hall Zoo!

Suddenly...

Look out!

Eek!

I wonder where those circus folk were going in such a hurry.

Let's follow them and find out!

The children watched as the clown car pulled up outside Wangcombe-on-Sea Art Gallery...

ART GALLERY

Hmm... That's decidedly odd.

I wonder what they're up to...

NOW ON SHOW AT WANGCOMBE-ON-SEA ART GALLERY

THE MONA LISA!

ON LOAN FROM THE LOUVRE, PARIS

Of *course!* That's it!

What?! I don't understand!

SNAP!

Don't you see, Tina? These circus baddies are planning to use their big top skills to steal the Mona Lisa - the world's most expensive work of art!

Gosh! But how!?!

LetterbОocks

letters@viz.co.uk

IF former MP Ann Widdecombe ever decides to get married, I think she could do a lot worse than marry the similarly named diminutive comedian Josh Widdicombe. That way, she wouldn't have to change her name with the banks and what have you. Well, not much anyway.

Iain Devenney, Abingdon

GOOD things come to those who wait, they say. Well I waited 45 minutes for the number 87 bus yesterday, only to sit next to an old man who talked about his haemorrhoids and farted all the way into town. I wonder if the so- called experts can explain that one.

Horatio Flunge, Sheffield

THE Covid vaccine is a fantastic thing but, shortly after being given one, you require a booster. I'm no conspiracy theorist, but Bill Gates has been putting money into vaccine development, and getting something and then it immediately needing to be updated has the look and feel of a Bill Gates product to me. I bet the boffins can explain this one, but don't want to.

James Wallace, Belper

IN America, toilets are called restrooms. But when I fell asleep in one in Disneyland, after a heady morning of vodka and benzodiazepines, they called the police and had me thrown out of the park. Honestly, make your mind up.

Charles Menton, Glastonbury

WHILST walking my dog in the park recently, I noticed that geese do not actually goose step. Moorhens however, do. I have no wish to rewrite one of the darkest chapters in our history, but I think that we have been incorrectly describing the way Herr Hitler and his brutish hordes would march.

Heinz Ketchup, Orkney

WHY are small things measured by comparison to a human hair? – this wire is the thickness of a human hair, or that spider's silk is one tenth the thickness of a human hair. Surely there are better things to use than human hair, and it's not fair on men who are bald.

Jeremy Balding, Spalding

WHEN ladies' nipples are visible through their clothing, men commonly remark that they could "have someone's eye out with those". I wonder if any readers who work in a hospital A&E department could confirm whether this is actually possible? If so, I would suggest that such a remark is a legitimate health and safety warning rather than an unacceptable sexist comment. I would appreciate a swift reply as there is an industrial tribunal riding on this.

Brian Westcountry Faggots, Orkney

STAR LETTER

I WAS travelling to London from Newcastle the other day, and just outside Newark Northgate I saw a man in a field with his trousers round his ankles having a shit. I wouldn't have minded so much, but I'd upgraded my ticket to first class, and it's not the type of thing you expect to see out of a first class window.

Bertram Crisps, Wallsend

WITH the popular vote so close to 50-50, has America ever considered having two Presidents, one Republican and one Democrat? They could both live in the White House – which is plenty big enough – and just try to get along and sort everything out. And if it turns out not to be a great way to run a country, they could always flog the format to Channel 5.

D Cox, Poole

FIVE years ago my wife and I visited Lisbon zoo, and whilst looking at the tropical birds I espied a grey parrot who looked like he might enjoy being taught some English. I spent ten minutes repeating a word that I thought suitable for him until I was moved on by a member of staff. I have no idea if my efforts have borne fruit, so could I ask readers of your publication if they have ever been to Lisbon zoo and heard the word "bollocks" emanating from the bird house?

Bob Pitt, Kendal

I CANNOT remember the last time I had a hole in my pocket that I could stick my finger through and poke my nob. Well done trouser boffins. You've got that sewn up.

Stuie, Bunny

WITH regard to *Viz* reader Dominic Twose's problem of getting an international Airport named after himself *(page 11)*, much like that personalised car number plate Top Tip that you keep getting sent, the obvious answer would be for him to change his name to that of an existing airport. I suggest Charles De Gaulle or Indira Ghandi would do nicely, though Dallas Fort Worth also has a nice ring to it. I did this once to win a bet and have never looked back.

Chicago O'Hare, Aberdeen

✱ *Thank you Mr O'Hare. And thanks to the many Viz readers who also came up with this idea, as well as the ones who will write in suggesting it as a Top Tip for many years to come.*

WHY are good things said to be "The Bee's Knees"? The knees are perhaps the most rubbish bit of a bee. I think its fuzzy arse with a big, barbed sting sticking out is much better. "The Bee's Bum" would be a much more appropriate expression.

Billy Bookcase, Guildford

IF companies like Deliveroo had been around in the 1970s, the whole plot of every *Terry and June*, with Terry's boss Sir Dennis unexpectedly coming around to dinner most evenings and June having no food ready, would have been ruined.

Phil Godsell, Bedford

IF extraterrestrials do exist, it would be great if they could land their spaceship in my neighbour's garden in the dead of night and shit him up a bit. To be honest, the bloke's an absolute helmet.

D Danter, Cardiff

HOW come no one ever farts on ITV's *Tipping Point*? There's been so many episodes of it, surely someone must have dropped their guts on it at least once. I wonder if they put corks up the contestants' arses to stop them from trumping during the show, or something.

David Wardle, Manchester

✱ *Let's see if our readers can throw any light on it, David. Perhaps you work on the Tipping Point production team and could let us know how you stop contestants from breaking wind. Or perhaps you have been a contestant on the show and could tell us what they did to you in order to keep you from blowing off. All letters will be treated in the strictest confidence.*

WHY isn't *Viz* stocked in my local Waitrose? Surely the upper class love a tit or bum gag as much as the rest of us. Come on, Waitrose. Let's spread some great fanny jokes to our revered betters.

Adrian Newth, Stratford upon Avon

TERRY and DUNE

Walk across the patio without rhythm, dear.

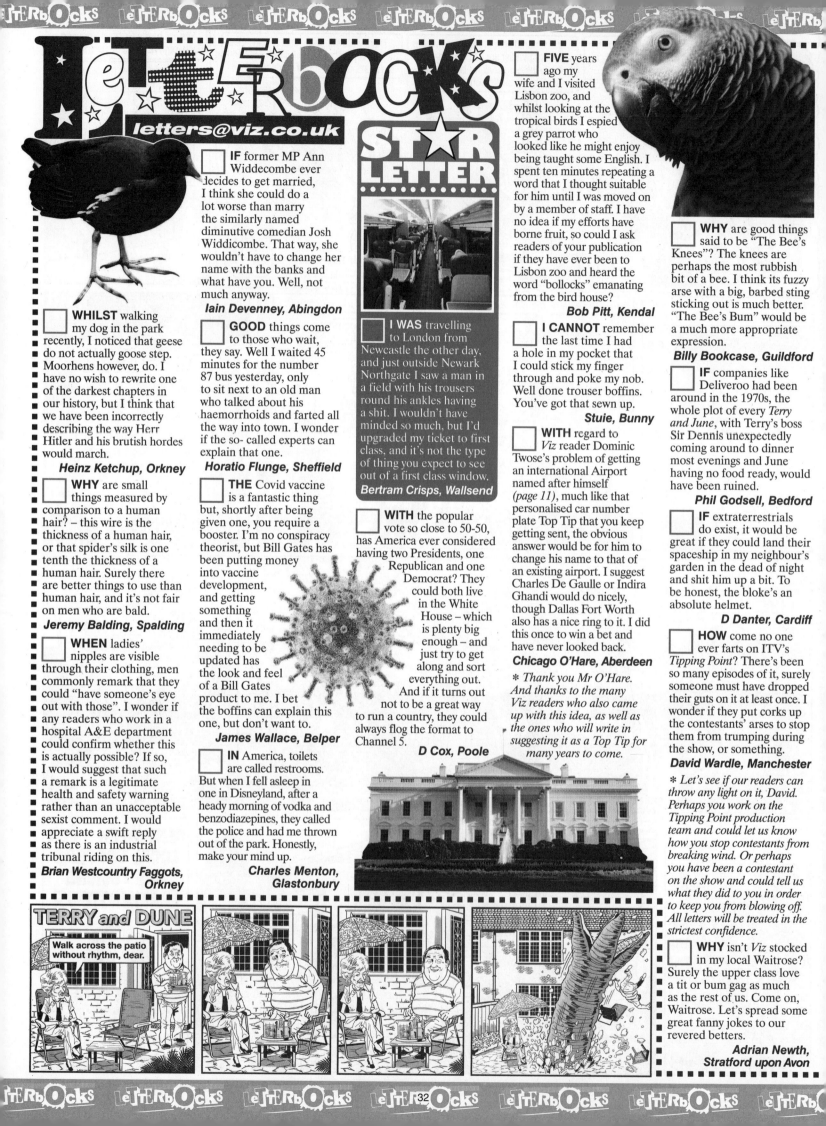

Gary Neville gives passionate must-watch anal...
Sky Sports Football
1.2M views

MY ENGLISH friends often ask me why soccer never caught on here in the US like it has in the rest of the world. I give you Exhibit A. You people need to get professional help.

Derek P, Massachusetts

WHEN 007 gets rained on or falls in the sea whilst fighting, he's invariably bone dry before he zooms off in his Aston Martin with some saucy minx at his side. But if I dribble down my beige slacks, it takes hours to dry and the wife disowns me. Once again it's one rule for Her Majesty's Secret Service agents and a completely different rule for gentlemen of advancing years.

Stuie, Bunny

TALKING to a friend the other day, I suddenly realised that he's really thick, and has been for a long while. Then I thought that I must be even more stupid for not noticing it before. Do any so-called scientists have an equation to decide which of us is the most dense?

Jimmy Big-Guns, email

BIRDS teach their chicks how to tap their feet on the grass to attract worms. Judging by the amount of them this has fooled for thousands of years, it would seem that worms don't teach their children to avoid the danger. There is clearly a massive imbalance between worm and bird education.

Andrew McGuigan, Blaydon

I CANNOT recall the product that was for sale on a recent TV advert where a bulldog prats around on a skateboard. Whatever it is, I will not be giving the company the benefit of my custom because they failed to get the CGI people to give the dog an arsehole. If they can't even ensure an accurate depiction of a dog with an arsehole, I'll be fucked if I will trust them with my cash.

Bob Pitt, Kendal

ALWAYS park next to cars of the same colour at supermarkets, so when neighbouring car doors are opened, the scratches match your paintwork.

David Craik, Hull

GYM goers. Rather than fighting each other to park nearest the gym entrance, simply park further away, count the number of steps you take to the gym door and deduct them from the thousands your are about to do on the treadmill.

Jock Itch, Gorbals

EMPLOYERS. Cut time lost due to staff toilet breaks by placing cat litter trays strategically around your workplace.

Marty H, Bradford

SCAMMERS. Improve your revenue exponentially by simply running a spelling and grammar check before sending out millions of emails that don't even make sense.

Bing Crosby, Cockermouth

CONVINCE neighbours you are highly sought-after violin teacher by putting a sign in your garden that says "Violin Lessons: Sorry, No Vacancies."

John Moynes, Dublin

HAVE press studs surgically attached in a circle around your head. Corresponding ones on your hat means you can look stylish and debonair no matter how windy it gets. Having the press studs lower on one side of your head will allow you to tilt your hat at a rakish angle.

Sam Green, Exeter

SAVE money on model railway equipment by simply walking to the top of a hill near a railway station and looking down. Hey presto! Your own perfect replica, accurate in every way, including delayed trains and muffled PA announcements.

Willosaurus, Bath

CONFRONTED by your wife over whether you have slept with her mother? Buy some much needed thinking time by indignantly accusing her of "playing politics" and insisting you are focused on getting on with the job of putting the bins out.

Kevin Caswell-Jones, Wrexham

TiPs

toptips@viz.co.uk

WHY, oh why, oh why are TV camera operators at major sporting events always told by the studio directors to pan their cameras away from streakers? I think I speak for most right-thinking viewers when I say that a bollock-naked piss artist legging it across the hallowed turf whilst being pursued by a posse of overweight security guards in hi-viz jackets is arguably one of the funniest spectacles on the planet. The prospect of either party going arse over tit renders the actual scoreline of the game completely irrelevant.

Kevin Caswell-Jones, Gresford

I'M as patriotic as the next man, but if I was offered a New Year's Honour I would turn it down. The extra letters before or after my name, a knighthood or an OBE would honestly be nothing more than a nightmare. Thanks but no thanks, Your Majesty. Give it to a deserving pop star or actor for services to one thing or another.

Cumcise Analpr, Bradford

MY friend was telling me that his son is being badly bullied at school. It's a sad indictment of today's education system that kids these days aren't even any good at making weaker kids' lives a misery. Back in my day, it was the only thing me and my mates were good at. It's hardly surprising that all the apprentices we take on at work only last a couple of months.

Steve Crouch, Peterborough

LONG LIVE LONG KING DONG

HAD HE lived, mythical 70s and 80s playground porn legend King Dong would have been 70 this year, or possibly even 80. In fact, depending on which website you go on, he may even still be alive. Regardless, he touched many of our lives and to mark of these two potential milestones and also possibly his death, you've been sending in your playground rumours about him.

...IN 1978, a mate's brother reckoned King Dong's cock was 3 foot long and that he'd pass out if he got a hard on, so all his scenes were done using a rubber nob.

Brian, Leeds

IN 1983, a rumour started at school that King Dong was our geography teacher's brother. We all drew cocks on our homework asking our teacher to get his brother to autograph them for us. However, it turned out our teacher's brother was actually John Holmes, so we never got the autograph.

Tony, Ripon

IN THE late seventies, a lad in my class said his dad made porn films in America and he got to help out during the school holidays. He met King Dong and he said he had to carry his nob around in a wheelbarrow to give it a rest between scenes. He said he was forced to sign a confidentiality agreement that meant he could only tell the other kids in his year at school and not the newspapers, so word never got out.

Rocco, Dewsbury

IN THE 70s, we had an art teacher who, according to a rumour, had posed nude in Playboy. Nobody had ever seen it, but this did not stop it being believed true, and this led to a rumour that she had also made a film with King Dong before she did her PGCE. Barry Whiting said his dad had a 10th generation VHS of it, and he had watched it while his dad was out and it was definitely her.

Graham, Nottingham

I GREW up in the 70s in San Fernando Valley in California – the famed home of America's porn industry. We would often see King Dong around town or when he was on his lunch break. It was no big deal to us and subsequently we had no schoolyard tales about him, except for the one about him passing out if he got a hard on. But he came in to school to give us a talk on road safety one time and he said it wasn't true.

Leonardo, Los Angeles

FRUGAL Sharkey

Hmm, could go a cuppa.

I'll see where I'm at on the smart meter.

Bloody Nora!

I've *already* blazed through two of today's five kilowatt minutes!

TODAY: £00.12

Oh, sod it! It's only your birthday once a year - live a little, man!

Cut loose!

Actually, to hell with scrimping for one day!

Treat yourself to a virgin bag!

one brew two brew three brew

Ok. *Calm*. There's exactly one cup of water in there. *Relax*.

H-here goes...

Come on. *Come on!*

Boil, damn you! Boil! *BOIL!*

TODAY: £00.28

Phew, glad that's over

If I'd eaten today think I might have thrown up there.

Two portions of milk, and why not? I'm worth it!

Besides, I need to get through 'em - they're four years out of date.

Not that UHT ever *actually* goes off...

That's the point, it lasts forever. Like coleslaw.

KNOCK KNOCK

Kevin, to what do I owe this unexpected pleasure?

Whatever you're after'd best be free!

Just here to wish my favourite cousin many happy returns!

Oh. Thanks, very kind.

I've no pressie or nothing, but I did knock up a really cool arrangement of *Happy Birthday* on my synthesiser, especially for you!

He'll expect refreshment.

Sorry, I'm busy. With... things

Aww, go on, *please*. I got the Human League in to advise me and everything.

That frigging Human League!

I'll set up here, shall I?

Mind my tea!

Oh, soz.

But if you're putting on the kettle again, I could murder a-

I'm not. *Ever.*

Where can I plug in?

Whaat? Doesn't that thing run on batteries?!

Don't be daft, cuz. It's a 1979 Moog Prodigy!

Never even a battery model available!

Don't you want a happy birthday? Don't you want one, ohhh, oh-oh-oh!

TODAY: £01.35

Don't - aw.

Okay, thanks. I get the general idea.

Now I can't shower for a fortnight.

Cockney Wanker

ONE MORNING...

ORWIGHT, WANKAH? WANT SOME GAWDFORSAKEN AN' EGGS, DO YA?

NO FANKS, SHIRL... AR'M GOIN' AAHT

SHAKE A LEG, JUNIOR... YOU'RE CAMMIN' WIV ME

WHERE TO, DAD?

T' THE BOXIN' GYM, MAR SAN

WOT FOR?

WE'RE GOIN' T' 'AVE A **FIGHT**, SAN... A BIT OF A DAST-AP

A DAST-AP!?!.. WHY? AR AIN'T DAN NAFFINK WRONG, 'AVE AR!?

NO, YOU 'AVEN'T, SAN... BAT IT'S A TRADITION IN THE FAAAAAAAAAMLY!

EVERY WANKAH WHEN HE TURNS SIXTEEN GETS IN THE RING WIV 'IS OLD MAN...

HMM?

...IT'S A RITE O' PASSAGE, SAN

AN' YOU'VE CAM OF AGE... YOU'LL CLARM IN THAT RING A **BOY**...

...BAT YOU'LL BE CARRIED AAHT OF IT A **MAN!**

Ye Olde Apples & Pears

RIGHT

WHEN AR WAS SIXTEEN, MAR OLD MAN TOOK ME IN THE RING AN' KNOCKED SEVEN BELLS O' TOM TIT AAHT O' ME...

...IT 'URT AT THE TIME, SAN, BAT IT MADE ME THE MAN AR AM TODAY... AN' AR FANK 'IM

AN IN A FEW YEARS TIME, YOU'LL BE WALKIN' INTO THIS FAT BOY SLIM WI' **YOUR** BOY, READY T' MAKE A MAN OF 'IM IN THE WANKAH TRADITION

...IT'S THE CIRCLE O' LARF... AN' IT MOVES AS AWL

ARSEHOLE'S GYM

HMM

NOW, AR WANT YOU T' GINE AS GOOD AS YOU GET TODAY, SAN

'COS AR'M GOIN' T' GO FOR YER, MAR BOY... NO SHAWT MEASURES

YUS, DAD

AR WARN YER...YOU'LL TAKE A RART OLD PASTIN' IN THAT QUEEN AN' KING TODAY... AN' IT'LL 'URT

IT'LL URT BAAAAD!

HMM!

BAT IT'LL BE THE **LARST TIME** ANYONE LAYS A FACKIN' FINGER ON YOU... ORWIGHT...

HMM?.. YUS

PUT THESE ON

THIS IS TAFF LAV, THIS IS.. **TAFF LAV!** AN' IT'S COS AR LAV YER SO MATCH THAT AR'M GOIN' T' 'URTCHAH!...

BAT IT'S GOIN' T' 'URT ME MORE THAN IT 'URTS YOU, TRAST ME

BAT WHEN IT'S DAN, WE'LL BOFE GO DAAAHN THE RAB-A-DAB FOR A NARCE PINT O' KING LEAR...

...FARVA AN' SAN TOGEVVAH!

YOUR GOIN' T' LOOK BACK ON THIS DAY WIV **PRAARD**, SON...

...THE DAY YOU BECOME A MAAN!

DON'T BE SCARED, SAN...

...THE PAIN WILL BE MOMENTARY... THE EFFECT WILL BE ETERNAL!

JAST REMEMBAH... AR LAV YAH!

SECONDS AAHT... RAAAHND ONE!

DING! DING!

SMACK!

OOOOF!

ONE... TWO... FREE... FOUR...FARVE... SIX...

WOT THE FACKIN'!?

SEVEN... EIGHT... NARN... **AAHT!**

YOU BARSTAD...YOU LITTLE FACKIN' BARSTAD!

YOU CAM AT ME WHEN AR WEREN'T READY

YOU FACKIN' TOERAG, YOU... YOU CHEATIN' LITTLE FACKAH!

'ITTIN' A GEEZER IN GLARSES, AN' AWL...

GAW!

NEXT DAY...

ORWIGHT, WANKAH? WANT SOME GAWDFORSAKEN AN' EGGS, DO YA?

NO FANKS, SHIRL... AR'M GOIN' AAHT

WHERE WE GOIN' DADDY?

T' THE BOXIN' GYM, SAN...

...EVERY WANKAH GETS IN THE RING WIV HIS OLD MAN WHEN HE TURNS SIX...

...IT'S A RITE O' PASSAGE

LOVE 'EM or hate 'em, you just can't avoid 'em. And if you've ever been higher than 10 storeys in a building, chances are you've been in one. Unless you used the stairs. They're LIFTS, and they've been taking us up and down buildings for decades. We take lifts for granted, jumping in, pushing a button, watching as the doors close, then open again, then pushing the button again rapidly in frustration before the doors finally close and we are whisked off on a vertical journey. And you probably think you know all there is to know about these miraculous ascending and descending boxes. Well, think again. here are...

20 THINGS YOU NEVER KNEW ABOUT LIFTS

1 If you look it up in the dictionary, the word 'lift' means to raise something up to a higher level. However, a lift can also lower things down, for example when moving people or goods from a higher floor to one below. So the dictionary is actually wrong on this count.

2 Whilst most people wear their shoes in lifts, some people wear lifts in their shoes! Short-arsed celebs such as **SYLVESTER STALLONE**, **TOM CRUISE** and **VLADIMIR PUTIN** are all rumoured to secrete hidden wedges – known as 'lifts' – in the heels of their footwear to make it appear that they are of normal height.

3 Lifts have been the subject of countless children's books, such as Roald Dahl's *Charlie and the Great Glass Elevator* (the American word for lift) and many more too numerous to mention.

4 Some of the earliest known lifts were used in the Roman Colosseum. There were around 25 lifts, each powered by eight men, which could raise a cage of lions 23 feet in the air. Although this was a popular spectacle at the time, it was to be another few years before the Emperor Domitian had the idea of putting the lifts under the floor of the Colosseum, so that the animals could be lifted up and let out at the top.

5 After the success of the1975 film *The Towering Inferno*, the Union of American Elevator Operatives (UEAO) specified that every Hollywood blockbuster was required by law to have an action scene set in an 'elevator' – the American word for 'lift'. Famous examples include *Die Hard* (the bit with man in the lift) and *Die Hard 3* (the bit with the men in the lift).

6 The most famous lifts in the world are those at the back of the clothing department in 70s sitcom *Are You Being Served*. However, the show – set in the fictional Grace Brothers department store – was actually filmed on a phoney BBC Television Centre soundstage, and the 'lifts' were fake and not connected to any other floors.

7 The world's smallest lift was owned and operated by **CALVIN PHILLIPS**, the world's smallest man. It consisted of ten matchboxes Sellotaped together with a single inner drawer pulled up and down inside the 'floors' by a length of string over a cotton reel at the top. However, Phillips never got to take a ride in it as, despite being the world's smallest man, he was much too large to fit inside a matchbox.

8 According to an internet article we found by googling the words "famous people sex in a lift", actors **BENICIO DEL TORO** and **SCARLETT JOHANSSON** have consistently failed to deny having it off during an 8-floor lift ride at Hollywood's Chateau Marmont hotel in 2004. Other people who haven't denied having sexual intercourse during a half-minute-long elevator trip at the luxury Tinseltown inn include former Lib-Dems leader **NICK CLEGG**, TV weatherman **MICHAEL FISH** and *Corrie* battleaxe Ena Sharples, aka 122-year-old actress **VIOLET CARSON**.

9 Googling "famous people sex in elevator" yields similar results.

10 Lifts aren't only used for carrying people. Tiny little lifts called "dumbwaiters" were invented in the United States in the early nineteenth century to carry food between floors of tall buildings. However they only really caught on in the 1840s when an eagle-eyed engineer realised that the buttons used to operate the lift were best placed on the outside of the lift, rather than the inside.

11 Many well known songs about lifts have made it into the hit parade, such as *Love in an Elevator* by Aerosmith, *Elevator* by the Pussycat Dolls, and *Elevator* by Flo Rida featuring Timberland.

12 And *Lift* by Radiohead, which was released in the US under the title *Elevator*.

13 Back in 2016, pop star **PRINCE** – also known as a squiggle – died in the lift at his Minnesota mansion following an overdose of the painkiller fentanyl. It is believed that the Norman Wisdom-sized sex-mad *Purple Rain* Jehovah's Witness could have lain dead in his luxury Paisley Park elevator – an incorrect American term for a lift – for up to 6 hours before being discovered. That's almost long enough to have watched all 3 original *Star Wars* films back to back.

14 The only bit he would have missed would have been the last quarter of an hour of *Return of the Jedi*, where the ghosts of Obi-Wan, Yoda and Anakin Skywalker appear in a sort of Ready Brek glow.

15 A 2018 survey completed by over 200 lift repair companies across the world revealed that the lift button which required replacing most often due to wear was the one for the ground floor. This is the same in all lifts, no matter how many floors they service. "Every button should statistically have the same chance of breaking due to wear and tear. Why it's always the ground floor ones that go first we'll never know," said University of Oxford mathematician Professor Marcus du Sautoy.

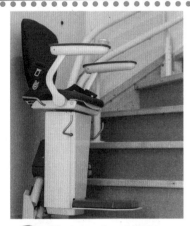

up to 30 times more dangerous than travelling in a proper lift. However, fatalities are rare and generally, if you mis-time your entrance or exit, the worst you can expect is to lose a foot or possibly a leg.

19 On average, 30 people die each year in America as a result of accidents in elevators (the term Americans mistakenly use when they mean lift), while up to 17,000 people are injured – that's the same as the population of Dorking in Surrey.

16 The opposite of 'lift' is 'stairs' – the familiar rise of evenly spaced horizontal struts which enable non-powered passage between different levels of a structure. However the two commonly co-exist in the form of a stairlift – or a seat fitted to a rail which facilitates bidirectional travel along the same trajectory as the stairs. You couldn't make it up!

17 At 418 feet, Northampton's National Lift Tower is Britain's tallest test facility of its kind and contains half a dozen state-of-the-art high speed lift shafts. However, all the researchers who work there suffer from claustrophobia, and in order to get to the research labs they are forced to take the 725 stairs to the top.

18 Travelling in a 'paternoster' – an old-fashioned elevator (the American misnomer for lift), in which the cars loop around without stopping - is

20 Famous past residents of Dorking include actor **LAURENCE OLIVIER**, Gold 104.3 DJ **CHRISTIAN O'CONNELL**, *Robinson Crusoe* author **DANIEL DEFOE**, and *Come Play With Me* porn star **MARY MILLINGTON**.

3...2...1... LIFT OFF!

Your lift questions answered by a reputable lift engineer with one average review on Trustpilot.

Q. I'M HEALTH CONSCIOUS and I understand that you burn more calories taking the stairs than if you use a lift. But the stairs in the block of flats where I live reek of piss and I'm reluctant to take them. Would I burn just as many calories if I were to jog on the spot whilst in the lift?

A. Probably, but I wouldn't recommend jogging on the spot whilst in the lift as the extra commotion could destabilise the sheave (the pulley the wire cables are wrapped around) and cause uncoupling of the elevator cart. Why not take some light dumb bells in the lift with you and do some slow squats?

Q. ARE LIFT MECHANICS responsible for the music we hear in lifts? The lift in my workplace only plays *In The Air Tonight*, but I only need to go three floors, and I always exit before the good bit where the drums kick in. Could we not have more songs where the chorus appears sooner, or ideally, have a song that starts with the chorus like *She Loves You* by The Beatles or *Build Me Up Buttercup* by The Foundations?

A. Sadly we lift engineers are not responsible for the muzak heard in lifts. Why don't you simply press all the buttons of the lift when entering? That way it will stop at each floor, open its doors, wait and then close again. I'm sure this will enable ample time for the drums to kick in.

Q. I SAW *Fatal Attraction* the other night and couldn't help but admire the virility of Michael Douglas and his impromptu shag with Glenn Close in a lift. I just wondered if people really do this, and what are the actual odds of getting caught shagging in a lift?

A. It really depends on many factors, including how quickly the lift travels between floors, the number of people using the lift per hour, and the time it takes the shagging couple to complete the sex act. If you're thinking of giving it a go and don't want to get caught, choose a lift that will be quiet, such as an out of town shopping centre car park lift on a Sunday evening. Or you might consider moving to Sweden where public nudity is considered normal in most places, including lifts, and displays of affection are not as frowned upon as they are here in the UK.

▲ LIFT LOCK-IN ▽

IT'S THE STUFF of bad dreams. To be in a lift which breaks down between floors, stuck having to make small talk with a stranger for a couple of hours until your eventual release. How much worse it would be if it were somebody like Nigel Farage, Naomi Campbell, or him out of *Mrs Brown's Boys*? On the other hand, you could be trapped with one of your favourite celebrities and have them all to yourself for a couple of hours as they entertained you with stories and anecdotes from their life in showbiz. *It could be the best two hours of your life!* We went on the streets to ask ordinary people which famous person they would like to be trapped in a lift with for a couple of hours...

...I'VE always loved Pavarotti, so being trapped with him for 2 hours in a lift would be wonderful. It would be a bit of a squeeze, as I weigh 28 stone, as does he, which may explain why the lift broke in the first place. And I imagine he wouldn't be able to sing to me, as it would be far too loud for such a small space. So we'd just have to chat about classical music or something until the engineers came.

Edna Ballsup, shop assistant

...I'D like to be trapped in a lift with Gary Lineker. I've followed his career since he started at Leicester in 1978 and I think he is a tremendous ambassador for the game. And if there was ever a lull in the conversation, we could have a bit of a kickabout in the lift with the football that I always carry with me just in case this situation ever arises.

Stan Broadleaf, cabbie

...I'D like to be trapped in a lift for a couple of hours with Jeffrey Archer. We could chat about all the great books he has written over the years. Then after that, we'd probably just stand in awkward silence for an hour and 58 minutes until rescued.

Troy Beesting, plumber

...JOHN Cleese would be my favourite broken lift companion. I grew up with Monty Python and I know all their sketches off by heart, and I'd spend two hours repeating all the best ones for his amusement, doing the voices and everything. He'd have a great time and we'd probably agree to keep in touch with each other after our ordeal was over.

Billy Cheeses, office worker

...I'D love to be trapped in a lift with one of my favourite comedians, Rod Hull. I dare say he get up to all sorts of tomfoolery, grabbing me by the genitals, wrestling me to the ground and pulling off my shoe. It would be hilarious. And if he had his emu puppet with him, all the better. I assume this is hypothetical and the fact that he's dead doesn't make any difference.

Frank Brush, electrician

GOVERNMENT IN CRISIS!

Fears for Democracy as No.10 runs out of pens.

A DOWNING Street whistle-blower has blown the whistle on dangerously low stationery levels at the heart of government. And in a document leaked to *The Times*, they reveal that after more than half the stock was removed without authority, Whitehall staff now say Number 10's stationery cupboard is 'running on empty'. The resultant shortage of envelopes, pens, typewriter ribbons and duplicating paper leaves the governance of the country in a parlous state in the run-up to Christmas.

PEN-DING INVESTIGATION: *An anonymous source revealed 10 Downing Street's stationery cupboard had over half its stock taken without authority.*

The famous cupboard – often cited as the true heart of government – ensures that pens are always available for ministers to approve catastrophic legislation or sign-off taxpayer-funded infrastructure deals for chums. But the revelation that it is near-empty has rocked Britain's seat of power to its foundations. And worse, the whistle-blower says that *a former Prime Minister was behind the thefts*.

espadrilles

The anonymous civil servant, dubbed 'Basildon Bond', says that former PM Liz Truss was seen wearing larger dresses than usual in the final few weeks of her few-weeks-long premiership. According to Bond, these dresses would mysteriously bulk out during the day. He also revealed that Truss was often seen with a full array of coloured pens and pencils in her handbag.

sofa

The famous walk-in cupboard – often used as a secure meeting place for discussions of an intimate nature – is situated between the Cabinet Office and the PM's rooms. The source said that the quiet location of the cupboard would have afforded the former Prime Minister ample time to clear its shelves of taxpayer-funded stationery.

The nameless Whitehall mandarin catalogued a wide range of missing items, from reams of A4 paper to half-full boxes of staples and the Chancellor's favourite treasury tags, along with civil service pens, pencils, erasers, sharpeners, whiteboard markers and coloured post-it notes.

hoisin

The long time Downing Street staffer also claimed that a toaster and several coffee mugs disappeared 'into thin air' from the communal kitchen on Mrs Truss's last day. They accuse the short-lived PM of stuffing these kitchen items into a Tesco bag along with teabags and sachets of No. 10 Ketchup and HP Sauce. These were then handed to an aide to hide in the boot of her car before she was driven to Buckingham Palace to hand in her resignation to the king.

A spokesman for the record-breaking PM refused to comment. We also approached the Official Keeper of the Governmental Stationery for a statement, but they didn't answer our calls. Although we might possibly have dialled the wrong number.

COUNT THE SPOONS

FAILED Prime Minister Liz Truss may or may not be the latest incumbent of Downing Street to have allegedly helped herself to freebies from the government stationery cabinet, but she is by no means the first. Accusations of prime ministerial light fingers have dogged many of the country's leaders during their time in Number 10...

THE MILK'S NOT FOR TURNING: *Thatcher (left) would sneak pintas (above) from neighbour's doorstep.*

● **IN 2016,** *PM David Cameron resigned after his attempt to placate the UK Independence Party by calling a referendum on Britain's membership of the EU spectacularly backfired. On leaving number 10, he reportedly went round the building's 100 rooms and removed all the light bulbs, telling staffers that they were his. When his successor Theresa May took office later that night, she found the place in complete darkness and almost tripped over Larry the cat whilst trying to find her way to the Prime Ministerial apartments.*

Attorney General Jeremy Wright QC later ruled that in law, the bulbs constituted 'fixtures and fittings' and as such must be returned.

● **MARGARET THATCHER** *earned the nickname 'Milk Snatcher' after her unpopular move to cut free milk in schools. But the nation's children were not the only ones to lose out on the white stuff. For* Thatcher would regularly steal milk from her next-door neighbour, Chancellor Sir Geoffrey Howe. Sleeping only a few hours a night, the Iron Lady would rise at 4.30 each morning, sneak out of the famous front door and half-inch a pinta from the step of No. 11. She was eventually spotted by a neighbour returning early from a night-shift, who reported what was going on to Howe.

Keen to avoid a scandal, Sir Geoffrey did not confront the PM, but bought a special 'lockable doorstep milk bottle box' from Argos, and the thefts stopped.

● **THE LAST LABOUR** *leader to hold the top office in the country – Gordon Brown – was shown the door after coming second in the 2010 general election. When his successor David Cameron moved into the property the next day, he was shocked to see that the fireplace in the famous cabinet room had been ripped out. Security footage of Brown's final meeting with his top ministers showed clearly that the fireplace was in situ the day before, and that it must have been removed the day before Cameron moved in.*

The new incumbent reported the matter to police who, after a tip-off, discovered the ornate 18th century marble surround propped up in the back yard of a house in Fife. The occupier of the house? A certain Gordon Brown MP.

THE BOTTOM INSPECTORS in... TERROR on LUST Island!

...I'M STARTING TO WONDER IF JACK'S GOING OFF ME... HE'S SNOGGED FOUR OTHER GIRLS TODAY AND HE WON'T EVEN TALK TO ME...

MAYBE HE'S JUST A BIT SHY...

TRIIING!!

OH WOW! I'VE LIKE... GOT A TEXT?!

OH! MY GOD! THAT'S AWESOME!

IT SAYS THREE NEW GUYS ARE GOING TO BE JOINING THE ISLAND IN FIVE MINUTES!

WAIT..! IT SAYS "AND FOR TODAY'S TASK, YOU MUST COMPLY WITH THE GUYS' INSTRUCTIONS"!

"...# BOTTOMS UP! # AN INSPECTOR CALLS!"

WHAT DO YOU THINK THEY'LL MAKE US DO?

DUNNO. BUT HOW EXCITING!

THAT DOESN'T SOUND RIGHT... YOU DON'T THINK IT COULD BE... THEM, DO YOU..?

NO, NO... THEY COULDN'T...

...THEY WOULDN'T...

THEY COULD!

THEY WOULD!

...AND THEY DID!

...IT'S THE BOTTOM INSPECTORS!

SCREAM!

THAT'S NOT FAIR! THE PRODUCERS SAID WE'D BE SAFE ON THE ISLAND!

...AND SO YOU ARE...

...IF YOU HAVE COMMITTED NO BOTTOM CRIMES!

THEY TOLD US LUST ISLAND WAS OUT OF YOUR OFFICE'S JURISDICTION!

HA! NOWHERE IS OUT OF OUR JURISDICTION!

...NOW BARE YOUR BOTTOMS!

HMM... THIS BOTTOM LOOKS IN ORDER...

...BUT WAIT!

...AN INTERESTING PATTERN OF SUNTAN HERE...

...INTERESTING AND HIGHLY ILLEGAL!

YOU WILL BE LEAVING FOR A VERY DIFFERENT ISLAND TODAY..! THE ISLAND OF ALCATRARSE, WHERE NO SUNLIGHT WILL REACH YOUR BUMCHEEKS...FOR THE NEXT TEN YEARS!

...DEAR OH DEAR, YOU HAVE A RATHER SWEATY CLEFT!

IT'S VERY HOT HERE... I COME FROM THE NORTH...

...I'M NOT USED TO THE HEAT..!

THAT IS EASILY CORRECTED...FIVE YEARS IN A SIBERIAN BUMCONTRATION CAMP AND YOUR CLEFT WILL FORGET HOW TO PERSPIRE!

TAKE HIM AWAY!

NO!

HMM...THIS IS NOT GOOD. YOU HAVE WHAT APPEAR TO BE LOVE BITES ON YOUR BUTTOCKS!

IT WAS CINDY! SHE DID THAT! TAKE HER! NOT ME!

SILENCE!

YOUR BUTTOCKS..YOUR CRIME! YOUR TIME ON THIS ISLAND IS OVER, AND YOUR TIME IN A BOTTOM CORRECTION CENTRE IS ABOUT TO BEGIN!

...AND AS FOR YOU, THERE'S NO NEED FOR YOU TO BARE YOUR BOTTOM...

PHEW!

...BECAUSE THIS PHOTOGRAPH OF YOUR BARED BOTTOM POSTED ON YOUR INSTAGRAM CLEARLY SHOWS A PIMPLE ON YOUR LEFT BUTTOCK!

WHAT THE?!

PERHAPS NEXT TIME YOU WON'T TAKE YOUR BOTTOM SELFIES IN 4K HD..!

YOU NEXT! BARE YOUR BOTTOM!

YOU HAVE AN ABRASION PATTERN RUNNING VERTICALLY UP YOUR CLEFT..! IT WOULD APPEAR THAT YOU HAVE BEEN WEARING A THONG DURING EXCESSIVE BUTTOCK MOVEMENT!

...THAT IS A CATEGORY TWO BOTTOM CRIME...!

IT...IT WASN'T MY FAULT! WE WERE TWERKING!

CHELSEA! QUIET!

WE ALL HAD TO TWERK. THE PRODUCERS MADE US DO IT!

TWERKING IS A CATEGORY ONE BOTTOM CRIME...

...AND YOU HAVE JUST IMPLICATED ALL OF YOUR FELLOW ISLANDERS...

WE'RE GOING TO NEED A BIGGER BOAT.

NEXT WEEK! ESCAPE FROM ALCATRARSE!

FOREIGN POWER BUYS NON-LEAGUE MINNOWS

Despotic regime's cash injection could spell success for struggling side

THERE WAS dancing in the streets of Barnton last night as locals learned that the town's floundering football club is being bought by a consortium-led by the wealthy rulers of a foreign country.

Rumours of a buy-out of non-league Barnton Academicals FC by the Krastikovs, ruling family of Russian satellite state Krastikova, have been circulating for a while. But at 10pm last night, fans finally heard the news they had been waiting for as the fabulously wealthy family signed a deal to buy the ailing club.

And not only has the secretive, autocratic state bought the club and its Tuphill Recreation Park ground, it has also snapped up much of the surrounding land, including all the real estate in and around Barnton itself.

But while Amnesty International raised the alarm regarding the regime's 'appalling' record on human rights, supporters of the Midland Athenian League Division One side remained upbeat.

"As fans, you've got to be allowed to enjoy a bit of hope," said season ticket holder Nobby Bleach. "It's not about human rights and all that tonight. It's about hope for the club and the area. That's the priority right now."

And reports that the Krastikovs are planning to triple all rents in the town – a move which could see hundreds of Barnton families end up homeless – left jubilant fans undaunted.

"What's important is that the club is getting a crucial injection of cash which will make us contenders for promotion to the Midland Athenian Premier division," said Sidney Chops, President of the BAFC Supporters' Club.

boot

Civil rights campaigners slammed the club for entering into a deal with the despotic state which regularly executes political dissidents and anyone critical of the ruling regime, citing more than 130 journalists who have 'disappeared' in Krastikov this year alone. But Academicals fans were more upbeat.

"Certainly, the new owners come from a different culture and some of their ways might seem strange to us," said club treasurer Arnold Brasso. "But the £1000 they've pledged to build a 25-seat covered stand is not to be sniffed at."

The first part of the Krastikovs' plan to catapult the non-league minnows into the top flight of football is to bulldoze the town's war memorial and erect a 100m statue of Emperor General Ivan Krastikov who has ruled the totalitarian state for the past 68 years.

"Building that thing is going to create ten new jobs at least," said council leader Len Mollusc. "So not only will the deal make our club a force to be reckoned with on the pitch, it will also do a lot to help local unemployment."

kedgeree

Although representatives of the barbaric regime have confirmed that all Barnton residents will be required to kneel before the towering granite effigy of Emperor Krastikov every day, and that anyone refusing to do so will be shot in the back of the head, jubilant local supporters were undeterred.

"They're paying the players' wages, and they've promised £2000 to get a new striker," said Reg Horseman, secretary of the BAFC Away Game Travel Club. "With money like that we could even tempt somebody from a couple of leagues above, so I'll happily be bending the knee."

But what has concerned a few residents is that the deal also includes a clause which allows the club's new owners to ship

PITCHED UP: *Barnton Academical fans over-the-moon with club buy-out by Russian satellite state Krastikova.*

Barnton's children 2,500 miles to Krastikov to work in the country's cadmium mines. However, supporters of the 2021 Barnton Pork Sausage Cup-winning side believe this is definitely a price worth paying.

"We'd rather not condemn our children to enforced labour in a toxic chemical mine, but what's important is that the club is getting a substantial investment of cash which will allow us to get the midfield right," said manager Billy Limp, waving goodbye to his three children as they were loaded into the back of a Krastikova-bound army truck.

"What's more, they've put up £3000 to refit the match day snack bar. Well, that's silly money, that is," he added.

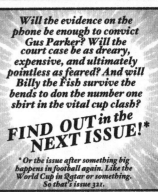

WHEN IN ROME!

We team up with top history buff to assess how the celebs would have fared in classical antiquity

ASK anyone from Land's End to John O'Groats where they would go if they suddenly had access to a time machine, and the answer will always be the same: THE WILD WEST! But for the sake of this article, we're going to say the answer is ANCIENT ROME.

This dangerous – yet glamorous – period of history quite simply has it all: war, death, glory, political turmoil, snazzy clothes, glitzy palaces, mass orgies, and best of all, big fuck-off chariots with all swords coming out the wheels. "It's an utterly compelling turning point in modern civilisation," agrees amateur historian PEVERSLEY CAPSLOCK.

Clinically obese Peversley has devoted his entire life to studying the Roman Empire. From producing an acclaimed glitter-and-glue-based collage of a centurion at primary school, to regularly googling pictures of Lucy Worsley in a toga, the Redcar-based bachelor is the country's self-dubbed 'leading expert' on Italian classical antiquity.

"Mary Beard can kiss my arse," boasts the 64-year-old jobless scholar. "If you want to know owt about Ancient Rome, I'm your man."

The period between 753 BC and 476 AD saw seismic advances in law, architecture, education and medicine on the Italic peninsula and throughout the Roman Empire. But Capslock considers his area of expertise to be the *everyday life* of the ordinary Roman citizenry. "Just imagine watching them big gladiator blokes knocking fuck out of each other in the Colosseum before nipping out to a sex orgy with a load of randy farm girls. Phwoarrrr!" says the distinguished academic, pumping his fist into the crook of his elbow and doing a Les Dawson face.

NO PLACE LIKE ROME: *Self-proclaimed Roman life expert Peversley Capslock reveals how today's stars would have coped in olden days Rome.*

For a bit of fun, we asked Capslock to use his historical expertise to assess how five modern-day A-List celebs might have fared in Ancient Rome. Would they have thrived in this perilous and tumultuous period, perhaps becoming fearsome gladiators, rich tradesmen or famous senators? Or would they have simply got crucified or fed to some lions? Let's find out now, as we see how the stars handle themselves... *WHEN IN ROME!*

Roman A-Lister 1: JEFF BEZOS

Slap-headed CEO Jeff is one of the world's most successful businessmen, having founded the iconic Amazon virtual shopping site back in the 'nineties. For this reason, Capslock believes the hairless entrepreneur would have one glaringly obvious option open to him if were magically whisked back to classical times... to become a MERCHANT in the bustling Roman Forum!

"Bezos has made an absolute killing off of Amazon, so once transported back two millennia, there's no reason why the shiny-domed capitalist

couldn't use that same business savvy to conquer the Ancient Roman marketplace.

He couldn't flog low-cost books, CDs and DVDs over the internet, because it wouldn't exist, but he would likely launch a physical stall – *Amazoniae Dotcommus* – in the centre of the busy Esquiline Hill district, where he would knock out silks, spices, wines, statues and mosaics at low, low prices.

Within months, Jeff's technique of severely undercutting his fellow tradesmen would have worked wonders, and *Amazoniae Dotcommus* would quickly be delivering goods to customers all over the Empire. Of course, in the 21st Century, Bezos' chosen delivery method is by drone – another technology that did not exist in classical antiquity. However, the non-hirsute industrialist could easily come up with a suitable alternative – perhaps strapping small products to magpies or starlings, and using eagles for larger shipments.

Jeff is also renowned for his adventurous nature, famously jetting off to space in his own personal rocket ship. But this tendency to roam into unknown territory may prove to be his downfall in the first century AD. If he chose to charter a fleet of merchant ships and sail along the eastern trade route to Phoenicia, he would most likely encounter vicious bands of marauding pirates. The good ship *Amazoniae Prima* would promptly be plundered for its spoils, and Captain Bezos would be gagged, bound and tossed overboard, where he would sink to a watery death at the bottom of the Erythraean Sea."

42

Roman A-Lister 2: PROFESSOR RICHARD DAWKINS

Aside from building roads, murdering each other and having group sex, the fourth favourite hobby of the Ancient Romans was persecuting Christians. As soon as Jesus Christ was born on the 25th of December 0BC, the citizens of the Empire were all lining up to torture, stone and crucify any of the Son of Man's followers. Among the modern-day celebrity set, there is no-one who enjoys harassing churchgoers more than blasphemous brainbox Richard Dawkins. For this reason, Capslock believes that the egg-headed heathen would make a fabulous Roman **CENTURION!**

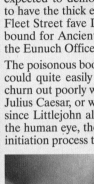

"Centurions were big cocky bastards who dressed up in all gold helmets and whatnot and went around enforcing the Roman law, but according to Wikipedia, they were also prominent figures within the Senate. As such, they regularly addressed huge crowds in the Forum, and as a seasoned lecturer in universities and on telly, Dawkins would be quite at home in this high-profile, public-facing role.

But let's not kid ourselves, the appeal of the job for Richard would be the chance to legally kick seven shades of shit out of any Christian he came across. The *Selfish Gene* author's intense dislike of God and Jesus is well publicised, so he would thrive in this violently Christ-phobic age. Here in the 21st Century, the Oxford boffin is only permitted to express his contempt for religion via scathing tweets and the occasional arse-numbing book. But as a Centurion in the Roman legion, he would have free reign to subject god-botherers to whippings, beatings, crucifixion or lion-based public consumption, as he saw fit. He would be as happy as a pig in shit.

However, the Roman Empire converted to Christianity under the Emperor Constantine around 313 AD. So if Dawkins arrived after this date, his aggressive atheism would receive a far less warm welcome. Unable to resist belittling and mocking the Emperor for believing in 'a right load of old bollocks', Centurion Dawkins would likely find himself stripped of his titles and armour, nailed to a wooden cross and left in a field for the vultures."

Roman A-Lister 3: PETER KAY

From the iconic 1776 volume The Decline and Fall of the Roman Empire *by Edward Gibbon to the shit 2006 potboiler* Dream of Rome *by Boris Johnson, the age of Caesar and Nero has been written about constantly for the past two millennia. However, much of the greatest Roman history comes from within the period itself, with contemporary authors such as Tacitus, Livy and Pliny the Elder setting down the trials and tribulations of the Empire as they occurred. And for Capslock's money, there would be no better A-List Roman* **HISTORIAN** *than roly-poly* Phoenix Nights *funnyman Peter Kay!*

"Peter is the absolute maestro of memory. Whether he's asking an audience if they remember clackers, asking an audience if they remember Angel Delight, or asking an audience if they remember *The A-Team*, there is absolutely nothing from the recent past that the *Car Share* jester cannot recall in intricate detail and then comedically ask an audience if they remember.

Were Peter to be magicked back to the Italian peninsula circa 25 AD, his faultless recollection skills would put him in pole position to become one of the Empire's most accomplished documentarians. In the hustle and bustle of the Forum, the big-boned Boltonian would delight passing citizens by asking them if they remembered the Overthrow of Tarquin the Proud, the Second Punic War or those fiddly old ten-denarii coins brought in by Theodosius II.

And since Ancient Rome is the birthplace of garlic bread, Kay would be sure to find a perfect audience for his iconic catchphrase. *Or so you might think.* Because unfortunately, the Ancient Romans didn't call it 'garlic bread'... they called it *'Allium panem'!* Unaware that his side-splitting slogan was being lost in translation, Kay would become increasingly irate as he bellowed "GARLIC BREAD!?" over and over at the baffled crowd. Before long, a passing centurion would most likely accuse the *Max and Paddy* star of breaching the *Pax Romana*, and promptly run Peter through with his broadsword to shut him up."

Roman A-Lister 3: RICHARD LITTLEJOHN

Top Daily Mail hack Richard is a devoted acolyte of both the Royal family and the Conservative government, using his weekly column to heap praise on Tory MPs and Mountbatten-Windsors alike. He is also – if cruel and unsubstantiated rumour is to be believed – the owner of a laughably small penis.
With these two facts in mind, Capslock believes the purple-faced gobshite would thrive in Ancient Roman times... if he became a **EUNUCH** *at the Emperor's court!*

"Eunuchs, castrated males who served as Imperial court officials, were expected to demonstrate fanatical devotion to those in power, and also to have the thick end of fuck all going on in the trouser department. So, if Fleet Street fave Littlejohn was bundled into a time-travelling DeLorean bound for Ancient Rome, he would be well advised to get straight down the Eunuch Office and see if they are hiring!

The poisonous bootlick's talent for brown-nosing right-wingers and Royals could quite easily be transferred to the Roman senate, where he would churn out poorly written propaganda pieces in support of Nero, Augustus, Julius Caesar, or whoever happened to be in charge when he arrived. And since Littlejohn allegedly already possesses a cock that's barely visible to the human eye, there would be no need for the traditional – and painful – initiation process that usually comes with the job.

However, most Roman leaders were hell-bent on expanding their territory, pushing the borders of Rome out into Europe to transform various different nation states in one cohesive 'European Union'. Given his rabid hatred of the Bonkers Brussels Bureaucrats, Littlejohn would most likely be fervently against this tactic, branding the Emperor a 'woke loony left snowflake' for his desire to unite the continent under one single banner. The micropenised *Mail* man's tenure as Chief Eunuch would then be brought to an abrupt close as he is dragged screaming to the Roman Colosseum, stripped naked and fed to lions for the amusement of a baying crowd."

Roman A-Lister 4: THE STIG

Held at the vast Flavian Amphitheatre, the Roman Games were the highlight of every ancient citizen's calendar. These breathtakingly dangerous events featured everything from live displays by ferocious wild beasts to bone-crunching clashes between the Empire's top gladiators. But according to Capslock, there would only be one member of the 21st Century showbiz set who could cut it in this blood-soaked circus of death – mysterious Top Gear star The Stig, who would enjoy great acclaim as a **CHARIOT RACER!**

"For decades, masked driver The Stig has delighted *Top Gear* viewers with his high-octane antics. So, there's no reason why he wouldn't excel on the racetrack at the Colosseum too. Swapping his Ferrari F430 for a two-wheeled horse-drawn cart and whip, the anonymous telly fave would tear around the amphitheatre in his trademark white jumpsuit and crash helmet, making every other charioteer look very much like 'Captain Slow'!

Of course, chariot drivers were always on the same bill as gladiators, so any aspiring racer would need to be able to hold their own in the dressing room with these bloodthirsty musclebound maniacs. But having worked with producer-thumping petrolhead Jeremy Clarkson for many years, The Stig has picked up a thing or two about fisticuffs. Consequently he would be more than capable of serving up a knuckle sandwich if one of the gladiators starts giving it the big one.

However, one potential problem might arise after the race finishes. Having wiped the floor with his competitors, The Stig would be personally congratulated by the Emperor, who would ask him to remove his helmet and state his name, like what Russell Crowe gets asked to do in *Gladiator*. Aware that his anonymity is a vital part of his brand, the enigmatic chauffeur would refuse point blank to take off his full-face headgear for fear of angering the *Top Gear* fanbase. The Emperor would promptly order one of his lackeys to lop the driver's still-helmeted head clean off, and it would be fed to a pack of hungry bears."

NEXT WEEK: *'It's All Greek To Me!' Capslock selects five top A-Listers and tells us why they would all die in horrific ways if they were transported back to Ancient Greece.*

WHEN THE **FUN** STOPS

JACK POTTS

44

BEFORE THE BUSES

A-List hunk Gosling signs on for Blakey blockbuster

TOP DECK ENTERTAINMENT: *Gosling (above left) to play titular hero in gritty new blockbuster 'Blakey'.*

FROM *Joker* to *Cruella* to *Maleficent*, dark and gritty 'origin story' films have been setting the box office ablaze in recent years.

Delving deep into the psyches of Hollywood's most seminal villains, these movies unravel their protagonists' murky pasts, uncovering the sinister reasons they turned to the dark side. And fans of the genre will be rejoicing today, after Universal Studios announced the latest mega-budget blockbuster to focus on a famous screen antihero... the cruel bus inspector *BLAKEY*.

Set to hit multiplexes in the summer, *Blakey* will chart the formative years of iconic *On The Buses* antagonist Cyril 'Blakey' Blake, showing how the character gradually morphed from a mild-mannered Wapping teenager into a neurotic, pen-pushing megalomaniac.

conference

At a press conference in Los Angeles, Universal chief executive **THOMAS L WILLIAMS** outlined the studio's motivation for the project. Williams told reporters: "Darth Vader, Hannibal Lecter, Cruella De Ville – all these fictional icons of evil have had their backstories told on the silver screen. Yet the origins of arguably the most complex and intriguing villain ever created - Blakey out of *On The Buses* - have remained untouched for decades."

"Now is the time to finally lay bare Blakey's turbulent past and introduce a whole new generation to the Luxton & District Traction Company Extended Cinematic Universe."

Williams added that *Blakey* will be rated 18 due to scenes of graphic violence and explicit language, and its budget will clock in at a whopping **$300 MILLION**, making it one of the most expensive films ever made.

indoor

"To do this thing right, we had to spend big bucks," Williams admitted. "The *On The Buses* fanbase is one of the largest, fiercest and most loyal on the planet. There would be rioting in the streets if we cut corners when depicting such an iconic character."

And the studio boss was keen to assure fans that pre-production was already going smoothly.

"The script is dynamite," he gushed. "No spoilers, but audiences are set to discover everything about young Cyril's transformation into the villainous, stammering bureaucrat we know as Blakey."

The film will touch on many intriguing themes that have remained unexplained throughout

EXCLUSIVE!

On The Buses's 74 TV episodes and 3 feature films, including:

- *Why Blakey joined the Luxton & District Traction Company*
- *Why he abhors lateness*
- *Why he has that moustache*

But the main focus of the film will centre around the events that caused the inspector to become the arch nemesis of feckless bus crew Stan Butler and Jack Harper.

standard

Williams confirmed that *Inception* visionary **CHRISTOPHER NOLAN** is set to direct the movie, with **QUENTIN TARANTINO** and **MARTIN SCORSESE** acting as executive producers. And if that wasn't enough to send fans into a frenzy, the studio head also revealed that *Blade Runner* star **RYAN GOSLING** will be donning the iconic peaked cap and black mackintosh to play the title role.

"We had several encouraging meetings with Joaquin Phoenix, Daniel Day-Lewis and Christian Bale," said Williams. "But Ryan's commitment and passion for the character shone through above all the others."

"He grew a toothbrush moustache especially for the audition, and lumbered in completely in character, leering at us and groaning. When he tucked a clipboard under his arm, bobbed up and down on his tiptoes and said 'Eeeeer! I 'ate you, Williams,' we all knew we had found our Blakey."

La La Land fave Gosling, 41, told *Vanity Fair* that he will be working with Tinseltown's top gurning consultants to achieve Blakey's singular facial spasms and bizarre range of guttural noises.

"I see the film very much as a character study," Gosling said. "A chance to explore the inner recesses of this man's mind and discover why getting Stan and Jack sacked became his raison d'être, and why he is so intolerant of Butler's sexual advances towards the female clippies."

table

Rumours have also circulated that Universal plans to further broaden the OTBECU (On The Buses Extended Cinematic Universe), with the release of *Olive* in 2026. The film will chart the origin story of Stan Butler's dowdy, bottle-bottom-bespectacled sister, who is set to be played by **ANYA TAYLOR-JOY**.

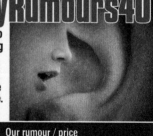
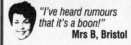

E(ASTENDERS) = MC (ALBERT) SQUARE(D)

New 'Time Travel' plot set to thrill sci-fi soap fans

THE BBC has announced a bold new fantasy plotline for *EastEnders* later this year, which they hope will thrill watchers of the popular BBC1 soap and draw in a new audience of sci-fi fans. The daring new storyline will see Sharon Watts discover a strange portal behind The Queen Vic, through which she travels back in time in an attempt to convince her teenage rock group The Banned not to split up.

Something Outta Space: Sharon (right) gets caught in futuristic time portal to save her teenage band.

Back in 1986, the primetime soap's viewers were enthralled when youthful characters Sharon Watts, Ian Beale, Kevin Carpenter and Ian 'Wicksy' Wicks formed a musical group. Subsequent episodes chronicled The Banned's career – from their disastrous debut gig in the Queen Vic, through all the arguments over musical differences and direction. The storyline came to an end when the group split up acrimoniously following an embarassing performance in a Walford 'Battle of the Bands' competition after disgruntled former member Harry Reynolds sabotaged their equipment.

"If there's one thing that everyone at *EastEnders* regrets, it's that we didn't see more of The Banned," producer Sharon Batten told us. "They were young, cool, talented, and authentic. They had it all going for them, and it's time to bring them back."

curly

The new storyline begins with Sharon discovering a portal through time whilst stacking empty kegs round the back of the Queen Vic, and travelling back to 1986. There she sees The Banned – including her younger self – performing their hit *Something Outta Nothing*. Shocked and afraid, Sharon stumbles back into the portal and returns to the present day. In an attempt to conceal what has happened from other pub-goers, she puts a bin in front of the rip in the space-time continuum.

Later on, she finds herself humming the tune that she saw the band perform

EXCLUSIVE!

35 years in the past. Cockney co-star Danny Dyer notices and asks her what the song is, but she brushes him off by telling him it was just something she heard on the radio. In that moment, Sharon realises that The Banned had something special. Returning to the time-travel portal after closing time, she once again goes back to 1986 to convince the group not to split up.

mo

"As with all time-travel plotlines, there are lots of paradoxes and impossibilities," said Batten. "We had to be careful that Sharon didn't interact with her younger self, which could lead to a temporal causality loop."

"Instead, our story sees Sharon approaching Simon Wicks, The Banned's keyboard player, and telling him how good the group is. Flattered by her attention, he makes a pass at her and they begin a passionate 'May-and-September' affair."

larry

According to Batten, the storyline will leapfrog across the decades, with modern-day Sharon attempting to stop The Banned from breaking up in the past, while trying to keep her time-travelling fling with Wicksy concealed from her jealous younger self.

Script writers are aware that if modern-day Sharon is successful in her bid to keep The Banned together in

1986, it could change the whole course of Albert Square history. "Sharon could return to present day Albert Square only to find a 70-year-old Dirty Den and Ange, complete with silver corkscrew hair, still in charge of the Vic," said Batten. "Or Arthur Beale could have found a copy of the Racing Post from the future in a bin and won a fortune at the bookies."

She continued: "To stop that happening, the new story will see The Banned stay together, but move to Australia so their career will have no impact on the goings on in Albert Square. That way, the past 35 years of the soap will still make sense."

perry

"The Ian, Kevin, Sharon and Wicksy who appear in the show post-1986 will be revealed as long-lost twins of the band members in Australia, who were adopted as babies or something."

"We haven't finalised it quite yet."

The younger versions of Sharon, Ian, Wicksy and Kevin will be played by the original actors using de-aging video technology. The computerised graphics system – the same as that which allowed 78-year-old Robert de Niro to play his lumbering youthful self in Martin Scorsese's *The Irishman* – will allow present day soap stars to play what younger versions of themselves would look like if they were played by older versions of themselves.

To coincide with the new storyline, the BBC plans to re-release The Banned's hit single *Something Outta Nothing*, along with a 'Greatest Hits' album featuring several remixes of *Something Outta Nothing*.

Time travel, gentlemen please: The Queen Vic yesterday

MEDDLESOME RATBAG

Bad Bob The Randy Wonder Dog

GLENPEEBLES police sergeant Greenock was making a special visit to Miss McFife in her cottage on the edge of the village of Glenpeebles. Miss McFife wanted her dog Mitzy to have a litter of puppies, and she had asked if the sergeant's dog, Bob, would help this miracle of nature come about.

"I'LL MAKE a cup of tea, Sergeant, whilst the wee doggies get doon tae their business," said Miss McFife. "I'm sure it'll nae tak him but a couple o' minutes tae… ahem… perform his duty," said the sergeant. Bob didn't need asking twice to get to work, and rushed across the kitchen.

THE RANDY terrier trotted straight past Mitzy and latched onto Mrs McFife's leg! "Ach! Get aff me, ye dirty wee beast!" she shouted. Sergeant Greenock ran foward to try to remove his hound, but Bob was gripped limpit tight. "Nae, Bob. Bad dog. Aff the leg! *Aff* the leg!" he cried.

GREENOCK pulled with all his might, tumbling backwards as Bob came free. "Och! Ye dirty wee animal," cried Miss McFife. "Look whit y've done tae ma tights." As Mitzy yapped around, the sergeant tried to pry the unruly mutt from his own leg. But Bob was approaching the Billy Mill Roundabout.

MISS McFife eventually wrested the dog from his owner's leg, but it looked like it was too late. "Good heavens, Sergeant," she cried. "He's starting tae twitch… he's got the jester's shoes!" Sergeant Greenock leapt into action. "Don't worry, Miss McFife," he cried. "I know a wee trick."

QUICK as a flash, the canny sergeant held Mitzy next to his leg. "Let him go!" he cried. Miss McFife released the priapic hound, who leapt towards his master's leg, landing straight on Mitzy's back. "Och! You've done it, Sergeant Greenock!" she cried. "And just in the nick of time."

NINE weeks later, Sergeant Greenock heard the news that Mitzy had given birth to a fine litter of six, strong puppies. "Come oan, Bob," he said to his excited pal. "Let's go an' see yir affspring." Bob looked every inch the proud father as he heard the yips of his puppies from inside the cottage.

BUT WHAT a commotion met the pair's eyes as they entered, to find the puppies latched onto Miss McFife and humping away! "Get the bluidy things *aff* me!" she cried. But there was little the embarrassed policeman could do. "Bad puppies!" cried Sergeant Greenock. "Nae milkies fir ye!"

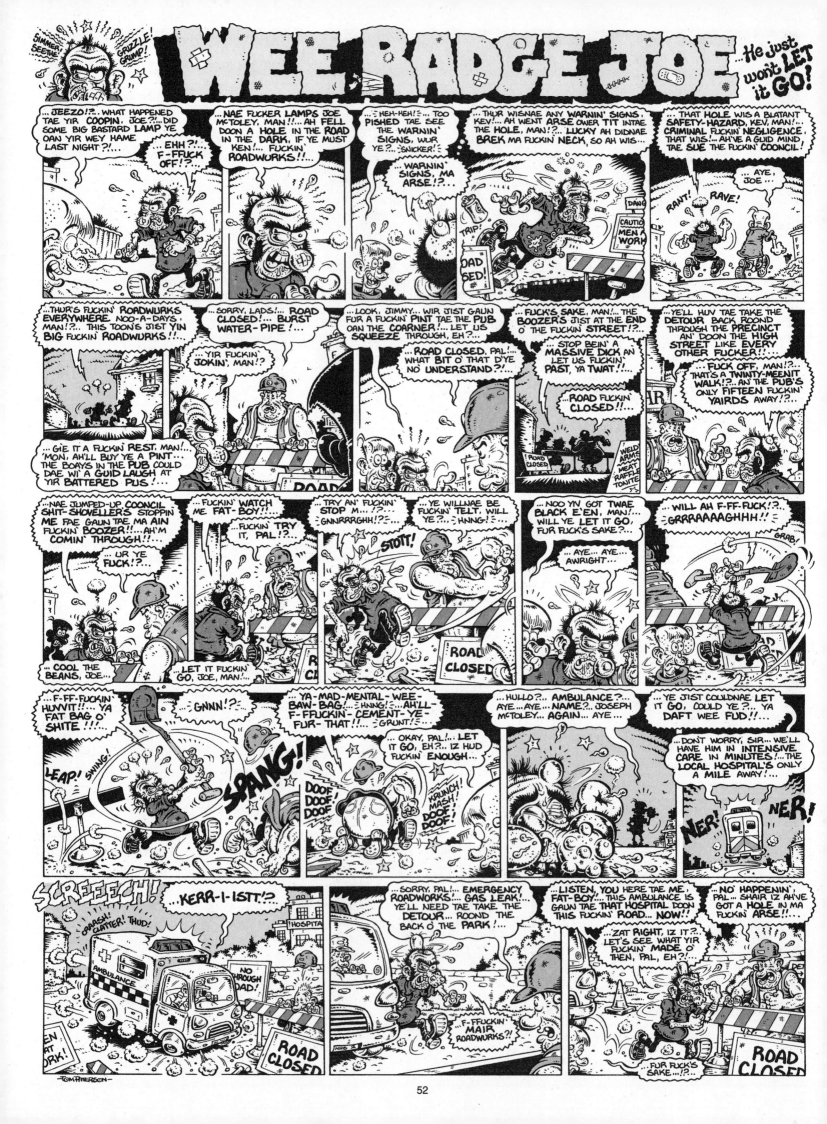

SID the SEXIST

'ERE SID... LOOK 'OO'S JUST WAALKED IN..!

EH!

SCHOOL REUNION

NOT SEEN HOR SINCE WUZ WUZ SIX, LADS..!

IT'S THAT LASS WOT USED T'BE IN W'NORSERY, MAN

YUZ MUST REMEMBAH HOR, SID...

MIND, WUZ'VE AALL FILLED OOT A BIT OVA TH'INTAVENIN' YEAZ, LIKE, HEVN'T WUZ..?

HEY! I RECOGNISE YOU..! IT'S ME! DEBBIE! WE WERE IN THE SAME CLASS AT SCROGG ROAD NURSERY!

OH AYE...

DON'T YOU REMEMBER ME?

LANG TIME NUR SEE, PET...

FANCY BUMPING INTO YOU! WE ALWAYS SAID THAT IF NEITHER OF US HAD GOT MARRIED BY THE TIME WE WERE THIRTY, WE'D GET HITCHED TO EACH OTHER...

DID W'!?

I MEAN, OH AYE...DEBBIE

WELL I'M NOT HITCHED YET, PET. HOW ABOUT YOU?

ERM...NAH...STILL FOOT-LOOSE AN' FANCY-FREE, LIKE, ME.

...I S'PURSE WUZ SHOULD GET MARRIED, THEN...JUST FER TH' CRACK, LIKE...

ERM... HANG ON...

...I'M JUST REMEMBERIN'...

...IT WASN'T YOU I SAT NEXT TO WAS IT.? IT WAS A SHORT LAD WITH A HEAD LIKE A RUGBY BALL..!

HOO LADS... JUST 'AD ME PISS, LIKE...

EEH, DO YOU REMEMBER THAT KID WHO SHAT HIS KECKS ON HIS FIRST DAY.? WHAT WAS HE CALLED.?

SID SMUTT, PET.

SHITTY SID!

WHAT A DOYLEM!

MAJOR MISUNDERSTANDING

DJ '22

SUNDAY MORNING

MORNING VICAR! THAT WAS QUITE A STORM LAST NIGHT...

ST QUAVER'S CHURCH

KEEP BACK, MISS GATSBY! STAY OUT OF THE CHURCHYARD!

THE CHURCH TOWER WAS DAMAGED IN THE STORM—THERE'S BITS OF MASONRY DROPPING OFF!

I'M AFRAID THE WHOLE LOT COULD COME CRASHING DOWN!

OUR RON'S A BUILDER—I'M SURE HE COULD SORT OUT A QUICK EMERGENCY REPAIR.

I'LL RING HIM NOW.

THANK YOU, MRS GATSBY! PLEASE TELL HIM IT'S VERY URGENT!

AH, I'M SORRY EVERYONE, THERE WILL BE NO SUNDAY SERVICE HELD IN THE CHURCH TODAY...

NOW, HOW DO I FIND RON'S NUMBER ON THIS THING...?

AND I SUPPOSE YOU WANT US ALL TO "DOWNLOAD" YOUR "APP" ONTO OUR PHONES INSTEAD?

PRESS THE BUTTON TO HEAR A SERMON, SWIPE LEFT FOR HYMN NUMBER FORTY TWO?

THE WHOLE WORLD HAS BEEN DEHUMANISED.

YOU CAN'T WALK INTO BARCLAYS AND SPEAK TO A CASHIER NOWADAYS. THEY TELL YOU TO GO HOME AND "DO IT ONLINE."

HAVE YOU STOPPED TO THINK THAT SOME OF US MIGHT PREFER TO ATTEND A TRADITIONAL SERVICE IN AN ACTUAL, PHYSICAL CHURCH?

WE DON'T ALL WANT TO SPEND OUR TIME SWIPING AND PRODDING AT OUR BLOODY MOBILE PHONES!

I HAD HOPED THAT THE CHURCH OF ENGLAND WOULD NOT SUCCUMB TO THIS INFANTILE FAD FOR COMPUTER GIMMICKRY.

CRUMBLE

ST QUAVERS CHURCH

SADLY, IT SEEMS THAT I WAS MISTAKEN.

letterbocks

....letters@viz.co.uk.......

WHY is it all buskers are warbling those dreary, mournful ballads that seem to be all over the radio these days. They're utterly depressing. Why can't buskers be more like Chas and Dave, banging out some cheerful sing-along tune about rabbits?

Felton Bellhew, Worksop

BACK in the 70s, men used to sing in the shower, but not these days. Yet another tradition lost to the 'Woke Brigade' no doubt.

Germaline Pie, Quibble

I WAS in Sainsbury's buying some food last week when a woman told another she was talking to that she had "had it up to here." Instinctively, I glanced to see exactly where she had had it up to. I caught the eye of another shopper who was also looking to see where she had had it up to. But in the end she didn't indicate. She just added "I really have."

T Waterman, Brighton

I'M a vegetarian who also eats meat, and it's absolutely great. You get the best of both worlds.

R. 'Tubby' Shaw, e-mail

IF I was the headmaster of Eton College, I would hope that every time Boris Johnson mentioned that he attended my school, people would think it was just another one of his fucking lies.

Bob Diode, Cromer

A FRIEND of mine's cock and balls are so big that he is unable to fit them into one of those dimpled pint glasses. Does anyone know if there is another series of *Britain's Got Talent* planned?

Tom Beetroot, M'borough

I'VE just watched yet another Netflix show set in a post-Armageddon dystopian future and I have to say, it looks a bloody horrible place. I for one hope we never have one of these ruddy nuclear conflicts if that's the end result.

Bob Locke, Herts

WHEN I was a nipper in 1963, our milkman drove an electric milk float. If he had only known that 60 years later everyone would be driving electric vehicles, he could have made a million and retired, instead of working till he was 67 and dying of a stroke at 68.

Terry Farricker, Blackpool

STAR LETTER

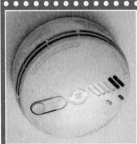

I RECKON that with a few slight modifications, the 'Cooking Bacon' detector we have on our kitchen ceiling could be turned into some sort of safety device to warn of fire. Come on, boffins. Get cracking.

Alex Stokoe, Newcastle upon Tyne

WHY on earth is April Fools' Day in April? If you really wanted to catch someone unawares, it would be much better to play your little trick at some other time of year. That's what will be doing this April fools' day. I refuse to kowtow to the authorities on this one.

Phil Kitching, Isle of Jura

ALTHOUGH I and fellow-drivers only use the left-hand side of the road, we are nevertheless charged the full Road Tax. What an absolute swizz! I shall be demanding a 50% refund from DVLA, and I shall keep your readers informed of the process of my claim.

Hamish McTumshie, Edinburgh

DOES anyone know how to delete that U2 album they loaded onto everyone's iPhone without asking a few years back? I'm sick and tired of having to scroll through the fucking thing every time I put my music on in the car. You must be able to dump it somehow. They can put a man on the moon, for fuck's sake.

Wheatstone Bridge, Hull

WITH reference to Mr Bridge's letter *(above)*. As a solicitor, I would advise people to write to Apple and ask them to remove the album from their device with immediate effect. Tell them that you will charge Apple a storage fee of £50 for each day the album remains on your device, and that their leaving it on your device constitutes acceptance of these terms.

George Capacitor, Leeds

COME on England. The controversial 'Hand of God' goal scored by Maradona was more than 35 years ago and the poor sod has been dead for more than 5 years, so there's no point in grizzling relentlessly over it and swearing every time his name is mentioned. Anyway, as a neutral Welshman, I have viewed the footage several times and I must say, it looked like a perfectly good goal to me. And regarding that 'second goal' that Hurst 'scored' in the 1966 World Cup final, the ball never crossed the line as long as I've got a hole in my arse.

Dai Llewellyn-Gogogoch, Cardiff

WHILST watching *Countdown* today, I was disappointed when Susie Dent failed to spot the word 'Roostied' during a letters game part of the episode. 'Roostied' is a term used to describe the act of 'cupping the balls' and is easily found in the urban dictionary. How could you possibly miss it, Susie? Amateur, very amateur indeed.

Peter Phyle, Rusty Cornhole

IMAGINE my embarrassment when looking through my local paper to see, splashed across the front page, the report of my court case, where I was given a £200 fine for sniffing my neighbour's underwear in her back garden. Fortunately, the paper doesn't have a big readership.

Percy Gladrags, Sligo

SOME people say that things were better in the past and I have to agree. But then I'm currently sitting at the dentist having root canal treatment with no anaesthetic, and *Achy Breaky Heart* by Billy Ray Cyrus is playing on the radio.

Jane Hoole Garner, St Ives

TO be honest, if you were hoofed in the face by Vampirella's stiletto boot you'd probably say the same thing.

Lewis Lloyd, Surbiton

ToP

HOME workers. Recreate the thrill of office working by inviting your neighbours round to use up all your coffee, choose a terrible radio station and stink up your toilet.

Paul Johnson, Glasgow

MONARCHS. Reduce energy bills by turning the heating down a few degrees in the rooms where you only store crowns and jewels.

Stuie, Bunny

FOOTBALL strikers. Score more goals by leaning slightly forward and keeping your knee above the ball when shooting.

Chess Player, Wirral

ask alexei

54

JUDAS Priest get hauled before the court because one of their songs, when played backwards, might just have sounded like someone saying "do it", allegedly encouraging youngsters to commit suicide. But when Van Halen have a smash hit with where you can plainly hear the lyric 'Go ahead and jump!' played forwards, they get away scot free. As usual it's one rule for rock bands who wear stripy trousers and another for rock bands who wear jeans.

Jack Spratt, Stourbridge

I CAN'T believe that in about 50,000 years artists have only managed to invent seven colours, one of which is indigo, whatever the fuck that is. Scientists on the other hand have come up with over 118 elements in only 200 years. It's easy to spot who's taking the piss here.

Ian Cat-Flap, Pilchard

I HAVEN'T bothered to look it up, but I reckon that in those languages that make every noun masculine or feminine, 'poo' will be masculine and 'wee' will be feminine, even though men do both and so do women. You couldn't make it up.

Martin Shithell, Bristol

DOES anyone else think that using mating calls when hunting birds is a bit messed up? Imagine getting a call from a woman to come round for a good time, only to get shot when you arrived. If it were me I'd be quite disappointed.

George Lawley, York

MY friend once told me a witch lived in the big tree in the school playground and I genuinely believed it all through primary school. I have recently realised that they were probably lying, and I looked like a gullible twat.

Lewis, Bristol

EVERYONE seems to be gobsmacked by the sudden huge hike in food prices, but I'm not surprised at all. Mind you, I am a frequent flyer with Ryanair.

Rick Pistol, Bottington-Under-Pants

I STILL don't know what percentage of current newsreaders own a Teasmade. Google is crap and I'm worried it will come up in a pub quiz.

Alphonso Mango, email

✳ *We would imagine the percentage of newsreaders owning a Teasmade will be the same as in the population as a whole. Could Viz readers write in and let us know if they own a Teasmade or not so as we can work out the percentage of readers who do. Using these figures, we can work out what percentage of newsreaders own Teasmades and announce the results in next year's annual.*

THESE Winter Olympics are an absolute con. The so-called 'athletes' get to the top of the various hills on lifts, and then they just let gravity take over! Where's the skill in that? I'm sure it would make better telly if they were forced to walk up the slope dragging their sledges and skis behind them. This would make the luge much more exciting for the casually interested.

Stuie, Bunny

IT'S true what they say about the supermarkets becoming monopolies. Only the other day I parked in Tescos car park next to a giant top hat, and there was a bloke driving out in what looked like a huge steam iron.

Jack Spratt, Stourbridge

I'M fed up with there only being 7 letters in music (A-G). I know there are sharps and flats and shit, but I think it's about time we introduced H to the musical scale. Just think what that would do for our hard-pressed music industry.

Dee Sharp, Belfast

WHY is it our moon is just called 'The Moon'? Other planets' moons have cool names like Hyperion and Ganymede. Uranus has a moon called Titania and that planet is named after a jacksy! Come on astronomers, get your priorities right.

Kevin Osborne, Bury St. Edmunds

I HAVE noticed that snow globe manufacturers are one trick ponies, doing only one type of weather in their globes. Come on globe producers, let's have a bit more variety, perhaps some rain, wind or thunder? It's not much to ask.

Ken Jenkins, Kings Langley

AT the height of the Cold War, Minister for War John Profumo was caught sleeping with the same prostitute as the Soviet Naval Attaché. These days, you just get Matt Hancock groping his adviser's arse and a few dodgy piss-ups at Downing Street. Come on, the government. Throw some hookers and a few lines of coke into your Wine Time Fridays and give us a proper scandal.

Lew, Birmingham

MY stomach just made a noise like Frankie Howerd. I don't care if your readers don't believe me, I know what I heard.

Andrew Morrice, Leeds

SAVE wear and tear on your brake pads when slowing down on motorways and road junctions by opening all the doors on your car like aeroplane flaps.

Samuel L Collins, Bristol

HAVING trouble paying for fuel for your open fire? Simply make one online enquiry into obtaining credit and Hey Presto! Guaranteed free fuel through the post, every day for years.

Lance Trumpet, Liverpool

HOMEOWNERS. Pretend you're appearing on an interior design show by getting a better-dressed, more-attractive friend to come round and swap your furniture for upcycled pallets.

Jombert Patisserie, Ballachulish

LADIES. If you want the man in your life to pay attention when you speak, simply say the word 'breasts' at the beginning of important sentences. You will then have about ten seconds or so until they lose interest owing to their short attention span.

Artferret, Hayle.

MAKE someone believe they are an actor in a stage play by knocking on their bedroom door and saying "Five minutes!"

Bath Bob, Bath

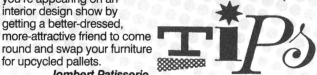

toptips@viz.co.uk

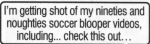

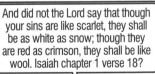

MINIMUM WAGE? MAXIMU

BACK IN MAY, the long-awaited Sue Gray Report into lockdown-busting parliamentary gatherings was finally published. One of the more incendiary details to emerge from the 60-page document was the claim that Downing Street officials had mistreated, mocked and been rude to security guards, cleaners and other low-wage staff employed at Number 10.

Clearly, this allegation was little more than sickening left-wing propaganda, designed to smear our noble prime minister and his loyal support team. But even more sickening was the reaction of the snowflake showbiz set. In the wake of Mrs Gray's traitorous 'report', members of the A-List Woke Brigade took to social media to condemn our hard-working government merely for indulging in a bit of horseplay with the people paid to scrub their red wine stains, break up their fights and mop up their vomit.

It was nauseating, borderline treasonous stuff. And it prompted the question: *How do these leftie celebs treat their OWN lower-income workers? Are they true friends to the salt-of-the-earth man in the street? Or are they a bunch* of two-faced sanctimonious arseholes who wouldn't PISS on a member of the working class if they were literally on fire in front of them?

Spoiler alert!: It's the second one.

Award-winning *Viz* investigative journalist MAHATMA MACAROON went undercover to expose the hypocrisy at the heart of our celebrity Wokerati. And what he found will make every right-wing right-thinking reader feel physically and mentally SICK to their stomach and brain respectively.

For the 'woke' A-Listers, it seems that MINIMUM WAGE equals MAXIMUM RAGE...

BY **VIZ** UNDERCOVER REPORTER
MAHATMA MACAROON

A-LIST CASE STUDY NO.1: GARY NEVILLE

IN RECENT YEARS, former Manchester United defender Gary Neville has become one of the Woke Mob's loudest critics of our green and pleasant government.

Capitalising on his vast social media profile, Sky pundit Neville regularly tweets his displeasure about Conservative Party policy, and he was among the many snowflake celebs to express 'horror' about Tory officials harmlessly humiliating their cleaners. But how 'clean' is Gary's own record when it comes to treatment of janitorial staff?

I aim to find out...

Arriving at Sky Sports' London HQ, I sneak past security and cunningly Taser a member of the cleaning staff. I dump his unconscious body in a broom cupboard and re-emerge wearing his yellow overalls. With my mop and bucket, I begin splashing bleach all over the lobby floor, whistling tunelessly to complete my transformation. It isn't long until I see former Red Devil Neville entering the building.

Knowing that he hails from Greater Manchester, I adopt a thick working-class 'Oop North' brogue, giving the Old Trafford fave a cheery nod and wink as he approaches. "Ayup, Mr Neville, sir!" I chirp, tugging hard at my forelock. "'Appen it's reet champion t' si' thee, an' naw mistek!"

A rictus grin spreads across Neville's face. The multi-millionaire footy ace is clearly *FUMING* at having to stop and interact with a lowly cleaner. "Good morning!" he seethes. "I don't think we've met yet – I'm Gary. What's your name?"

Unbelievable. The sanctimonious snowflake was first in line to criticise the 'rude' treatment of cleaning staff by Tory bigwigs – yet I've been on the Sky janitorial team nearly *SIX MINUTES*, and this ivory-tower-dwelling arsehole hasn't even *BOTHERED* to learn my name. To Neville, us low-wage grifters are simply interchangeable drones: subhuman 'worker bees' who are paid a pittance to wallow in his filth.

I quickly invent a pseudonym and the ex-England right-back shakes my hand. "It's great to meet you," he lies through his left-wing teeth. "And thanks so much for everything you do," he adds, almost certainly making a mental note to wash his hands at some point during the day after touching mine.

I am so utterly gobsmacked by this barrage of woke hypocrisy that I fail to spot the re-appearance of the cleaner I tasered earlier. He has apparently regained consciousness and is marching towards me with a face like thunder, flanked by a pair of irate-looking security guards. As my overalls are ripped off and I am brutally manhandled towards the exit, I appeal to 'Man Of The People' Neville for assistance. Surely this pleb-loving do-gooder will be there for the common man in his hour of need?

"Eeh, can tha do owt t'elp me, Mr Neville, sir?" I bleat, pathetically. "I've got bairns t' feed!" But rather than rushing to my aid, two-faced Gary simply feigns confusion, and as I am hurled through the revolving doors in my vest and pants, he barely even deigns to look at me. He made a grand show of pretending we were equals, but when push comes to shove this stuck-up snob considers my kind too far beneath him to bother with.

Neville was one of England's finest defenders. But when it came to defending the country's low-income workers, he dropped the ball.

A-LIST CASE STUDY NO.2: FRANKIE BOYLE

ONCE UPON A TIME, near-the-knuckle funnyman Frankie represented everything the Woke Brigade stands against. Penning a superb regular column for Britain's finest newspaper – *The Sun* – and cracking side-splitting jibes about paedophilia and the Queen's vagina, the outrageous Scotch jester was the scourge of the snowflake liberal elite.

But in recent times, Boyle appears to have been brainwashed by Marxist propaganda, and his Twitter feed is now a constant stream of four-letter abuse of our brave and brilliant Tory government. And you can bet a Scottish ten-pound note that freshly-woke Frankie was gloating his sporran off when news broke of No.10 staff mocking a security guard who tried to break up their lockdown party (which, incidentally, wasn't even a 'party' – merely a work event that happened to feature cake, wine and some light vomiting).

Boyle was quick to slam the Tory cabinet's good-natured pleb-baiting then – but can the risqué comic really say he treats his **OWN** security staff any better?

Let's see, shall we...

Disguised as a bodyguard, with black bomber jacket, shades and a sturdy leather cosh, I approach the London studio where Boyle films his satirical TV show, *Frankie Boyle's New World Order*. I'm hoping he will employ me as his new security detail so I can begin an undercover investigation into how he treats me. First, however, I need to convince him that he actually *needs* a security detail.

Using the crowbar concealed up my sleeve, I give Boyle's dressing room window a hard tap. It shatters easily – an encouraging sign that he will have good use for my services. Clambering inside, I seal the deal by systematically destroying all his possessions and doing a shit on his carpet. When Boyle sees there's been a 'break-in', he's sure to sign me straight up.

Just as I'm laying my cable, I hear footsteps down the corridor. Boyle appears at the door as I am pulling up my trousers, and quick as a flash I adopt a flawless proletarian Scottish accent as I address my new employer. "A'right Muster Boyle, sur, bonny tae meet ye," I cluck, in my finest Highlands brogue. "Thir's been a wee brekk-in, as ye kin see. But yir nae tae worry. Ah'm yir noo security guaird, an' ah'll get tae the bottom o' it, nae bother, Jimmy."

Given his pompous fury about how Downing Street officials 'mistreated' their own guards, I'm assuming that bleeding heart Boyle will rush forward to greet me with a warm, welcoming handshake.

I could not be more wrong.

Gary Neville at least made an effort to conceal his seething hatred of low-income workers, but Boyle does nothing of the sort. Coming face to face with a minimum-wage slave, his anger and fear are palpable. "What the fuck do you think you're doing in here?" he demands, staring at the cosh in my hand and the freshly crimped shite on his floor.

Disappointment courses through my veins. Boyle won't even tolerate the mere *presence* of a lower-class labourer within six feet of him. We've barely been introduced, and he's already launched a potty-mouthed stream of abuse at me. As I leap out of the window and disappear into the bushes, I reflect that this so-called 'liberal' so-called 'comedian' likes to pose as a socially conscious do-gooder – but his behaviour is just as disrespectful as the politicians he criticises. Not that theirs was disrespectful.

Boyle made his name cracking edgy jokes on shit panel show 'Mock the Week'. But apparently this self-righteous stand-up also likes to 'Mock the Low-Paid Workers'.

A-LIST CASE STUDY NO.3: EMILY MAITLIS

DESPITE **WORKING** for years at the supposedly 'impartial' BBC, former *Newsnight* crumpet Emily has long been a card-carrying member of the Woke Cabal. During her time on the Beeb's tawdry flagship current affairs show, the shapely snowflake made a habit of publicly humiliating good men such as Donald Trump and HRH Prince Andrew by smearing them in interviews with her left-wing 'facts' and 'evidence'.

Nowadays, Maitlis uses social media to virtue-signal her dislike of the current government, and she was particularly critical of Tory officials' treatment of staff during their light-hearted illegal work events during lockdown. But when push comes to shove, does the high-and-mighty Miss Maitlis treat her *own* minimum wage labourers any better?

*Breaking news!: does she **BOLLOCKS!***

Disguising myself as a traditional 'cock-er-nee' chimney sweep, complete with soot-smeared donkey jacket, red neckerchief and a flat cap worn jauntily askew, I knock at the door of Maitlis's swanky West London home. As she opens the door, I affect a pitch-perfect Dick Van Dyke East End brogue: "Wotcha, Missus!" I chirrup, leaping into the air and clicking my boot-heels together. "Lahvly day forrit! Sweep yer chimney for tuppence?"

Maitlis adopts a look of vague bewilderment to hide her obvious revulsion at having to engage with a member of the hoi polloi. "Yes, all right, why not," she says, through a friendly smile that presumably masks her violent rage. "Please do come in."

The not-unattractive anchorwoman shows me to the fireplace in her bedroom, and after fetching me a cup of tea and some biscuits, she leaves me to my work.

So far, so respectful. *But things are about to take a turn for the worse...*

From my jacket, I remove my homemade chimney brush which

consists of a standard toilet brush sellotaped to twelve 'selfie sticks'. In the process, however, I accidentally unhook the buckle of my belt. My trousers and pants tumble down around my ankles, and I trip and stagger forward, grabbing hold of what turns out to be Mrs Maitlis' underwear drawer to steady myself, the drawer coming open in the process.

Hearing the commotion, Maitlis returns to the room – and this time she **CAN'T** hide the expression of superior elitist disgust on her face. As I am half-naked, clutching a fistful of her scuds in one hand and my penis in the other, I admit the scene might look a tad suspicious at first glance.

But it's quite clearly a simple misunderstanding that could happen to anyone. Indeed, had it been one of Maitlis's high-earning middle-class peers – such as Christian Fraser or Ros Atkins – getting caught in that situation, you can bet they would all be chuckling about it at their next Islington dinner party. But as far as she is aware, I am neither high-earning **NOR** middle-class. I am but a humble chimney sweep – and in the Maitlis household, that means different standards apply.

As the supposedly 'egalitarian' broadcaster chases me from her property whilst phoning the police, I reflect on yet another dispiriting brush with woke showbiz royalty. Calling a minimum wage worker every name under the sun while you forcibly eject him from your home seems a *touch* more disrespectful than anything those Downing Street officials did. But I wonder how much space Sue Gray will devote to *this* incident in her next 'report'?

NEWSFLASH! The thick end of FUCK ALL.

A-LIST CASE STUDY NO.4: SIR KEIR STARMER

AS THE **LEADER** of the loony left Labour Party, immaculately coiffed former barrister Sir Keir is pretty much the commanding officer of the Woke Mob.

And surprise, surprise – when Sue Gray's epic work of fiction was released back in May, the Swiss Toni-haired MP was one of the first to start crowing about 'shameful behaviour' and 'lack of respect'. But it's one thing to virtue signal about the treatment of low-paid workers from afar: *how will this Oxford-educated toff comport himself when he himself comes to face to face with a real-life minimum wager?*

I intend to find out.

After a spot of research, I discover that Keir has plans to visit a newly opened burger restaurant in his Central London constituency at the weekend. Since catering staff are some of the most poorly paid workers in the country, this is the perfect opportunity to see if the side-parted snowflake can back up his big talk about treating poor people as 'equals'.

On Saturday night, I sneak into the Holborn eatery and shrewdly Taser one of the waiters. I quickly don his logo-embossed polo shirt and fluorescent visor and step out onto the restaurant floor. At that precise moment, Sir Keir enters. He clocks my low-income presence, and the fear and loathing on his face is clear as day – or at least it would be if it wasn't hidden behind a warm smile. I go to remove his coat for him, but the pauper-phobic politico stops me. "Oh, please don't worry, I can do that myself," he says.

I stand rooted to the spot, too stunned to speak. This haughty snob cannot even bear to be **TOUCHED** by a member of the working class. Clearly, he thinks that I and all my proletarian brethren are little more than lice-riddled thieves.

Shaking with anger, I retreat to the kitchen to bring the two-faced opposition leader his meal. But my hands are still trembling as I return with the grub, and I end up dumping a whole plate of ketchup-slathered fries all over Sir Keir's left-wing head.

It's the kind of commonplace gaffe that occurs in restaurants the world over every day. So surely this so-liberal snowflake will take pity on a stressed and struggling busboy by simply laughing the incident off? Think again.

Incandescent with elitist rage, the pleb-loathing knight of the realm launches a spittle-flecked tirade of verbal abuse in my direction. "Whoopsie-daisy," he chuckles, furiously. "No worries, accidents happen."

I cannot believe what I'm hearing. This pampered fop hasn't done a proper day's graft in his entire privileged life, and now he's belittling *my* efforts to put food on the table, accusing me of causing 'accidents'. The disrespect is staggering. But worse is yet to come.

On their lowly wages, Britain's poverty-stricken waiters rely heavily on tips to keep them afloat, and it's good manners for a customer to leave at least a ten per cent gratuity. But a professed 'friend to the working class' like Keir might be expected to stretch to twenty, you might suppose. So imagine my horror when I discover that the tight-fisted front-bencher *has not left a single penny!*

According to my fellow catering staff, Keir has 'misplaced' his wallet and will have to return tomorrow to settle up. *What a coincidence!* This smug hypocrite values key workers so little that he doesn't even think we deserve paying.

Luckily, I won't be out of pocket, as I had the foresight to lift Starmer's wallet when I attempted to take his coat earlier. But a less savvy wage slave would simply have had to do without their precious service charge – and all because this so-called socialist despises the common man.

As I begin making copies of all Sir Keir's credit cards, I feel genuinely sick to my stomach.

As a barrister, the Labour chief specialised in Human Rights. But his contempt for minimum wage workers is quite simply a Human WRONG.

NEXT WEEK – 'YACHT A SCANDAL!' Mahatma poses as a billionaire oligarch to expose the 'woke' soap stars' unfair treatment of the super-rich!

A PICTURE OF LOREN GRAY
TikTok star says she's never heard of herself

SOCIAL media superstar **LOREN GRAY**, who boasts over 50 million followers on TikTok, was left red-faced last night after revealing to fans that she had never heard of herself.

Gray posted a clip which quickly went viral on the social media site, in which she admitted that she had no idea who Loren Gray was.

video

"I mean, I'm hearing, like, so much about this Loren Gray all over TikTok, and I'm sure that, like, she is super-talented, you know?" she said in the video. "But I just don't know who she is."

"I guess that's because, like, I'm just so super-busy with my singing and, you know, my dancing or whatever it is, and, like, just my whole TikTok lifestyle," she continued.

"So, you know, good luck Loren, hope you're not offended, and I hope you have a super-great career."

Within seconds of the clip being uploaded onto the platform, Gray's fans began posting their responses.

EXCLUSIVE!

"OMG! Loren… It's YOU! Facepalm!!!!!!!" said one, whilst another posted a red-faced emoji with the message "Don't know who Loren Gray is? Ask your mom, Loren!!!!!!!!!"

"Loren's standing in front of your bathroom mirror now. Go look, girl!!!!!!!!!!!!" another quipped, putting no fewer than 12 exclamation marks, several small yellow faces and a picture of an eggplant after the final word for emphasis.

sorry

Within minutes, the 19-year-old megastar, who has twice been nominated for the *Teen Choice Muser* of the Year award and recently launched a jewellery brand, realised her blunder and took to TikTok to release a tearful and emotional video in which she apologised for her earlier mistake.

"Oh my God, that's, like, so embarrassing, and I'm just so, so sorry. I love you all so much and, like, I feel I've let you down," she gushed, her voice breaking with emotion as she theatrically dabbed her eyes with a $2000 Louis Vuitton handkerchief she had been given for free.

"I'd like to apologise to myself, like, not knowing who I was?" she added, making it sound like a fucking question.

GRAY EXPECTATIONS: *Loren's fans responded in their milions (inset left) to star's confusion on popular social media platform.*

HEELYVEL KNIEVEL

After buying a pair of Heelys in a charity shop, Albert Clubmoss fulfilled his lifelong ambition to become a stunt performer. And with a boiler suit, a crash helmet, and a small curtain from the same shop, his transformation to his alter-ego **Heelyvel Knievel** was complete. Performing his daredevil shows in front of amazed crowds, he soon became the talk of the north Northumberland area…

It was the day of the Alwinton show, and Heelyvel had been booked to perform one of his breathtaking stunts…

LADIES AND GENTLEMEN, BOYS AND GIRLS… THE SPECTACLE YOU ARE ABOUT TO WITNESS, I GUARANTEE WILL STAY WITH YOU ALL YOUR LIVES…

…FOR YOU ARE ABOUT TO SEE ME CHEAT DEATH AS I HURTLE DOWN THIS RAMP ON MY HEELYS AND LEAP OFF THE END, SOARING LIKE AN EAGLE OVER NOT ONE, BUT *TWO* BALES OF HAY!

GASP!

BUT REMEMBER… I AM A PROFESSIONAL STUNTMAN. UNDER NO CIRCUMSTANCES SHOULD YOU ATTEMPT A FEAT LIKE THIS YOURSELF.

The crowd watched with their hearts in their mouths as Heelyvel started his descent…

TRUNDLE! TRUNDLE! TRUNDLE!

WHOOOOOOSH!

CRUMP!

GNNNNN!

GASP!

For a terrible moment, it looked like Heelyvel Knievel's double hay-bale jump had been his last…

But then…

HE'S OKAY! OH, THANK GOODNESS!

HOORAY!

THANK YOU…

NOW BEFORE I GO, I HAVE AN ANNOUNCEMENT TO MAKE…

THAT STUNT MAY HAVE LEFT YOU SPELLBOUND, BUT NEXT WEEK, AT THE ILDERTON SHOW, I SHALL BE ATTEMPTING TO BREAK A WORLD RECORD!

… A RECORD WHICH HAS STOOD UNBROKEN FOR *THIRTY YEARS!*

I SHALL ATTEMPT A HEELY RAMP-JUMP OVER A RUNNING COMBINE HARVESTER, SMASHING THE WORLD RECORD FOR THE MOST FOOLHARDY THING TO DO!

WOW!!!!

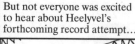

But not everyone was excited to hear about Heelyvel's forthcoming record attempt…

SO… HE WANTS TO TAKE MY WORLD RECORD FROM ME, DOES HE…?

WE'LL SEE ABOUT THAT!

Three decades earlier, Tommy Liverwort had climbed the fence of the tiger enclosure at Twycross Zoo in order to retrieve a Rizla which blew out of his hand whilst he was making a roll-up…

DANGER!

Tommy had survived the ordeal and took the record for the Most Foolhardy Thing To Do, presented to him by Guinness Book of Records editors Ross and Norris McWhirter…

Most Foolhardy Thing To Do World Record. Tommy Liverwort

PERHAPS HE WILL FIND MY RECORD HARDER TO BREAK THAN HE THINKS…

The day of the Ilderton show came, and a crowd had gathered to witness Heelyvel's record breaking act of stupidity…

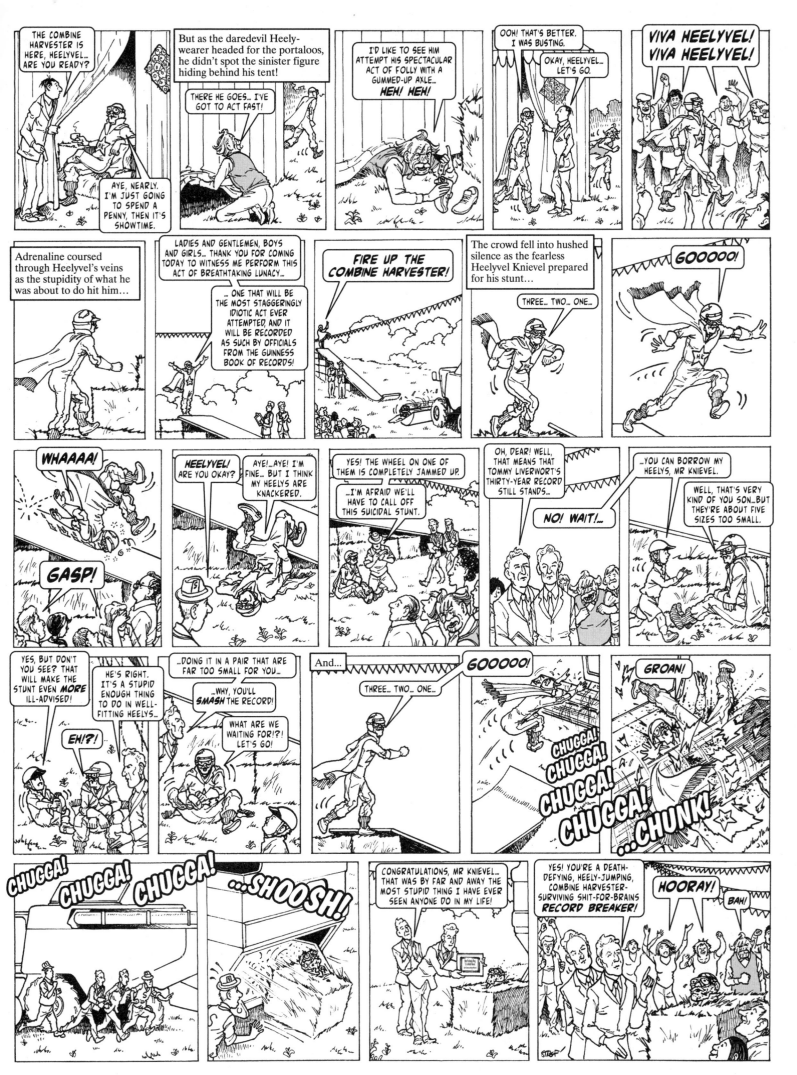

HOPELESS ROMANTIC!

BRITAIN is a nation of romantics, and every one of us looks forward to Valentine's Day. Come February 14th, there is simply no greater feeling on Earth than showering chocolates, flowers, and all manner of other amorous gifts onto that one person we cherish most in the world – our partner, be they boyfriend, girlfriend, husband or wife.

But for one Nuneaton-based bachelor, February 14th is not only the most special day of the year – it's also the *busiest*. That's because 62-year-old **DIDSBURY PARSON** is officially **THE MOST ROMANTIC MAN IN BRITAIN™**!

"It's true," chuckles the jobless quadruple divorcee. "I'm a big old softy, me – I can't get enough of anything Valentine's related."

"Cut me and I bleed Love Hearts!" he laughs – a joke with a clever double meaning, since according to his GP, Didsbury's blood sugar levels are dangerously high.

For years, romance-obsessed Parson did everything in his power to orchestrate the perfect February 14th for whichever of his four ex-wives he happened to be with at the time. But sadly, the luckless Romeo's best-laid plans never quite panned out the way he hoped.

"No matter what ultra-romantic gift or experience I roll out for my beloved on Valentine's Day, it always seems to go tits up," sighs the medically obese Prince Charming. "Sometimes I think I'm not only the Most Romantic Man In Britain™ – I'm also the Unluckiest."

Now Didsbury is about to hit the lecture circuit, describing to paying audiences how his doomed romantic gestures led to the tragic collapse of his previously happy marriages. And he hopes that the gruelling three month tour of low audience capacity venues in and around the Nuneaton area

Shed-over-heels: Parson's garden parfumerie was raided by police.

EXCLUSIVE!

will help prevent other hopeless romantics from making the same mistakes as him, and also leave him financially solvent for the first time in 38 years.

Stop Making Scents

Didsbury's run of Valentine's bad luck began when he was still with his first wife, Denise. The pair got married back in 2010 and he was an exceptionally attentive husband from the word go – despite what his wife would later tell the divorce courts and local paper – going out of his way to make sure that each February 14th was more special for her than the last.

> **I slapped a padlock on the shed to keep the local scrotes out**

I always did my best, but Denise was a particularly hard woman to please. One year, things had been quite prickly between us, due to my being sacked from my janitorial job following wrongful allegations of sexual misconduct. As February 14th loomed into view, Denise was grumbling about having to support both of us on just her wages. I decided I needed to pull something SERIOUSLY romantic out of the bag this time.

I thought long and hard until a suitably extravagant idea popped into my love-addled brain. Denise had always been keen on her posh perfumes, so what if I whipped her up her very own 'signature fragrance'... *Eau de Denise!*

It would be a charmingly unique and thoughtful gift which she could cherish for years to

Love goggles: Is Didsbury Parson the most romantic – and unlucky – man in Britain?

come. And the memory of it would last forever, if not longer, I thought.

Excited, I got to work straight away. While Denise was out doing double-shifts at the mini-mart, I toiled away in my shed, mixing the ingredients for my romantic Valentine's aroma in an old bathtub I had found at a local fly-tipping hotspot.

Denise is something of a 'foodie' – she regularly eats at least three meals a day and calls salad cream 'mayonnaise' – so I decided the base notes of her custom scent should be food-related: potatoes, yeast and crushed barley grains. For the top note, I thought a lemony tang would work well, so I added an industrial-sized can of citric acid. Perfumes also traditionally contain between sixty and seventy per cent alcohol, so I made sure to add a few bottles of methylated spirits into the mix, too. A quick splash of iodine for good measure, and hey presto – 'Eau de Denise' was complete!

The fermentation process for the perfume took a couple of weeks, so I covered the bathtub with cheesecloth, and slapped a padlock on the shed to keep the local scrotes out. I couldn't wait to see my Denise's face on Valentine's Day when I presented her with her very own unique eau de cologne – hand-made by her loving hubbie!

Unfortunately, I would never get the chance.

One night, as I was bottling up the fragrance, my shed was raided by several fuck-witted members of the Warwickshire constabulary. The blundering bobbies slapped me in handcuffs, spouting some ludicrous cock and bull story about a dangerously strong home-brewed "vodka" that was being sold to vagrants down the local precinct. Apparently a few of them had gone blind from drinking this fictional bootleg liquor, and the filth were hauling me into the station for supplying it. You couldn't make it up.

I told the coppers that I was merely infusing a romantic signature scent for my wife as a Valentine's gift, but they wouldn't listen. The fact that it was early May, and February 14th was over nine months away, seemed to

> **As usual, I was thinking with my head, not my heart**

support their argument. But there was a perfectly simple explanation; in my haste to surprise my beloved missus I must've got my dates slightly muddled. As usual, I was thinking with my heart, not my head.

The long and short of it was that I did a bit of bird for the mix-up, and Denise chucked me the minute I went down. She got the house, the shed and even the bathtub in the settlement – but she never got the one thing that mattered most to me: *my beautiful Valentine's gift.*

66

Massage-y Bargy

Shortly after his release from prison, Parson met and married his second wife, Sue. Once again, the modern-day Don Juan proved to be the most caring and conscientious husband any woman could ask for, despite what Sue, her immediate family and her lawyer said later. But in 2015, after a few years of blissful companionship, he began to feel that the spark was fizzling out in their relationship.

" Sue was focused solely on her career – she would regularly work 16-hour cleaning shifts while I sat home alone, unable to find gainful employment due to being placed on the sex offenders' register following a misunderstanding at a leisure centre. We hadn't been intimate in months, and as February 14th drew closer, I decided to inject some passion back into our relationship the only way I knew how: *with a delightfully heartfelt Valentine's gift!*

I knew Sue liked nothing better than a long hot soak in the tub, so I decided I would organise a blissfully relaxing Valentine's 'spa day' for her. She would be preened, pampered, spoiled and indulged to her heart's content – before I whisked her home for a tender, moonlit knee-trembler she would *never* forget.

A great massage is the foundation for any successful spa day, and as luck would have it there was a house across the road from us with a sign in the window saying 'MASSAGES GIVEN HERE'. I'd often noticed the place because it had a quirky red light bulb in the front room, so I decided to pop in and enquire about the possibility of booking my beloved Sue a romantic rubdown.

The lady at the counter suggested I try one myself – just to make sure their quality was up to scratch – and it seemed like a good idea. Four minutes later, I left the place feeling significantly more relaxed than I had when I went in.

But I wanted the absolute BEST for my beloved Sue, so I decided to shop around a few other parlours before I made any concrete arrangements.

Over the next fortnight, I painstakingly located every other massage establishment in the Nuneaton area, and sampled what each of them had to offer. I slogged from Burbage to Hinckley and from Tamworth to Maxstoke, searching for the PERFECT set of magic fingers. My heart thumped with excitement at the thought of how my Sue would react on February 14th when I presented her with my considerate gift.

But then as usual, the unthinkable happened.

Love in bloom: Didsbury hoped that his floral gift would ignite the flame of love with wife number four.

I was conducting my final round of auditions at a luxury parlour above a chip shop in Caldecote, when some local constables kicked the door down and barged inside. I was so relaxed that I must of fallen asleep, and my underpants must also of got snagged on the therapy table, because they'd come off altogether. The young woman giving me the massage must of tried to pull them up for me, but she'd obviously got muddled up and had accidentally grasped my manhood instead. By which I mean my cock.

It was the kind of straightforward mix-up that must happen a hundred times a day, if not more, in every parlour. But the brainless tit-heads refused to see the evidence that was right in front of them. Before I knew what was happening, I was being hauled into a police van, and Sue was filing for divorce. I tried to explain that I was merely organising a romantic spa day for her Valentine's gift, but unfortunately I'd got my dates confused again, and it was June 6th, so she didn't believe me.

My heart sank. I was facing a second failed marriage and a second stint in the big house – but my greatest sadness was that my precious Valentine never received her priceless pressie. "

Darling Buds of Dis-May

The next few years were the same story for unlucky Didsbury. Weddings and divorces followed in quick succession after more bungled attempts to give his third and fourth one-and-only unforgettable February 14th gifts.

" I thought it would be a wonderful surprise if I learned how to dance so that I could take wife number three, Marion, for a romantic Valentine's waltz at a ballroom. I found the number of a local female dancer in a phone box, and she'd been giving me private lessons. Everything was going to plan until one day Marion came home early from work and caught us practising.

We'd been rehearsing a particularly tricky foxtrot, and our bodies had become entangled, and also our clothes must of got snagged on something because they'd all come off. My missus put two and two together to make five, and *Wallop!* That was the end of my third marriage.

> ## We'd been rehearsing a particularly tricky foxtrot and our bodies had become entangled

So when I met and married wife number four, Linda, last year, I knew I had to tread carefully. Whilst my other three missuses had turned out to be lying, hatchet-faced gold-diggers, Linda was very definitely the love of my life. It was vital that our first Valentine's together was extra special. And I knew immediately what I would get her.

A bunch of flowers.

That may seem a particularly unimaginative gift to give someone special, but this would not be just ANY old bouquet, I thought. These would be flowers *I had grown myself, from seed!* The idea was so simple, so *devastatingly* romantic, that when I handed it over, it would be a pound to a penny she'd let me on the nest.

I was after something more exciting than your bog-standard roses or tulips, and a mate of mine who's got an allotment suggested trying a quirky flowering plant that grows in Asia. Its blossoms were a beautiful dark green colour, he explained, sprawling outwards in a star-like shape. The seeds were expensive, and their upkeep even more so; due to the plants' exotic nature, I would also have to fork out for a pricey 'UV' lighting rig and an industrial silo to house the hydroponics system. But Linda deserved the best, so I dug deep and bought the lot.

My mate generously let me pitch my silo on his allotment patch, and over the next few months my hand-nurtured Valentine's blossoms began to bloom. As well as being beautiful to look at, they also had a deliciously heady scent – earthy and herbal, thick, pungent and musky. My yield was so good I decided it would be selfish to keep all the flowers to myself. After all, there might be other Romeos out there who wanted to treat their Juliets, too!

The utter softy that I am, I began selling offcuts of the plants in little plastic bags for a tenner a pop. My heart swelled at the thought that I was pumping pure, uncut romance into the streets of Nuneaton. I couldn't wait to see my own beloved's face when I handed over her sweet-smelling bouquet when Valentine's came around.

Suffice it to say, that moment would never come to pass.

I arrived at the silo one morning to find it surrounded by coppers. Before I could ask what they were all doing – confiscating arguably the most romantic Valentine's gift of all time – I was rudely slammed to the ground and told that I had the right to remain silent and anything I did say could later be used against me in a court of law.

I had to chuckle as there had obviously been some silly mix-up. But my laughter soon turned to tears as the doughnut-munching shitwits explained that I was "under arrest" for apparently being "North Warwickshire's leading drugs kingpin!" I've said it before and I'll say it again: *you couldn't make it up.*

To my immense shock and dismay, I was informed that the beautiful blooms I'd been lovingly harvesting to present to my beloved wife weren't technically legal in the UK. As a result, I'm now looking at the thick end of a decade in clink, not to mention a fourth round of nuptials down the pisser. "

Parson is currently out on bail and his case will not be heard until after Valentine's day. He intends to use the time before his trial date in May to perform his lecture tour. But this time next year, it is far from certain that he will be free to make any kind of romantic gesture to wife number five. He may be spending the next February 14th - and many more over the years to come - at His Majesty's pleasure.

"As Shakespeare said, the course of love never runs smooth," he told us. "But if you'll pardon my French, romance has proved an effing rocky road for me."

"And by effing, I mean the 'F' word. You know, fucking," he added.

Robbie's Robot Carer

Ahhh, that'll be Coral.

Right on time.

Come on in love.

The kettle's –

Good morning Robbie.

SPRING

What – how do you know me?

I am from the council. My name is Martin.

I will be executing your statutory homecare visit entitlement from now on.

W-where's Coral?

You will not miss Coral.

I am equipped to perform all her functions.

And more, faster, cheaper, I do not take holidays, I am never ill, I have no problems.

Well...

We usually have a cup of tea and a catch-up first.

I do not need tea.

I don't talk with so many folk now, face-to-face like, so it's nice, to have a little natter.

Coral tells me how her son is getting on at university.

He sounds like a right grand lad...

I am interested in your stories Robbie.

Please continue your stories.

Soon

ZZZZ

Robbie?

Robbie?

DUGGA! DUGGA! DUGGA!

Do not be afraid, Robbie, blanks. I am also purposed for crowd control situations.

Have you made toilet?

Do not upset yourself Robbie.

Loss of bladder and/or bowel control is common among humans nearing death.

ZZZZ

DUGGA! DUGGA! DUGGA!

Statutory homecare visit entitlement period concludes in ten, nine, eight, seven, six-

NEWS AROUND THE WORLD
AROUND THE WOR-ORLD
AROUND THE WORLD, A-ROUND THE WOR-ORLD

with retired robotic electro-popsters Daft Punk

MICE DOING BUSINESS WITH YOU

THE COST of mice in pet shops spiked last night after it emerged that corporate giant Unilever had made an aggressive takeover of the small rodents.

Markets around the world rocketed in reaction to the news, which saw the $6 billion multinational acquire a controlling interest in the planet's 21.7 billion mice, putting £0.25 on the cost of an animal at the counter.

"This is a big day for Unilever," said CEO Kirby Lonsdale. "The company has long had an excellent reputation for asset enrichment, and we're proud to be taking over mice at this exciting time for the species."

Insiders suggest that the verminous rodents will be streamlined in order to achieve greater efficiency, with one source suggesting that the creatures will be required to eat 30% less cheese while increasing productivity against a range of KPIs, including frightening women onto chairs, pissing everywhere, dying under the floor, and squeaking.

"While mice have very solid brand recognition, any honest person will admit they've not been at the top of their game for a while now," says City-watcher Robert Peston. "So really they were a sitting target for a takeover like this."

The news saw Siemens immediately float their shares of ferrets which saw the stock price of the trouser-dwelling mammals fall by two points overnight.

LINE OF BOOTY

BEYONCÉ KNOWLES has shocked the entertainment world by announcing that she is leaving the music industry to become an anti-corruption officer at Scotland Yard. "It's true," she told her disappointed fans. "From now on, I'm interested in one thing only, and that's bent coppers!"

Knowles formed a strong interest in rooting out police corruption after binge-watching *Line of Duty* during lockdown. "My friends kept going on about how good it was, but I was always too busy touring and recording to watch any of it," she explained. "Then the pandemic hit and I was stuck at home, so I thought I'd give it a go. And I soon realised that the idea of policemen breaking the law makes me really, really angry!"

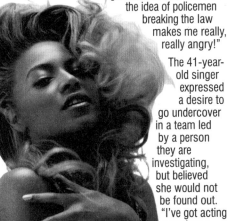

The 41-year-old singer expressed a desire to go undercover in a team led by a person they are investigating, but believed she would not be found out. "I've got acting experience from being in the 3rd Austin Powers film, so I definitely could pull it off," she said. "I mean, one police officer pretending to be another one. How hard can it be?"

A senior anti-corruption officer, who gave his name only as 'H', offered a cautious welcome to the force's newest recruit. "Obviously every new person who joins the police force strengthens it," he said. "But I have to question the suitability of Ms Knowles for undercover work. She has a very recognisable face, which I feel might be something of a disadvantage."

But Knowles was quick to dismiss the criticism. "I'll just cut my hair short and stick on a pair of shades, so they wouldn't know it's me," she responded. "Plus I'll wear one of my really short stage costumes, so none of the bent coppers will be looking at my face anyway."

WHATEVS THE WEATHER

A WORRYING survey published by Newcastle University has revealed that many children are leaving school unable to distinguish between the long, hot summer of 1976 and the terrible winter of 1963, leaving them ill-equipped to correctly allude to watershed weather events as adults.

"Thirty years ago, everyone left school being able to give a full run down on the summer of 1976, including stories of eggs being fried of car bonnets, old men getting sunburnt in deckchairs and kids having water fights in flares," said a spokesman for the Department of Education.

A modern focus on core subjects such as Maths, Science and English has created a generation with no climate-related frame of reference when referring to very hot or very cold weather.

A snap poll of 16-25 year-olds showed that 80% were unaware of even the hottest recorded temperature that summer. More worrying, many year 10 pupils regularly confuse the bad winter of 1963 with the Winter of Discontent. When questioned about the winter of 1963, one 15-year-old asked "Was that the one where they couldn't bury their dead or where all the reservoirs were empty?"

That's all for this week. More news from Around the World, A-round the Wor-orld, Around the World, A-round the Wor-orld next week.

Daft Punk xx

The Conspiracy

DID YOU KNOW that the Apollo astronauts never set foot on the Moon despite photographs showing they clearly did? Did you know that far from dying in 1977, Elvis Presley is still alive and well and living in Scotland? And did you know that the 9/11 attacks were actually organised by US President George Bush in order to spark a war with Iraq and secure a pipeline deal for Dick Cheney's Halliburton Group? *No?* Well you do now. And it's all thanks to the tireless work of Conspiracy Theorists.

Many people believe that conspiracy theories are simply lunatic ideas dreamed up and perpetuated by crackpots with little grip on reality. But if you take the trouble to examine the evidence in plain sight, it is clear we live in a world where many people are trying to deceive us to further their own ends. Why should we believe a virologist who says a vaccine is effective against a virus simply because they have thirty years experience and have tested it rigorously? Perhaps they have an ulterior motive in getting us to inject their death serums into our arms. Perhaps they actually do contain microchips which track our every movement. Conspiracy Theorists force us to question what we believe to be the case, and as such they are vital tools in getting to the truth.

But how do their theories come about? How do they start one? And how do they promulgate it so that it becomes accepted as gospel truth by everyone wearing a MAGA hat? Here's a step-by-step guide to how the Conspiracy Theorist operates…

2 **THE SKELETON** of your conspiracy is formed. But just like in the scientific realm, it is initially merely a loose hypothesis; in order for it to become a theory you will have to provide solid evidence to back it up. For scientists, this step involves years of painstaking research and experimentation, followed by a rigorous process of peer review and reassessment. Fortunately, the burden of proof for the Conspiracy Theorist is far lower. A blurred photograph of the Queen with two women of similar height alongside her is evidence enough. As is the testimony of a man in the pub who says he knows for a fact that the Queen once opened a supermarket in Aberdeen at exactly the same time as she was Trooping the Colour in London.

3 **YOUR THEORY** - now backed up by irrefutable photographic proof - is complete, and you are ready to let the world know the truth. Just a few years ago, this would have been done by writing to the newspaper, or standing on the corner of your local high street with a placard, handing out flyers whilst being kicked up the arse by schoolboys. But today, social media has made the dissemination of information as quick as the speed of an electron. With a click of your mouse, the world can instantaneously know that the United Kingdom has *three* Queen Elizabeth IIs.

5 **THE WHOLE** world has now heard about Britain's three Queens. The truth is like a juggernaut; once it builds up momentum, nothing can stop it, so you may think you are home and dry. But this is the most dangerous time for a newly minted conspiracy theory. There are many people who have a vested interest in keeping the fact

that there are three Queens secret, and they will stop at nothing to silence you. 'Woke' comedians will crack feeble jokes at your expense, and left-wing columnists will mock your theory in their tawdry newspaper columns in the mainstream media. Their first line of attack will be to attempt to discredit you and your fellow believers, claiming that other causes you espouse - like the earth being flat, or that they've found a cure for cancer that costs pennies but the drug companies are suppressing it - are somehow proof that you are mentally deranged.

6 **WHEN IT'S CLEAR** to all that you are an intelligent, clear thinker, they will turn their attention to discrediting your theory itself. They will use facts, figures and verifiable evidence as so-called 'proof' to support their position that there is just one Queen Elizabeth. You could bring in more evidence if you wish - for example, more blurred photographs, contradictory Royal engagement lists found on the internet, further evidence from the man in the pub. But remember, you do not need to counter their arguments. The burden of proof is upon *them* to demonstrate that there is just a single Her Majesty the Queen, which they know they cannot do. Because there are three.

Theorist

1 THE FIRST STEP in developing a new conspiracy theory is to think about something that almost everyone accepts as truth. For instance, there is only ONE Queen Elizabeth II. That is so obviously a fact that it would seem madness to even question it. *But do we know that for sure?* Human beings are blessed with inquisitive minds which seek the truth. Why should we believe something simply because everyone else believes it? Could there not actually be two Queens? Or three? *How do we know that they have not cloned her majesty not once, but twice, and that our country is being ruled by the actual monarch, aided by two replicants?*

4 HOWEVER, it's likely that you are still building up your Twitter following, so your theory will probably only have been read by four or five people. So it is important to send it to the right channel, to someone who will not only see the truth in what you say, but who has an online following in the hundreds of thousands. Until recently, sending it to Donald Trump was a guarantee of your theory becoming fact, but unfortunately he was removed from Twitter under instruction from the CIA, who are in the pay of Barack Obama. Fortunately, you are still spoilt for choice. Clear thinkers like Laurence Fox, Julia Hartley-Brewer, Alex Jones and Right Said Fred are good conduits to get the truth out to the masses.

7 THE TRUTH is now too widespread to ignore, and everyone else who has a conspiracy theory of their own will now believe yours. Reciprocally, you must sign up to every one of their theories, no matter how crackpot they may appear at first. If you think about it for just one second, it's obvious; *their apparent unlikelihood simply makes them all the more credible.* Everything - from the fact that Denver Airport stands above a secret underground city and pipe-smoking former PM Harold Wilson was a KGB agent, to the attempted murder of Pakistani female education activist Malala Yousafzai which was organised by her father and carried out by actor Robert de Niro - must not only be believed, it must be linked. The Conspiracy Theorist Brother and Sisterhood has strength in numbers and together we will get the truth out there.

A TSAR IS BORN

Diplomatic role for fave Corrie milquetoast

Won't really know: Coronation Street's Mavis Wilton (top left) to become government's first Toothless Criticism Tsar, Johnson (bottom left) announced yesterday.

BORIS **Johnson has announced that all token half-arsed criticism of China's human rights record will now be outsourced to Mavis Wilton off** *Coronation Street.*

The fictional corner shop worker will become be the government's first official Toothless Criticism Tsar, with duties to include giggling nervously while looking at the ground and getting in a quiet huff with autocrats and dictators.

face down

According to a government spokesperson, former Kabin shop assistant Mavis has all the qualities necessary to face down the Beijing regime. "Mavis ticks all the boxes," he told us. "The combination of cowering subservience, an inability to criticise, and long-winded, polite requests that sound like apologies, means that she will be the complete pushover the British government needs her to be in Anglo-Chinese negotiations."

Fictional stationery salesman Derek Wilton's former on-screen wife fought off stiff competition for the high-powered role from *Dad's Army*'s mild-mannered Sergeant Wilson, *Are You Being Served* middle-manager Mr Rumbold and *EastEnders* pushover Lofty Holloway.

According to the government source, the Chinese hardliners are in for a tough time when negotiations open. "Timid Mavis won't mince her words when it comes to making a statement that is supposed to sound tough, but somehow comes out like a compliment," he said.

EXCLUSIVE!

Zeguang: Warning.

Chinese ambassador Zheng Zeguang yesterday warned fictional TV soap characters not to meddle in his government's affairs. But a planned visit to Weatherfield from China's trade commisioner to cement a deal providing butter and tomato sauce to Roy Cropper's Roy's Rolls Cafe was cancelled without warning last night, hinting that the appointment of the Kabin sales assistant, once wooed by Victor Pendlebury, has rattled the superpower.

hands up

The actor who plays mouse-like Mavis was last night unavailable for comment as she was away on 3-day trip to Syria, where she has been giving President Assad a telling off over his questionable human rights record by drinking half a lager and lime whilst tutting quietly.

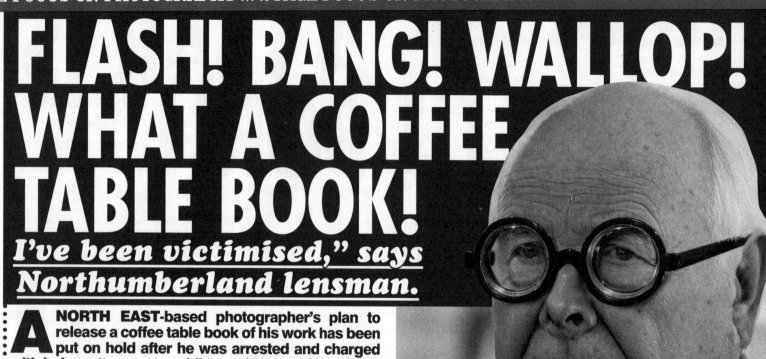

FLASH! BANG! WALLOP! WHAT A COFFEE TABLE BOOK!

I've been victimised," says Northumberland lensman.

SNAP JUDGEMENT: *Cornstalk's saucy book led to brush with the law.*

A NORTH EAST-based photographer's plan to release a coffee table book of his work has been put on hold after he was arrested and charged with indecent exposure whilst working on his project.

Wallis Cornstalk has spent the last 45 years behind the lens, photographing the countryside in and around his native Northumberland, and his work has appeared on several greetings cards which he has sent to family members. But this summer, he sidelined his love for landscapes when he came up with a plan to produce a raunchy collection of photographs on the theme of 'Sexuality'.

"I was inspired by that book *Sex* that Madonna brought out," said Cornstalk. "I'd bought a copy from a car boot at Newbiggin, and I thought it was very thought provoking."

"Of course, Madge's book came out in 1992 when the world was a very different place. It has dated quite badly, so I thought it was high time its themes were revisited," the self-styled David Bailey of Ashington went on.

version

The 66-year-old retired frozen food worker hoped that his book *Sex 2022* would prove as popular as the Grammy-winning singer's original version, and started working on the content in July.

"It would be so easy to get a book like this wrong and produce some trashy

EXCLUSIVE!

bit of filth," he confessed. "So I was determined that every shot would be tasteful and artistic."

And in a brave, modern twist, Cornstalk decided that although the book would feature explicit photographs, none of them would depict the female form.

"I abhor sexism in all its forms, and my book was going to strike a blow for women's lib by depicting only blokes in sensuous poses," he said.

However, on the eve of the project, Cornstalk suffered a major blow. "I was making last minute preparations when I received a phone call from the model agency," he recalls. "They told me that all the models with six-packs I had booked for my forthcoming session had been asked to do a Jean Paul Gaultier advert for a hundred quid. And that was each."

"I was told by the agency that unless I could match Gaultier's offer, they were going to have to let me down. Well, I can't compete with that kind of money, so that was that," he said.

camera

Cornstalk decided to have a drink in his local pub to gather his thoughts and formulate a solution. But then he was dealt a second – and more serious – blow.

"The landlord of the pub had barred me from taking my camera into the bogs with me after a bit of a misunderstanding a few weeks earlier. So, when I needed a piss, I left it on the table," he said.

"Of course, when I came out, it was gone."

With no models to photograph, and without a camera, many people would have given up. But Cornstalk decided that the book would be published despite his

seemingly insurmountable setbacks. "I decided that I would be my own model in the book. And there was a perfectly good photo-booth inside a branch of B&N Bargains in town," he told magistrates.

Cornstalk wanted the first picture in his magnum opus to be an evocative study of the male genitals, so he went into the booth, dropped his trousers and started shooting.

"It was all going great," he told the court. "I'd closed the little curtain for privacy and I was getting some really good, artistic shots."

"When it comes to my work, I'm a bit of a perfectionist, so I was in there quite a long time, rearranging my tackle to make sure the composition was just right."

"I had done about eight strips which had come out the front of the machine, when an old woman waiting to do her bus pass saw them and called the police," he said.

joko

Cornstalk was arrested and taken to the police station on Lintonville Terrace where he was charged with indecent exposure and outraging public decency. After being found guilty yesterday at Ashington Magistrates court, and asking for 23 similar

charges to be taken into consideration, the amateur photographer was bound over to keep the peace for 18 months, fitted with an ankle tag and put on the sex offenders register.

"It's just so unfair," he said. "I mean, if the woman who reported me is offended by art, then she shouldn't look at the stuff, the old cow."

"And if I've got to wear a tag and have my fucking front windows smashed in, then I think Madonna should too," he added.

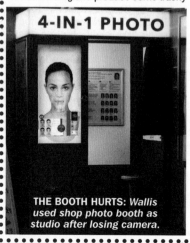

4-IN-1 PHOTO

THE BOOTH HURTS: *Wallis used shop photo booth as studio after losing camera.*

SNAP

Dear Arthur, **I'VE BEEN** married for 40 years, and whenever I take a photo of my wife, she always does this stupid, self conscious smile. It's a completely unconscious reaction to the camera and she doesn't even know she is doing it. I have tried shouting at her to stop it, but that just seems to cause her to do it all the more.

I love her very much, but in every picture I have of her she is pulling this ridiculous 'Cherie Blair' gurn. She is even doing it on our wedding photos. I would love just one picture where she is looking normal and wondered if you had any advice.

Albert Unicycle, Penge

Arthur says... After 40 years, I doubt your wife will be able to stop herself from gurning when she sees the camera. The only way you will get a picture of he looking normal is to catch her unawares when she doesn't know the camera is on her. Perhaps you could try poking your camera through a crack in the bathroom door while she is having a shower, or perhaps you could set up a hidden surveillance camera to catch her on the toilet. It seems a lot of trouble to go to, but you will at last have a nice picture of her to put on the mantlepiece.

PHOTOGRAPHY has been a popular hobby since humans first scratched photos onto the walls of their caves with sticks. And while it used to be the pursuit of the wealthy, cameras are now cheap enough that everyone can join in. And even if you don't think you have a camera, you probably have… because chances are there's one in your phone!

But whilst everyone can join in, there is more to taking a good photograph than pointing your camera at an attractive or interesting scene and allowing light to pass through a small hole and be captured on a piece of film or an electronic sensor. *Much more.*

If you want your snaps to stand out from the crowd, follow these simple but effective tips to give your photos the *'wow'* factor.

SAY CHEESE!
OUR TOP TEN TIPS FOR TAKING TOP PHOTOS

1 Understand your camera
You will never be able to create the perfect photograph unless you know your camera intimately and fully understand what is going on inside. So, before you take another photograph, completely dismantle it and examine all the components. Touch them, feel them, discover what they are for and see how they interact with each other. You will quickly feel a deep connection with your camera. Once you do, put it back together (remembering to tighten all the tiny little screws), and you are ready to go out and capture some magic.

2 Get the lighting right
Photography is all about capturing the subtle, fleeting effects of light, so if that isn't perfect, your pictures won't be perfect either. Natural outdoor light is ideal for taking pictures, with the brightest and clearest illumination occurring at 12:26pm on June 22nd, so try to take all your photographs then. If your shoot takes place indoors, make sure you put all the lights on or use the 'flash' function on your camera. Of course, it is technically possible to take photographs at night, but you will have to keep your lens open longer, so remember to keep your camera very still.

3 Think about composition
Composition can make or break a photograph, so think carefully about how things will look before you take your shot. If you are photographing a person, don't just have them standing up looking straight at the camera in the middle of the frame. Look through the viewfinder and check there isn't a tree growing out of someone's head; if there is, remember to adjust your composition or cut it down before you take your picture. If there is something interesting nearby, such as a castle, a telephone box or something on fire, have them stand next to that to give the photograph extra interest.

4 Change perspective
We observe our world looking straight on at eye level because that is how our vision works. But the camera is different to our eyes and there is no reason to photograph our world from that same perspective. Try dropping down on one knee and pointing your camera upwards like photographers do in films. If your camera has one of those big 'fuck off' lenses, then zoom in or out to change the shot. Put it on the floor, tilt it slightly to one side or turn it upside down. A new and interesting new perspective will make your photograph really stand out.

5 Take the lens cap off
There is nothing more infuriating than doing a fashion shoot in the Bahamas, only to return to the hotel at the end of the day to find you have left the lens cap on. Forgetting to take the lens cap off is photography mistake 101, and it is made by professionals and amateurs alike. Get into the habit of taking your lens cap off before you do anything else. Or better still, simply don't bother putting it on in the first place.

6 Have fun
Everyone loves a quirky picture, and if you have fun with your camera, this humour will come across in your photos. Be imaginative and original. Don't take a shot of somebody simply standing next to the Leaning Tower of Pisa – frame your picture so it looks as if they are pushing it straight. Don't just snap your subject in front of a sunset – frame them so they appear to be holding the sun between their thumb and forefinger. Try not to stare into the sun for too long as you might damage your camera or go blind.

7 Get naked
Photographing the nude is an art form in itself, and some of the most memorable photographs ever taken have depicted the naked form. A well lit, tasteful, artistic photograph of a nude is a thing of beauty. Next time you are at a party or a wedding, ask all the guests to take their clothes off while you snap away. If your shots are in black and white rather than colour, the results will look even more artistic.

8 Create depth
A flat photograph is less interesting than one with depth. If you are photographing people, have your subjects stand in front of something big but far away, such as a building or mountain. If there is nothing there, create a sense of depth by asking some of them to stand further away from the camera than others. If you are photographing jockeys and basketball players, sending the jockeys to the back will heighten that sense of depth, whereas bringing the jockeys to the front would make everyone look the same height and flatten the picture.

9 Put a tiger in the frame
With their rich orange and black stripes, piercing green eyes and strong, muscular bodies, tigers are the most photogenic of animals. There are many thousands of photographs with tigers in and all of them are striking images. If your picture does not feature a tiger, it is at an immediate disadvantage to one that does. So rent a tiger from an animal theatrical agency, or if you live near a zoo, pop along and take all your photographs there.

10 Use effects
The camera never lies, but it can be made to spin the truth. There are many special effects lenses on the market but these are very expensive and similar results can be achieved at little cost. A piece of blue cellophane held across the top half of the lens will give any landscape a brooding sky, while a bit of vaseline smeared on the lens can make plain-looking people slightly more attractive. For people like Anne Widdecombe and Ricky Tomlinson, use a bit of industrial strength axle grease.

HAPPY
Your Photo Queries Answered by Viz photographer Arthur Snap

Dear Arthur, I LOVE taking snaps of my family, but my 14-year-old daughter is a vegan and she refuses to say 'cheese' when photographed. Is there another vegan-friendly alternative word I can ask her to say when I get my camera out?
Ada Brainwash, Braintree

Arthur says… The idea behind saying cheese for a photograph is that the mouth is naturally pulled into a smile whilst doing so. As such, any word with similar phoenetics will work. 'Beef', 'Meat' and 'Cream' would work perfectly, but I imagine these would similarly be unacceptable to your daughter. She could say 'Mead', unless she is one of these vegans who won't even eat honey. If she is, then 'Seed', 'Beet' or 'TVP', extending the last letter (ie, 'Peeeeeeeee') should be acceptable to anyone who eschews animal products.

Dear Arthur, I'VE BEEN trying to take a 'dick-pic' to send to a woman at work. I would like it to look sexy and alluring, but I can't seem to get it right. I thought it might be the camera on my phone that wasn't up to the job, so I upgraded to an iPhone 13, but it still comes out looking like something from a medical textbook. Having to take it myself doesn't help matters, but I can't ask my wife to do it for obvious reasons. Do you have any tips for getting a half decent snap of my tackle?
Mr B, Essex

Arthur says… When it comes to genital selfies, it is always the lighting that is the enemy. It is naturally quite dark 'under the bridge' and so some form of supplementary illumination is essential. Never use the flash on your camera as this is too stark and will always produce an unflattering result. Try changing the bulbs in your bathroom for LED daylight bulbs which produce a more natural light and therefore a better picture of the fruit bowl. Of course, actual daylight is the best source of illumination, so if you can snap your tackle outdoors without getting arrested, that will produce the best results.

Mrs Brady OLD LADY

OOH, HE'S LOVELY, THAT LENNIE BENNETT.

...WE'LL BE BACK WITH MORE LUCKY LADDERS HERE ON CHALLENGE AFTER THIS..!

...WILL NO-ONE HELP THE BEARS..?

EEH! LOOK AT 'IM THERE ALL IN A CAGE, LOOK...

...SOMEONE PLEASE HELP THE BEARS...

THEY SHOULDN'T BE IN CAGES, BEARS...

...IT'S NOT RIGHT.

...TEXT "CUDDLY TEDDIES" TO 01 8118055 TO GIVE £5 A WEEK TO A BEAR IN A CAGE.

I'M DOIN' THAT.

...HOW CAN YOU LOOK THIS ORPHAN CAT IN THE EYES..?

THE POOR MITE!

...IT'S SHAMEFUL WHAT HE'S BEEN PUT THROUGH, THAT PUSS!

...HE HASN'T GOT A BALL OF WOOL TO PLAY WITH...NO-ONE TO TICKLE HIM BEHIND THE EARS...

WHERE'S ME PHONE..?

...TEXT "HELP THE LITTLE KITTEN" TO GIVE JUST £8 A MONTH TO HELP ORPHAN CATS LIKE TIDDLES ENJOY A HAPPY LIFE...

H...E...L...P...

TAP-TAP.

...THIS LITTLE BUNNY RABBIT'S MAMMY'S BEEN RAN OVER BY A STEAMROLLER...

AW..! ≥SLOOP!≤

...HE'S SAT IN THE WOODS AND HE DOESN'T KNOW WHERE SHE'S GONE AND HE'S HUNGRY AND AFRAID...

LOOK AT 'IM...

BLESS 'IM, WITH 'IS BIG EYES AN' 'IS WHISKERS...

...BUT YOU CAN MAKE HIM SMILE AGAIN WITH A TEXT MESSAGE TO DONATE JUST £10 A WEEK TO BUY HIM SOME CARROTS...

TAP-TAP.

DONE.

...LOOK AT THESE FOREIGN DONKEYS WITH THEIR HOOVES ALL BENT...

EEH..! THAT'S TERRIBLE IS THAT..!

...TEXT "HELP THEM POOR DONKEYS" TO THIS NUMBER TO GIVE JUST £20 A DAY TO HELP GET THESE LOVELY CREATURES' FEET TRIMMED...

P...O...O...R...D...

TAP-TAP...

HELP TA

...THESE ELEPHANTS ARE NATURE'S MOST MAJESTIC AND GENTLE CREATURES...

AW...

...BUT THEY KEEP GETTING MADE INTO PIANOS...

!

...A GIFT FROM YOU OF JUST £20 A DAY – THAT'S LESS THAN THE COST OF A FABERGÉ EGG – WILL STOP ELEPHANTS BEING MADE INTO PIANOS...

≥TSK≤

TAP-TAP...

I'M DOIN' THAT...

...THAT'S LEAST I COULD DO.

TAP-TAP...

TAP-TAP...

OH GOOD. ME PROGRAMME'S STARTIN' AGAIN...!

NEXT DOOR...

THAT'S ALL FOR NOW, BUT STAY TUNED FOR MORE CLASSIC LUCKY LADDERS ON UK GOLD AFTER THIS...!

...THIS IS ADA...

EEH...IT'S ADA..!

...ADA'S SPENT HER PENSION ON CHARITY APPEALS OFF DAYTIME TELEVISION...

FANCY.

...SHE HASN'T GOT ENOUGH MONEY LEFT TO BUY HERSELF A NEW FRUIT HAT OR A PAIR OF SUEDETTE BOOTEES...

AW...

≥SNIFF!≤

...BUT YOU CAN BRING SOME SUNSHINE BACK INTO ADA'S TRAGIC LIFE...

...TEXT "POOR OLD ADA" TO 0898...

TAP-TAP...

TAP-TAP...

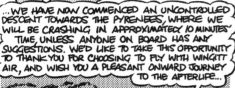

BREXIT IS TOP OF THE POPS

BRITAIN'S exit from the European Union has hit UK imports and exports badly, as HGV drivers trying to leave or enter the country find themselves mired in endless red tape. But the massive jams on the roads leading to our ports have led to an unexpected profits boost for soft drink manufacturers, as desperate truckers clamour to find something to piss in while they queue.

"Sales of bottled soft drinks at motorway services have seen a substantial increase since we left the EU," said UK Retail Industry spokesman Sir Brampton Ferrybridge.

irn

"Irn Bru, Lucozade Sport and Dr Pepper are just a few of the great British brands

BREXCLUSIVE!

that are coining it in thanks to HGV drivers needing emergency urine receptacles whilst stuck for hours in their cabs waiting for customs checks."

cppr

And the new figures seem to be supported

EU exit puts fizz in soft drink company profits

by anecdotal evidence. Motorists travelling up and down roads near major UK ports report increasing numbers of pop bottles containing alarmingly unhealthy-looking dark orange urine discarded along verges and central reservations by truckers who have been turned back

at customs due to incorrect paperwork.

"It's a real Brexit bonus for the soft drinks retail sector," barked Zippy-gobbed *GBNews* presenter Nigel Farage.

pltnm

"The brands with a wide neck on the bottle are particularly popular, as it's easier to get the end of your cock in," he added, whilst holding up a pint of John Smith's bitter made by Dutch brewers Heineken.

Farage: Zippy-gobbed.

Letterbocks

......letters@viz.co.uk......

WHAT'S the point of monks? They dress in a sack, grow bees, ring bells and never say a word. Frankly I think these chanting weirdos with their phallic haircuts should be sent to a prison camp. That would teach them.

Tilda Basmati-Rice, Orkney

PEOPLE use the expression "to make a beeline for" when they want to go somewhere quickly and directly. However, every bee I've ever seen tends to buzz around in the flowerbeds, flitting about all over the shop with no concept of urgency or direction at all. Surely there's a better expression. I often don't have time to flounce about all over the place when I need to get to the toilet in a hurry. I'm already on a yellow card from the missus after shitting myself when only halfway round the garden.

Fat Albert, Fort William

ON Pages 32 and 33, I noticed that there wasn't a single letter from a Hampshire resident. Come on, central southern England. Get writing and have your say.

Chess player, Wirral

"OUR house, in the middle of the street," sang popular North London ska band Madness in the eighties. But I can't imagine they were particularly popular with local residents if they had a house blocking the middle of the road. If their house had been at the side of the street like everyone else's, then perhaps their popularity wouldn't have steadily declined over the last four decades.

Micky Bullock, Bristol

YET again I'm watching a porno on my laptop and I notice the guy's cock is only halfway hard. Honestly, the lack of professionalism is so disappointing that I doubt I'll be able to complete my wank. Does no one take pride in their work any more?

Tommy Mack, email

I RECENTLY tried to draw Postman Pat for my young son. Unfortunately, it came out looking like Roger Mellie in fancy dress with a Husky instead of a cat.

Alan Jones, Cardiff

ACCORDING to the futurist Thomas Friedman, we live in an age of acceleration where everything we see, touch and feel is exponentially faster and more connected than at any time in the history of the human race. Yet I notice the speed of light has not changed since the 17th century, and even Albert Einstein couldn't make it go any faster. So come on physicists. Get your shit together and join the 21st century.

Pete D, Broxbourne

I WONDER what former Metropolitan Police Chief Cressida Dick will do now she's been given the boot? Panto is the obvious place for a celebrity failure, and she's already got a funny little uniform. As well as that, she'll know loads of bawdy jokes, she's a Dame and she's called Dick. She's an absolute shoo-in.

Stuie, Bunny

ME and my husband were talking about our kids the other night, and he mentioned that they're much better behaved than the ones he has with his mistress. The funny thing is, I didn't know he had a mistress and other kids, and I still don't know to this day! It's good that he can still make me chuckle after all these years.

Edna Baines, Chester

DOES Chewbacca have a human dick, or one of those red rocket things like dogs have? I wonder what your readers think, only George Lucas won't respond to my emails.

Daniel Crosby, Fareham

STAR LETTER

I JUST watched our pet cat jump, from standing, to the top of a chest of drawers some five feet high. It set me thinking that jumping six times my own height would be an impossible feat, and what a weak and limited species we human beings are by comparison to others in the animal kingdom. Of course, the fact that I am 23 stone doesn't help matters.

Athelstan Popkess, Nottingham

WITH reference to Martin Shithell's letter *(page 55)*, I can confirm that in the Romance languages, ie, French, Italian, Spanish, etc, the words 'poo' and 'wee' are both feminine, viz. la mierda, la cacca, la pisse etc. Millie Tant would be proud to know that her gender is both number one and number two in the war between the sexes.

Iain Bethune, email

I BET if Derren Brown borrowed a pen from you, he'd do some mad hypnotic bollocks to make sure you forgot to ask for it back. What an arsehole.

Chimney Magill, Colne

* Has Derren Brown ever borrowed a pen from you, and if so, did you get it back? Write in and let us know.

LIKE all of us, I was shocked to learn that Her Majesty the Queen was going to pay the £12m out-of-court settlement for Prince Andrew. But I shouldn't be judgemental as my mother paid my £40 fine when I was done for speeding in 1994.

Jared Goodhead, Nottingham

A GIRL I work with claims to be a feminist, but I know for a fact that she regularly wears cosmetics and has a boyfriend. It is people like her who undermine the credibility of worthy causes.

T O'Neill, Glasgow

GREETINGS From Mrs. Comfort Mohammed. I have a Mutual/Beneficial Business Project that would be beneficial to you. I only have two questions to ask of you, if you are interested. 1. Can you handle this project? 2. Can I give you this trust? Please note that the deal requires high level of maturity, honesty and secrecy. This will involve moving some money from my office, on trust to your hands or bank account. Also note that I will do everything to make sure that the money is moved as a purely legitimate fund, so you will not be exposed to any risk. I request for your full co-operation. I will give you details and procedure when I receive your reply, to commence this transaction, I require you to immediately indicate your interest by a return reply. I will be waiting for your response in a timely manner. Best Regard, Mrs.Comfort NOTE: If you received this message in your SPAM/ JUNK folder, that is because of the restrictions implemented by your Internet Service Provider, treat it genuinely.

Mrs Comfort, Email

* It did indeed go into our spam folder, Mrs Comfort, so thank you for reassuring us of its legitimacy. If any readers would like to get involved in Mrs Comfort's business project and 1) can handle the project, and 2) are able to accept Mrs Comfort's trust, then write in and we'll pass your details on.

The Devil Rides Out

*Vade retro Satana! Fututus et mori in igni!!

*Go away Satan! Fuck off and die in a fire!!

☐ **THE** tide of WW2 was changed in no small part by a ditty about Hitler only having one ball, sung to the tune of Colonel Bogey. With Europe yet again on the brink of war, I feel we should learn from past experience and start singing a similarly ridiculing song about Putin's wedding tackle, along the lines of –

Putin, has got a cock so thin,
His missus,
Can't feel it going in,
It gushes,
After two pushes,
Then it shrinks to the size of a pin.

If schoolboys across the land began singing this in the playground, it would be a big blow to Russian morale and could shorten the war.

Francis McConnell,
Mérida, Spain

☐ **I THINK** Francis McConnell *(above)* is onto something here. Maybe we could make the song Russian themed? I'm thinking something along the lines of the following, sung to the tune of Boney M's 1978 hit Rasputin:

Vla Vla Vlad Putin
cleaned his cock with Mr Sheen
it wasn't big,
but oh how it shone.

Happy to give up a couple of weekends on this, if it'll help.

Gordon Shatner,
Childs Hill

☐ **IMAGINE** how rich you would be today had you saved up all the money you'd spent on food in supermarkets. I have calculated that over 30 years – 18 of those raising three kids – I would be £147,000 better off.

Stephen, Widnes

☐ **HOW** do fish manage to hold their breath so long underwater?

Julian Wiseman, email

＊ *We can answer that for you, Julian. The simple answer is, they don't! Believe it or nor, fish actually 'breathe' water. Honestly, you couldn't make it up!*

WINTER OLYMPICS CORNER

Viz readers' responses to the Beijing Winter Olympics 2022

☐ **I DON'T** think the Olympic downhill skiers ought to be allowed to thwack those sticks out of the way during their race. If I was in charge, instead of being bendy, I'd make them out of steel pipe and concrete them in. Then they'd have to go round them properly.

Stuie, Bunny

☐ **CAN I** use the pages of *Viz* to put myself forward for selection of the next Winter Olympics men's curling team? I've never played, but after watching it for all of five minutes, my wife assures me it's "an absolute piece of piss. All you've got to do is push a fucking stone into a circle. How hard can it be? They don't even wear skates!" I look forward to hearing from the Olympic committee in due course.

Stu Perry, Peel Isle of Man

☐ **I GOT** a 9 while watching *Countdown* the other day. Unfortunately it was in the numbers round and the target was 583.

Ben Nunn, Caterham

☐ **ACCORDING** to Amazon, one of the best selling books of last year - *Entangled Life* by Merlin Sheldrake – ran to 360 pages and was all about mushrooms! Well, I'm no expert, but I'm sorry, there just isn't that much to say about mushrooms: they've got a stalk with a round bit on top, some you can eat and some you can't, and that's it. Two pages at most. The author must be laughing all the way to the bank.

Mike O'Riza,
Leeds

☐ **WE** all know that water always runs downhill and so do marbles. So why is it that you often see water in puddles at the bottom of hills but never pools of marbles. I'd like to see those so-called scientists answer that one.

Ivor Quilt, Exeter

☐ **BY** continually telling me how many stops away my parcel is, I think Amazon is overestimating my excitement. I've only ordered a washing machine hose for £6.57. It's hardly Christmas is it?

Micky Bullock, Bristol

TOP

INSTEAD of having your wife's name on a tattoo, just have one that says 'The Mrs' Instead. This will avoid any awkwardness in the event that you divorce and marry someone else.

Jack Spratt, Stourbridge

FOOL your neighbours into thinking your property is part of the National Trust by adding a gift shop by your back door.

Michael Thompson,
North Wales

IF YOU have a twin, convince someone that they are pissed by both of you standing in front of them whilst swaying from side to side.

Kev McLean, Peterlee

SAVE money when eating out at restaurants by having a big meal at home beforehand. You can then happily order a glass of water and a sprig of parsley as a main course.

Scarly, Sale

FEEL truly 'Presidential' when arriving home by pointing at random family members and pets as you walk through the house. An extra level of realism can be achieved if you act like you've never seen a balloon before.

Kevin Caswell-Jones,
Gresford

PREVENT hair loss by adding a few drops of Super Glue to you usual hair conditioner. Remember to wear goggles when rinsing to prevent your eyes getting glued shut.

Ian, Bletchley

SAVE money on a Hall of Mirrors by being 4' 3", 35 stone, and having a very pointed head.

Michael Thompson,
North Wales

TAKE advantage of any major storm that hits by throwing all your unwanted rubbish in your neighbours' gardens.

Geordie Pete, Reading

YOUNG people. Save time by not saying "literally" in every sentence, as it is already assumed. On the rare occasion you don't mean what you say literally, you can say "figuratively" or "metaphorically" as required.

Mike Taylor, Stalybridge

toptips@viz.co.uk

SOUP-ER BLOOPERS

BIG SCREEN BROTH BLUNDERS 'N' CHOWDER CHUCKLES WITH SOUP-LOVIN' CINEPHILE *Mark Commode*

The first appearance of soup on the silver screen was in **LAUREL AND HARDY**'s 1928 silent comedy *From Soup to Nuts*. Working as waiters at an upper-class dinner party, cack-handed Stan spills hot broth over Ollie's shoes as a title card reads: "Watch where you're dropping that soup, numbskull!" Jazz Age audiences were so busy chuckling at the slapstick hilarity, they failed to spot a glaring error, though... namely, *that Stan Laurel is wearing a **LIMP BIZKIT** T-shirt throughout the entire film!* "It was so embarrassing, because Limp Bizkit didn't even form until 1994, almost thirty years after my death," Laurel recalled in his autobiography. "Boy, were our faces red!"

The horse racing drama *Seabiscuit* features a scene in which Tinseltown ace **JEFF BRIDGES** is eating a bowl of tomato soup. However, eagle-eyed viewers will notice that the level of soup in the bowl does not remain consistent as the scene progresses. At the start, the bowl is seen to be nearly full, and by the end there is *no soup in the bowl at all!* Incredibly, this glaring blooper wasn't picked up on in post-production, and the finished film was released with the staggering soup-centric fuck-up included.

During filming of the 1986 horror movie *The Fly*, lead actor **JEFF GOLDBLUM** planned a side-splitting soup-based prank on his director, **DAVID CRONENBERG**. At lunch one day, Goldblum dressed up in his grotesque half-man-half-insect costume and hid inside Cronenberg's bowl of golden vegetable soup, planning to jump out crying "There's a fly in your soup!" as soon as the director sat down. However, before Goldblum could reveal himself, a ravenous Cronenberg took a big spoonful of his lunch... *swallowing Goldblum whole!* Co-star **GEENA DAVIS** had to rush across to the choking director and perform the Heimlich Manoeuvre, whereupon Cronenberg coughed up the 6'4" actor. "We all fell about laughing," Davis later recalled. "Except for Jeff, who was badly shaken and covered in phlegm."

More bouillon balls-ups and consommé catastrophes next time, you broth-bonkers film fuck-up fans! Mark xx

OH, LORDY!... IT'S THE **FAT SLAGS**

PREMARKED

EEH! LOOK AT THE PRICE O' KNICKERS THESE DAYS, TRAY... TWO FUCKIN' QUID!

AYE... BUT THAT IS F' FIVE PAIRS, SAN

I KNOW... BUT EVEN SO...

...TWO QUID!

WELL, LISTEN ... WHY NOT BUY 'EM AN' DO A "PREMARKED KNICKERS TRY-ON HAUL" VIDEO F' YOUTUBE?

EH!?.. WOT'S A TRY-ON HAUL VIDEO?

IT'S WHERE WOMEN FILM THEMSELVES TRYIN' ON STUFF THEY'VE BOUGHT AT THE SHOPS... THEY'RE DEAD POPULAR, SAN...

...'SPECIALLY WI' THE FELLAS

AN' IF Y' GET 100,000 VIEWS, Y' GET SOME MONEY OFF THAT BLOKE WOT OWNS GOOGLE

EEEH! THAT'S GOOD

AYE... FORGET PREMARKED, YOU'LL BE ABLE TO AFFORD VICTORIA'S SECRETS NEXT TIME Y' NEED SCADS.

AYE... AN I GET T' DO A PORN FLICK AN'ALL

OOH, NO... IT'S NOT PORN, SAN... THERE'S NO FANNIES OR OWT... YOUTUBE'LL TAKE IT DOWN IF THERE'S FANNIES ON IT.

WELL, WOT ABOUT THE ONE WE LOADED UP WI' BAZ DOIN' US UP THE ARSE?.. THEY'VE NOT TOOK THAT 'UN DOWN AN' THERE'S FANNIES IN THAT... TWO OF 'EM

THAT WEREN'T YOUTUBE, SAN. THAT WERE AMATEUR DIRT-BOX FUN DOT COM

OH, RIGHT

NO... TRY-ON VIDEOS ARE SEXY, BUT NOT GRAPHIC, SAN... THEY'RE **TITTILATIN'**

TITTILATIN'?.. I'D BEST GET THE BRA AN ALL, THEN

SHORTLY...

RIGHT... START BY 'OLDIN' 'EM UP IN FRONT OF Y' AN' STRETCHIN' 'EM...

...THEY USE THAT F' THE THUMBNAIL

RIGHT... THREE... TWO... ONE...

GO!

AYUP... I'M SAN, AN' WELCOME T' MY CHANNEL... AN' TODAY I'M GOIN' T' TRY ON THESE LOVELY SCADS WOT I'VE BOUGHT FROM PREMARKED..

...THEY'RE GORGEOUS, BUT NOT CHEAP AT TWO QUID F' FIVE PAIR

...SO LET ME PUT 'EM ON F' YER

AN'... CUT!

RIGHT... I'LL STOP FILMIN' WHILE YOU PUT 'EM ON

THEN WOT?

THEN Y' SHOW 'EM OFF T' THE CAMERA, SAYIN' 'OW NICE THEY FEEL AN' THAT... AN' PLENTY O' FLASHES O' STOCKIN' TOPS

RIGHT

AN' DON'T FORGET T' SHOW 'EM THE BACK... Y' CAN'T DO FANNIES ON YOUTUBE, BUT ARSES ARE OKAY... RIGHT...

...THREE... TWO... ONE... GO!

WELL... THERE Y' ARE... I'VE PUT 'EM ON... ...AREN'T THEY LOVELY?..

LIFT Y' SKIRT UP, SAN, WE CAN'T SEE 'EM...

...AREN'T THEY LOVELY?..

LIFT Y' TUMMY UP, SAN, WE CAN'T SEE 'EM

THEY'RE A CLASSIC, PLAIN DESIGN COTTON BRIEF WI' A COMFY ELASTICATED WAIST AN' LEGS...

...AN' THEY'VE GOT A NICE, HIGH CUT SIDE...

SEE...

AN' LOOK AT THE LOVELY THONG RIGHT UP YER CRACK SO NO 'ORRIBLE VPL

WELL, THAT'S IT F' THIS VIDEO.. DON'T FORGET T' GIVE ME A THUMBS UP AN' CLICK ON THE SUBSCRIBE SO I GET SOME MONEY OFF GOOGLE ...AN' I'LL BE BACK WI' A VICTORIA'S SECRET TRY-ON HAUL IN A FEW WEEKS

BYE-EEE! LUV YA!

THAT W' GREAT, SAN... DEAD SEXY... LET'S GERRIT UP ON YOUTUBE, WAIT FORRIT T' GO VIRAL, AN' WATCH THE MONEY COME ROLLIN' IN

8 WEEKS LATER...

LOOK AT THE STATE O' THESE FUCKIN' KNICKERS, TRAY! I ONLY BOUGHT 'EM TWO MONTH AGO AN' THEY'RE ALL STRETCHED T' FUCK AN' ALL THE ELASTIC'S GONE

...A WASTE O' TWO QUID... I'M TAKIN' 'EM BACK

I WOULDN'T BOTHER, SAN... YOU'LL BE GETTIN' SOME VICTORIA'S SECRETS, REMEMBER?

LET'S SEE 'OW Y' VIDEO'S GOIN'

OOH, AYE!

I RECKON YOU'LL GET TEN QUID PER MILLION VIEWS, SO YOU'LL NEED FIVE MILLION VIEWS F' A PAIR O' VICKIES...

FIVE MILLION... COME ON... FIVE MILLION...

OOH, SHIT...

FOUR MILLION, NINE 'UNDRED AN' NINETY NINE THOUSAND, NINE 'UNDRED AN' NINETY SIX... EEH!

EEH!.. SO I'M JUST A FEW VIEWS SHORT?

NO...

...YER FOUR MILLION, NINE 'UNDRED AN' NINETY NINE THOUSAND, NINE 'UNDRED AN' NINETY SIX SHORT...

...YOU GOT FOUR VIEWS!

HEY!.. THESE KNICKERS ARE ALL FUCKED AN' I ONLY BOUGHT THE FUCKIN' THINGS TWO MONTH BACK... I WANT SOME NEW UNS AN' ME MONEY BACK

YOU TELL 'EM, SAN

PREMARKED

79

FOR CRYING OUT LOUD

ONE TAKES TWO

ROYAL REPRESENTATIVES have announced that Prince Andrew is making preparations to have 'another go' at his disastrous *Newsnight* interview with journalist Emily Maitlis.

The tainted royal was subjected to the car crash TV quizzing in 2019, and his reputation was trashed as a result. But according to Palace insiders, after acknowledging a few flaws in his performance in the first exchange, Andrew has been working hard on arranging a rematch.

second

Royal insiders say he now believes he could 'nail it' second time around and get the British public on his side.

"His former Highness has been cramming for months in order to get all the questions right that Ms

EXCLUSIVE!

Maitlis puts to him," said a royal spokesman. "He really has got it spot on this time."

farm

It is believed that an Emily Maitlis lookalike has been hired to help prepare the Prince for his second attempt at the make-or-break interview, and she has apparently pulled no punches in her mock questioning. But according to Buckingham Palace,

Duke plans 'another bash' at TV interview

Andrew's performance is now word perfect. "He is hitting the mark on every question," said a spokesman. "He's knocking them out of the park."

back

Inside sources say the Prince is prepared to take part in the interview anytime, anywhere, and has told his private secretary to "bring it on".

NO SWEAT: *Prince Andrew aiming to produce the perfect interview.*

"His former Highness is pumped and ready to go," the spokesman said.

under

"The only conditions are that he has sight of Ms Maitlis's questions six weeks before the interview, that he can refuse permission for it to be broadcast if he is unhappy, and that he can have a third go if he ballses it up again," he added.

ROOM SERV-ICE

Mayor reveals plans for Lincolnshire 'Ice B&B'

ICE DO LIKE TO BE BESIDE THE SEASIDE! Skegness (inset top left) hoping to emulate success of Sweden's Ice Hotel with its Frozen Haven Guest House.

SWEDEN'S Ice Hotel was famously the inspiration for the Ice Palace, fictional headquarters of Korean diamond magnate Gustav Graves in 007 film *Die Another Day*. Since opening its doors in 1990, the luxury establishment in the village of Jukkasjärvi has spawned dozens of copycat projects around the world. And now a Lincolnshire lord mayor has announced plans to build the world's first *Ice B&B* in the Lincolnshire seaside resort of Skegness.

According to councillor Athelstan Popkiss, Skeggy's Frozen Haven Guest House will accommodate up to 10 holiday makers in 5 double bedrooms made completely of ice. The walls, floors, ceilings, doors and windows will be completely fashioned from frozen water, as well as all the furniture and fittings.

"The Frozen Haven B&B is going to be one of the Seven Wonders of Lincolnshire," he told local paper *The East Lindsey Fedora*. "Skegness already welcomes thousands of summer visitors from as far afield as Nottingham and Leicester, but our ice B&B is set to attract visitors from even further afield."

"It's going to put Skeggy well and truly on the map," he added.

reactor

Building work on the groundbreaking hotel will begin this winter, and is expected to use almost 2000 tons of ice shipped 30 miles down the coast from Grimsby fish market. Once completed, it is hoped that the famous 'bracing' Skegness weather will keep the sub-zero establishment frozen solid through the summer months when the resort is at its busiest.

"There's not a block of ice been laid yet, and we've already had a couple of dozen enquiries about bookings," said Popkiss. "It's going to be the most sought after accommodation on the Lincolnshire coast. We're going to be booked solid."

solid

The mayor said that despite its unique architectural qualities, the Frozen Haven will operate a traditionally strict 'no pets' policy in line with most other Skegness boarding houses. Guests will also be required to vacate their accommodation after breakfast each day at 9:00am, and will not be allowed back on the premises until 5:30pm.

"My sister-in-law Mrs Edna Scabies will be in day-to-day charge of the Frozen Haven," said Popkiss. "She is a seasoned landlady with over forty years' experience running the Lincoln Coast Retreat Guest House, and I can think of nobody better to ensure the comfort of all the guests."

lobster

Mrs Scabies has produced a list of rules which will be handed to each guest as they enter the ice B&B, setting out fines should any be broken. Food will not be allowed to be consumed anywhere in the B&B other than the ice-built dining room, and guests will not be allowed visitors in their room at any time.

"Patrons will be permitted one four-inch-deep bath every other day," said Popkiss. "Obviously it will have to be cold water because the bath is made of ice and it would melt if the water was hot."

"You'll get a maximum of two sheets of Izal per toilet visit, one to wipe and one to polish, and anyone blocking the ice-bog pan will receive a £10 unblocking fine," he added.

ICE TO SEE YOU, TO SEE YOU, ICE!

Call for greater winter ice visibility to save NHS

NO SKIDDING: Could colours used in ice lollies (inset left) be used to help prevent accidents caused by black ice?

SAFETY CAMPAIGNERS have called for ice to be coloured this winter in an attempt to prevent the thousands of accidents that result from people treading on the slippery substance. Each year, over 10,000 Brits find themselves admitted to A&E departments after falling on frozen pavements and steps. And the main reason seems to be that the ice is invisible.

"The problem is that ice is completely see-through," said Ursula Bear, president of the British Society for the Prevention of Accidents. "When you're walking along an icy pavement, you simply can't see the stuff. You can only see the pavement underneath it," she continued.

EXCL-ICE-IVE!

"It's like it's not there. No wonder so many people go arse over tit, if you'll pardon my language."

scientists

And the society called for scientists to ensure that this winter's ice is made completely visible so that people can take steps to avoid it.

"If they could make ice be blue or orange or something, then we'd all be able to see it and Casualty admissions would be falling rather than people," she said.

Bear admitted that she wasn't quite sure how ice could be coloured, but believed the same technology used in the manufacture of Zoom ice lollies could be used.

"I'm not a scientist, but surely the stuff they put in Zooms could be fired into the clouds to colour the rain and snow that forms the ice," she suggested. "I mean, they can put a man on the fucking Moon, if you'll pardon my language again."

And the BSPA have already enlisted the services of fashion guru Gok Wan to advise on the best colour for the winter ice. "You want something that stands out against the drabness of the season," he told *Take a Shit* magazine. "No pastels or delicate hues. You want colours that say 'watch that ice, girl!'. Something like a vibrant goji berry red or zippy bubblegum pink that will really pop."

magazine

But boffins at the Met Office said they were sceptical about whether the scheme would work. "We're sceptical about whether the scheme would work," said Tomasz Schaffernacker and Alex Beresford.

HE IS THE DUTCH phenomenon who has set hundreds of ultra-low temperature world records, from swimming under ice, lying down for ages in the freezing cold or running half-marathons barefoot in the Arctic Circle. He is *Wim Hof*, better known as The Ice Man. The bearded extreme athlete has developed a system of breathing, yoga and meditation to survive the cold by inducing a state of mental mastery. But what is Hof like underneath that flimsy cape thing he wears? Find out as we tell you...

-20 THINGS YOU NEVER KNEW ABOUT WIM HOF

COLD SHOULDER: *Ice Man Hof up to his neck in it.*

1 THE ICE MAN'S full name is Wimbledon Hofmeister, so called because his parents met whilst watching tennis, getting pissed up on truly awful 1980s lager and following a strutting bear wearing a pork pie hat and sunglasses.

2 WIM'S BODY is so precisely calibrated to ultra-cold conditions of around -45°C that he can never enjoy a Funny Feet ice lolly. Were he to eat one straight from the freezer at a mere -18°C, he would die… *of heatstroke!*

3 BELIEVE IT OR NOT, the Netherlands thermo-magician doesn't own a freezer or a cooker. Any food he wishes to store, he keeps down the back of his trousers where the temperature never rises above -30°C. When Wim fancies a Findus Crispy Pancake, he simply whips one out from between his icy buttocks and pops it in the fridge… *to cook!*

4 WIM CAME to fame presenting Reality TV's hit show *Freeze the Fear*, in which eight celebrities of screen and sport are guided through various frostbite-inducing tasks. The low-temp-loving lowlander auditioned for the role along with Alexander Armstrong, Bradley Walsh and Ben Shepherd. However, when the prospective presenters were asked to plunge their faces into a bath of liquid nitrogen during the audition, only one man was up to the task. Step forward, Wim Hof.

5 YOU MIGHT THINK that Wim's favourite cartoon is *Frozen*, but you'd be wrong. In fact he has called for the film to be BANNED because the characters are not cold enough, and last winter he led protests outside the Disney store in the northern Dutch city of Groningen wearing only his underpants.

6 IN HIS SPARE TIME, Wim is a keen musician and can often to be found playing an ice harp on top of a mountain in the Himalayas, bollock naked except for a headband.

7 YOU MIGHT THINK that Wim loves the music of bands such as Coldplay, Snow Patrol and Nine Below Zero. But ironically his favourite band is The Red Hot Chilli Peppers. "I hate their name," Wim told the *NME*. "But I love listening to their music whilst relaxing in a chest freezer, covered in bags of frozen peas."

8 HOF'S COLD survival methods are partly drawn from the ancient art of Tummo meditation, a Tibetan Monks' visualisation and breathing technique literally meaning 'Inner Fire'. It is a tantric practice, but one which keeps you warm rather than one which prevents your cock going off for 5 hours like it does with Sting.

9 THAT'S STING, the multiple Grammy-winning musician and former bass player from The Police, not the fanny-bearded American wrestler who, by a one-in-a-billion chance is also called Sting. *You couldn't make it up!*

10 IT IS UNLIKELY that the wrestler Sting would ever get a visit from Wim Hof. Real name Steve Borden, the AEW grapplemonger comes from Omaha, Nebraska where the average summer temperature is 30°C. In those conditions, Hof would simply desiccate into ash, a bit like Luke Skywalker in *Star Wars: The Last Jedi*.

11 IN *The Empire Strikes Back*, a planet in the Anoat Sector of the Outer Rim Territories of the galaxy is named 'Hoth', which sounds a little bit like Hof. Coincidentally, this planet is blanketed in snow and ice and unable to support any life forms… *except for Wim himself!*

12 AND SNOW LIZARDS called *tauntauns*, and *wampas*, which look a bit like a man in a yeti costume.

13 BECAUSE OF global warming, the future is looking particularly bleak for the ice-loving Hollander. Wim Hof thrives at ultra-low temperatures, and since our planet is inexorably getting warmer, scientists believe that polar bears and Wim could be extinct by 2050.

14 ALTHOUGH WIM can tolerate lower temperatures than any man or woman on the planet, even he could not survive at Absolute Zero, the lowest temperature possible. At -273°C, or 0 Kelvin, all the molecules in Wim's body would cease to vibrate, all his metabolic functions would stop and he would freeze solid. If dropped on the floor or struck with a hammer in this state, the frost-resistant Netherlander would shatter into a million pieces.

15 WIM WAS BORN in the Dutch province of Limburg, famous for its strong-smelling Limburger cheese. However, if you buy a block of Limburger from the supermarket, it will tell you clearly on the packet that it is unsuitable for freezing, unlike the region's most famous son.

16 AS A CHILD, Wim always made much bigger snowmen than his friends. While they were busy wrestling with thick socks, gloves and scarves, the future Ice Man was able to run into the garden in his pyjamas and get started on the construction. And when his peers had to go in after a couple of hours because their hands had gone numb, Wim was able to stay out all day working on his snowman.

17 FANS OF WIM will be excited to learn that he has written two books – *Klimmen in Stilte* (Climbing in Silence) and *De Top Bereiken is je Angst Overwinnen* (Reaching the Top is Overcoming your Fear). However, they will be disappointed when they get to the first page, because they are both written in *Dutch* and they won't be able to understand a word.

18 UNLESS THEY are Dutch, or can speak the language

19 MATTER EXPANDS as it warms up, and contracts as it cools, so you might expect Wim to become more dense when he takes his morning shower at 0°C. But you'd be wrong. Wim's body is composed of 75% water, a substance which contracts as it cools to 4°C, but then strangely *expands* as it cools to zero. You couldn't make it up!

20 MANY CELEBRITIES have signed up to have their bodies cryogenically frozen after death, but surprisingly Wim is not one of them. "I've spent my whole life freezing my knackers off, and I'm ready to be all snug and warm in the hereafter," he told *Titbits* magazine.

Summer Recipe
Nigella's Perfect Ice Cube

AS SUMMER temperatures soar, there's no better way to cool down than with an iced summer fruit juice cocktail. And here, Domestic Goddess Nigella Lawson brings *Viz* readers her recipe for the perfect ice cube.

"The secret of the perfect ice cube has to be the water, and you'll need about 10ml of it per ice cube. Perrier bottled water is the best, but the bubbles spoil the freezing, so pop it in a glass and leave it in the fridge to go flat. When the bubbles have stopped rising, pour the see-through liquid into a small container about an inch square. If you haven't got anything suitable, the ice cube tray from your fridge will do.

Now you're ready to turn it into ice. So take a fridge, a Fisher and Paykel or a £3,500 Smeg is best, and pop your water in the freezer box at temp mark -18 for about 8 hours. Keep checking every couple of hours to make sure it's okay. Test it by poking it with a skewer – when you can't push the skewer in, it's done.

Take it out and remove it from the container. Drop it in your summer fruit cocktail and serve immediately. *Divine!*"

83

Scum mothers who'd have 'em

HOW TV VOTE-OFF SHOWS ARE MADE

with Gregg Wallace

WOTCHA! I'm **Gregg Wallace.** It's pretty much impossible to turn on the box these days without there being a skill-based elimination show on. And I should know, I *co-present one myself!* Whether it's cooking, baking, sewing or pottering, have you ever stopped and wondered where they come from? Well, follow me as I show you around the **MASSIVE** factory where they're churned out! *Luvvly!*

EVERY great idea has to start somewhere, and this space-age machine is where it all begins. It chucks out a whopping **5,000 ideas-a-minute** and *every single one of them* is bought up by a production company and turned into a TV show for the plebs to enjoy. What's this one, then - *The Great British Punch-Up?* I'd love to watch that with an iced bun and a hot mug of cake. *Yum-my!*

OF course no elimination show would work without contestants to get rid of, which is where this clever bit of kit comes in. You simply enter in the confidence and ability levels on the keypad and this bit here phones 'em up and books 'em on to the show! And there's no waste, either. If you mistakenly set the confidence too high and the ability level too low, don't worry, they're booked on to *The Apprentice.* All clever stuff! *Do what?*

SO we've got the contestants, but there's something missing... That's right - presenters! *Easy-peasy!* You just switch this contraption on and it immediately gives me a call on my landline and a sexy female robot voice asks me I'm available. If I'm not about - maybe I'm doing a radio phone-in about veg or having a barney at a gourmet restaurant - a solenoid valve here kicks into action and books Alan Carr or Davina McCall instead. *Cor blimey!*

This bit of gubbins here is potentially the most important machine in the whole bloomin' factory; it's what they use to determine the optimal dramatic timing for the pause between the phrase, *"the first contestant leaving us is..."* and the poor sap's name. Its default setting is 7 seconds - the average time it takes to stifle a human sneeze - but it can be extended up to *three hours* to really pad out the dramatic tension! *Do me a lemon!*

WE love watching the winner being presented with their trophy at the end of each series almost as much as watching the others get the boot, but did you realise that *it's always the same trophy?* Well it is, and it was churned out on this conveyor belt here over twenty years ago. Each time this crystal offcut on a bit of old metal is presented to the winner, we put a different sticker over the old name and write the new person's name on in red biro. *Wa-hey!*

ONCE all the component elements for the show have been produced, they're gathered up and boxed in this area here, before being loaded onto these *massively* high shelves by forklift. They're so bloomin' high I can't even reach the bottom one! It's sort of like the warehouse bit of Ikea before you get to the checkouts, but instead of the boxes being full of flat furniture bits, they're full of TV shows that are all exactly the same! *Strewth!*

LIKE 'em or hate 'em, vote-off shows are here to stay. It's estimated that by the end of 2025, more than 98% of television programmes will involve a section where someone gets voted off - *even the news!* So next time you're sitting down watching a programme where a tearful wannabe gets handed their arse on a plate and sent packing for your entertainment, you'll now know where it came from. *Man up!*

NEXT WEEK: *Gregg takes a look round a factory and gets himself sucked up a chocolate pipe.*

A LIGHTER SHADE OF PAIN

Unrest sparks strike fears

RECENT strikes by rail workers, Post Office employees and barristers have caused havoc to a British population already struggling with high food prices, soaring energy bills and eye-watering mortgage rates. And things show no signs of getting better as union leaders representing Britain's cigarette lighter street vendors are now threatening industrial action following a downturn in the value of Sterling.

Recent turmoil in the economy which has led to the pound tumbling against the dollar has meant that the traditional cry of *"Lighters, three for a pound… Three for a pound, yer lighters!"* may no longer be heard on our streets.

"Britons have a proud tradition of being able to impulse-buy three poorly manufactured disposable fag-lighters for a pound on our streets and pop-up markets," said Ron Barrington, General Secretary of the Amalgamated Union of Tab Igniter Purveyors.

cabbage

Speaking to reporters from behind his suitcase on legs at Balham Tube Station, he continued: *"'Lighters, three for a pound…Three for a pound, yer lighters!'* has been the clarion call of our members for well over half a century."

EXCLUSIVE!

"However, since former Chancellor Kwasi Kwarteng's disastrous budget knocked 7% off the value of Sterling on the international currency markets, our members are faced with a stark choice."

"They must either absorb the additional costs, or pass the increase onto the consumer," he said.

Barrington warned that increasing the price in line with with inflation will not work, as the cry *"Lighters, three for one pound seven…Three for one pound seven, yer lighters!"* doesn't have the same ring to it and could spell the death knell of the cheap lighter industry.

Similarly, reducing the number of lighters customers receive in exchange for a pound would be equally damaging. "2.79 lighters for a pound would see my members' profits stay the same, but lighters have to be sold as complete units, otherwise there's flammable fluid everywhere," he added.

polaroids

In order to compete, union leaders are pressing the government to levy a windfall tax on fag-lighter 'big hitters' such as Clipper, Zippo and Bic in order to provide financial help to struggling low-budget cig-ignition-technology entrepreneurs. Ballot papers are already being sent out to members, but a series of walkouts this winter now looks inevitable.

"Spark-up hawkers have been a fixture on Britain's high streets for over half a century," said Barrington. "If we don't take action to protect the livelihoods of our members now, the familiar sight and sound of shifty and aggressive merchants supplying knocked-off eyebrow incinerators may disappear from our streets forever."

MONEY BY GASLIGHT: *Tradtional cheap lighter vendors to be hit by spiralling prices.*

SID the SEXIST

A Dr Rick Monroe MD Adventure

DR MONROE
AND THE RACE AGAINST TIME II

Brilliant surgeon Dr Rick Monroe and his dedicated assistants Nurse Todd and Nurse Erin arrive at London's Kings Cross station ahead of an important meeting at the British Medical Association headquarters in Tavistock Square…

I'm really looking forward to your talk on rectal prolapses at the BMA, Rick. It'll knock 'em dead.

Let's hope not, Todd…I'm in the business of saving lives.

Speaking of which, Rick, it looks like someone is in trouble!

Let me through, please… I'm a doctor.

HNNNNNG!

Looks like a myocardial infarction… Somebody call an ambulance.

Todd… can you pass me my bag?

Sure, Rick.

Diddly-diddly-diddly-deeee!
Diddly-diddly-diddly-deeee!

Diddly-diddly-diddly-deeee!
Diddly-diddly-diddly-deeee!

Can you take that, Erin?… it might be his next of kin.

I got it, Rick.

Hello!? No, it's not… he's here, but he's…

Pulse is very faint.

It's V-Mobile… They want to know if he wants to upgrade his package.

What!?… tell them to call back.

I'm sorry… could you call back?

How 'bout now, Todd?

Stabilising, but still faint.

Sorry, it's an offer they have today only…If he takes the Sky Cinema package for £12 a month, they throw in Sky Sports free for 3 months.

Ooh, that's a good offer…

Do you want to take 'em up on that, pal… They have some top films on there.

Pulse has gone, Rick.

HNNNNG!…Y…U…YE…NNNNNG!

Okay, Todd… time for CPR.

He said yes.

Yes, he'd like to go for that.

What's the first and third letters of his password?

What's the first and third letters of your password?

Here we go…

HNNNNNG!
NNNNNG!

I think he said L and B.

L and B… Lima Bravo.

One…Two… Three…Four…

No. it's not L and B… ask him again.

Okay… I'll just wait til he's finished having the kiss of life.

BENJAMIN'S BRITONS

YOUNG BENJAMIN BROWN WAS THE OWNER OF AN INCREDIBLE RADIO-CONTROLLED MECHANICAL MODEL ARMY OF BRITAIN'S GREATEST HISTORICAL HEROES.

IT WAS A FINE DAY AND BENJAMIN WAS HAVING A PICNIC IN LONDON'S HYDE PARK.

SIR WALTER RALEIGH'S SWORD IS PERFECT FOR BUTTERING SCONES!

SUDDENLY THE PEACE WAS SHATTERED BY AN ALARM BELL.

HELP! STOP THIEVES!

TOWER OF LONDON

A GANG OF FOREIGN CROOKS HAS STOLEN THE CROWN JEWELS!

CACKLING FOREIGNLY THE CROOKS SPED OFF IN THEIR GETAWAY CAR.

WE'VE GOT TO STOP THEM!

TOWER OF LONDON

VROOM!

ADIOS, EENGLISH!

HURRYING OVER TO THE CHILDREN'S PLAY AREA, BENJAMIN PRESSED THE RADIO CONTROL GADGET ON HIS WRIST.

THIS IS A JOB FOR KING HENRY THE EIGHTH AND FLORENCE NIGHTINGALE!

THE PORTLY 16TH CENTURY MONARCH JUMPED ONTO ONE END OF THE SEE-SAW, CATAPULTING FLORENCE NIGHTINGALE INTO THE AIR.

WHOOSH! BRITISH HISTORY'S MOST FAMOUS NURSE LANDED ON THE BONNET OF THE BADDIES' CAR.

ZUT ALORS! WHAT EES THEES?

FLORENCE NIGHTINGALE SWITCHED HER CELEBRATED LAMP ONTO FULL POWER, DAZZLING THE DRIVER.

AY, CARAMBA! I CANNOT SEE!

TOWER OF LONDON

ACHTUNG! ZE CAR EES GOING TO CRASH...

CLONK!

EES NO MATTER!

AIRFIELD

WE WEEL ESCAPE WIZ ZE CROWN JEWELS IN ZAT AEROPLANE!

WE'LL SEE ABOUT THAT — RIGHT, BRITONS?

AT THE TOUCH OF A BUTTON, BENJAMIN'S RADIO-CONTROLLED SIR ISAAC NEWTON JUMPED ONTO THE SHOULDERS OF THE EMINENT COMEDIAN BENNY HILL.

WHILE THE GREAT ENGLISH COMPOSER EDWARD ELGAR PLAYED A RENDITION OF 'YAKETY SAX', BENNY HILL RACED AFTER THE CROOKS USING HIS TRADEMARK "SPEEDED-UP" RUNNING ROUTINE.

BENNY HILL REACHED THE AIRFIELD JUST AS THE ROBBERS' PLANE WAS TAKING OFF.

TIME FOR SIR ISAAC NEWTON TO DO HIS STUFF!

THE TINY MECHANICAL 17TH CENTURY MATHEMATICIAN WAVED HIS SCIENTIFIC WAND.

GRAVITAS GRAVITORUM!

NEXT MOMENT

AY-AY-AY! NEWTON'S FORCES OF GRAVITY ARE ACTING UPON ZE PLANE!

VE CANNOT REMAIN AIRBORNE!

CRASH! THE FOREIGNERS' PLANE PLUMMETED INTO ENGLAND'S GREEN AND PLEASANT LAND.

AIEEE!

CRUNCH!

GREAT WORK, BENJAMIN! YOU'VE SAVED THE CROWN JEWELS!

THESE FOREIGN CROOKS WILL BE SPENDING THE REST OF THEIR DAYS LOCKED UP IN THE TOWER OF LONDON!

NO PROBLEM! BUT NOW ME AND MY BRITONS HAD BETTER RETURN TO OUR PICNIC!

IT'S NEARLY FOUR O'CLOCK — TIME FOR AFTERNOON TEA!

AND BENJAMIN WAS THRILLED TO BITS WHEN A VERY SPECIAL GUEST CAME AND JOINED HIM FOR TEA.

WELL DONE YOUNG MAN!

ANOTHER SCONE, YOUR MAJESTY?

THE LAST half-decade has been a time of tumultuous change. Six years ago the country was torn apart as we voted to leave the European Union, with the government moving quickly to the right to instigate a bitter culture war that still rages today. The scourge of Coronavirus, climate crisis and battles between vaxxers and non-vaxxers brought more conflict and upset into our daily lives.

But no subject divides the UK more starkly than this: *Just Who is the Best Max?* We all have our own ideas and beliefs on this red-button topic, meaning that agreement feels always beyond our grasp. Is it theoretical physicist Max PLANCK whose work on photons laid down the foundation for quantum physics? Is it Max CLIFFORD, the noncy PR guru who launched a thousand glittering careers before ending his own in a dingy prison cell? Or perhaps it's Max FACTOR, whose range of make-up graced the faces of a thousand glamorous stars in the Golden Age of Hollywood. Let's test these three contenders to the MAX as we ask the question…

PLAN WH

•••••••••••• PLANCK •••••••••••• | •••••••••• CLI

ROUND 1

ACTUALLY BEING CALLED MAX The baby who would one day discover energy quanta was born in Kiel, Germany, in 1858, and was baptised not Max, but *Karl Ernst Ludwig Marx Planck.* So not only did his name Max have an 'r' in it, but it wasn't even his second or third name; it was his *fourth!* It's a subatomic 'minimum' points for this so-called Max in round one.

Score 0

Ernst

ACTUALLY BEING CALLED MAX Before they were moved to St Catherine's House at Aldwych, documents kept in Somerset House registered the birth of the future PR guru and sex offender *Maxwell Frank Clifford* on April 6th 1943. The name Maxwell is of Scottish descent, and

ROUND 2

CELEBRITY SHOULDER-RUBBING Whilst attending Friedrich Wilhelm's University in Berlin, Planck collaborated with many great scientists, including physicists Hermann von Helmholtz and Gustav Kirchhoff, as well as renowned mathematician Karl Weiestrass. These people may have been giants in their field, but they were not exactly what you would call 'celebrities' like Marilyn Monroe, Alexa Chung or Will Smith. In fact, it is only the fact that the world famous celebrity Albert Einstein would pop round to his house now and again that stops Planck getting zero in this round.

Score 2

CELEBRITY SHOULDER-RUBBING Throughout his long career of dreaming up fictional stories to get his clients in the press, silver-haired Clifford regularly rubbed shoulders with the greats. The Beatles, Frank Sinatra, Muhammad Ali and Marlon Brando all found themselves represented at one time or another by the late PR-guru-turned-nonce-

ROUND 3

NOBEL PRIZES FOR PHYSICS The Nobel Prize for Physics is awarded each year by the Royal Swedish Academy of Sciences to those in the field who have made the most outstanding contributions for the benefit of mankind. And in 1918, the award went to none other than Max Planck for his discovery of energy quanta. So you would think it would be the full 10 points in this round. However, during the selection process, the Nobel Committee deemed none of that year's nominations to have met the criteria as outlined in the will of Alfred Nobel, and the award was reserved until the following year, meaning Planck didn't receive his scientific gong until twelve months later.

Score 6

NOBEL PRIZES FOR PHYSICS Future star wrangler Clifford left school aged 15 with no qualifications whatsoever. Without even a CSE grade 5 in Science, his teachers suspected that he would never be awarded the Nobel Prize for Physics. And their predictions came true as, at the

ROUND 4

GETTING HIT BY A DELIVERY TRUCK Outside of his scientific career, Planck led an interesting and varied life. He was a deeply religious man who married twice and fathered 5 children. He was also extremely interested in astronomy and a gifted musician, playing the piano, organ and cello, as well as writing several operas. However, in his posthumously-published *Scientific Autobiography and Other Papers,* Planck never mentions being hit by a delivery truck, so we can only assume that he never suffered such an accident, or if he did, it was of such insignificance that he felt no need to recall it in his memoirs.

Score 3

GETTING HIT BY A DELIVERY TRUCK Clifford was not known for being publicity shy, and had he been hit by a delivery truck at any point, it's a certainty that he would have had the news splashed across the front pages of whichever tabloid won the bidding war to cover the story, albeit with all the details and

ROUND 5

RIDICULOUS HAIR Most professors of physics have a wild, untamed mop of hair to accompany their often outlandish appearance and eccentric behaviour. However, Planck bucked this trend, sporting a neat, perfectly coiffed barnet in his early years. If the Goethe Prize-winning boffin had decided to go for a nutty "Mad Professor" look in later life, the option was taken away from him as, like up to 70% of adult men, he succumbed to male pattern baldness as he got older.

Score 3

RIDICULOUS HAIR While the late jailbird's dull-as-ditchwater hairstyle may not have been anything to write home about, the colour of it certainly was. For although the hair on his head went snow white at an early age, his eyebrows remained coal black all his life. It is this 'Alastair Darling'-style salt & pepper mismatch that gives the formerly-alive PR

ROUND 6

LEGACY The importance of Planck's work in the area of Quantum Physics is hard to overestimate. It has shaped almost all theoretical research that came after it, not least for the determination of the constant named in his honour, h, which describes the relationship between the wavelength of a photon and the energy that it possesses. Expressed in SI units, $h = 6.62607015 \times 10^{-34}$ J·Hz^{-1}, and without this constant, the science of Quantum Mechanics would still be in its infancy, However, it is not that much of a legacy as only a handful of weirdos understand what it is, so it's a low-scoring round.

Score 3

LEGACY It was often said that much of Clifford's work was unseen, as his job entailed keeping many stories *out* of the newspapers as he put in. But, disregarding for

HOW DID THEY DO?

PLANCK
(E=hv) by gum!

There's No(bel) prize for egghead Planck. Travelling at much less than the speed of light, the German-born boffin finishes the race in last place.

17

CLIFFORD

Close, but no great big, expensive cigar!

The disgraced sexcase PR guru may have been the self-

92

...K, CLIFFORD or FACTOR...
...O'S THE BEST MAX?

...ORD

...eans literally 'Mack's
...pring (or stream)'.
...owever, along with
...e Roman Maximus
...nd Maximillian, it is
...egularly shortened
...o plain Max. **Score** **8**

...onvict. However, at various times he also acted for
...onkers Scouse politician Derek Hatton, turd-sniffing
...utritionalist 'Dr' Gillian McKeith and Princess Di's self-
...tyled 'rock' Paul Burrrell, so that brings his score down
... bit in this
...ound. **Score** **5**

...me of his death in 2017, Clifford's name remained
...vell and truly OFF the list of winners of this coveted
...offins' accolade. And since there is no Nobel Prize
...or PR guru-ing or vile sex offences, Clifford
...ever became a Nobel Laureate in
...ny field, meaning 'PR' in this case
...stands for 'Poor Round'. **Score** **2**

...acts changed to make it more interesting and
...aleable. So the fact that we never heard a
...eep about it means that it almost certainly
...ever happened. It's another 'min'imal-
...scoring round for Max. **Score** **2**

...guru a sprinkling of
...uch needed points
...n this round.

...Score **7**

...a moment his long career as a serial sex offender,
...his legacy would have to be the 1986 *Sun* headline
...that stopped a nation, for we all remember where
...we were and what we were doing when we heard
...the news that comedian Freddie Starr had eaten
...somebody's hamster. Which he
...apparently hadn't done, because it
...wasn't true. **Score** **7**

...styled King of Spin,
...but he's a pauper at
...the court of
...the Maxes. **31**

FACTOR

ACTUALLY BEING CALLED MAX
Polish-born *Maksymilian Faktorowicz* has no more right to call himself Max than you do (assuming, that is, your name is not Max). Since his 11-letter birthname has no 'X' in it, it cannot legitimately be shortened to the particular shorthand spelling by which the Polish-born cosmetics mogul became famous. Were we asking "Who's the best Maks?" then this would have been a high-scoring round for the former apprentice wigmaker. But we're not. So it isn't. **Score** **0**

CELEBRITY SHOULDER-RUBBING
Over a 40-year career, Factor provided the make-up for almost every superstar who appeared on Hollywood's silver screen during Tinseltown's golden age. From Gloria Swanson and Jean Harlow to Joan Crawford and Ben Turpin, all of them benefitted from the famous Max Factor treatment before stepping in front of the cameras. Indeed, it would be quicker to list the A-listers who the cosmetician *didn't* rub shoulders with, such as Olivia Coleman, Idris Elba and the Chuckle Brothers. **Score** **10**

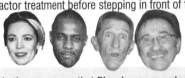

NOBEL PRIZES FOR PHYSICS
In the same year that Planck was awarded his Nobel Prize for Physics, Max Factor developed his "Color Harmony" range of face powder which, because of the huge range of shades available, allowed cosmeticians to customise make-up for individual actresses' skin tones. It was groundbreaking work, but Factor was never going to rival Planck that year, as his work was more in the field of Chemistry than Physics, and that year's Nobel prize for Chemistry went to Fritz Harber for his work on "The Synthesis of Ammonia from its Elements." **Score** **2**

GETTING HIT BY A DELIVERY TRUCK
In 1936, Factor was hit by a delivery truck outside his famous cosmetics studios on North Highland Avenue in Los Angeles. Tragically, although the cosmetician survived the impact, his recovery delayed the development of his 'pancake' make-up which, unlike the Panchromatic make-up then being used in Tinseltown's burgeoning movie industry, didn't leave a light sheen on the skin under studio lights. Even more tragically, he never fully recovered from the accident and died 2 years later. **Score** **9**

RIDICULOUS HAIR
In every photograph of Max Factor, the make-up artist to the stars appears with perfectly kempt hair in the usual style of the day. But before we award him *nil points,* remember that before turning to make-up, Factor was an expert wig-maker, and what we see may be simply one of his skilled trichological creations. Beneath that syrup, he may have had nightmare hair like Michael Fabricant, Zero Mostel or that bloke off *Time Team*. The benefit of the doubt brushes up the honorary Oscar-winner a median score in this round. **Score** **5**

LEGACY
Some people make such a mark that it is difficult to imagine how life would be had they not been born, and Max Factor is one of those world-changing people. Once upon a time, women could only choose from 3 colours of lipstick – pink, red or peach. Now, Max's avocado-butter-based Colour Elixir lipstick range gives them the choice of 29 delicious, craveable and kissable shades, ranging from Simply Nude and Toasted Almond, through Ruby Tuesday and Burnt Caramel, to Rich Mocha and Deep Mahogany. **Score** **8**

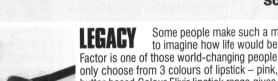

FACTOR
You couldn't make (it) up!
Cosmetics supremo Factor has put the blusher on the other two's faces and taken the title of the Best Max.

34

Next week:
CHARLTON
VS FISCHER
VS CRUSH
Who's the best Bobby?

ROUND 1
ROUND 2
ROUND 3
ROUND 4
ROUND 5
ROUND 6

RENÉ DESCARTES

HE THINKS, THEREFORE HE IS!

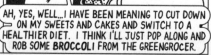

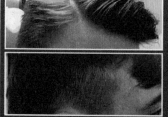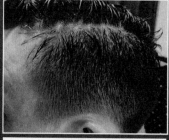

FOODIE BOLLOCKS

STAYBERKS COFFEE

Can I get...

Can I get...

Can I get a...

Can I get a regular *kopi luwak* to go?

Is that... like a cappuccino?

Ha ha ha oh my *GOD*.

What kind of a barista are you?

A zero-hours one.

No excuse.

If a job's worth doing it should be your life.

Besides, this is basic, day one stuff.

Kopi luwak is simply coffee which has passed through a civet.

Ring any bells? *Hmm?*

I think there's a tea-strainer behind here somewhere.

Civet! Civet!

A small cat-like mammal native to South and Southeast Asia.

They eat coffee berries, but only *partially* digest the beans.

Which pop out the other end.

These are harvested –

No way.

Yes, from civet faeces, then roasted and ground as usual.

But doesn't it taste of sh-

It's actually an incredibly smooth coffee experience.

And cheaper than you'd think.

These days you can get great kopi luwak for around three hundred pounds a kilo.

Three hundred quid?!

Yes, isn't it amazing?

Thanks to philanthropic entrepreneurs like Jonty Bloxham it's now within all our reach.

I carry his autobiography 24-7. It's the Bible of serious coffee enjoyers all over the world.

THE FIRED BEAN

His artisan roastery on Borough Market sparked a kopi luwak insurrection when Jay Rayner fainted during a tasting.

In 2005 Jonty's family hedge-fund took him east of Java, where the boss of a firm he was asset-stripping gave him his first cup –

– it was a literal epiphany!

He sold up a week later, spent half on a small island chain off Bali and 50,000 civets, and the rest is history.

Cool. Anyway, this is our only coffee.

What's its back-story?

Er, a bloke brings it twice a week on a van.

Sigh, okay, can I get a regular flat white?

Of course.

I take it you offer nut milk?

Oh yes, almond or coconut.

No.

Tsk, not malabar?

No.

STAYBERKS CO

Karuka?

No.

Kurrajong?

No.

Baru?

LetterbOcks

......letters@viz.co.uk......

LAST night I dreamed that I worked for Boris Johnson, and when I handed in my notice to go and work instead for Hercule Poirot, the Prime Minister gave me a really lovely, written reference even though at the time he was being pursued by a very angry man who I'd accidentally let into the building. When I woke up, I was touched by the sentiments in the reference and wondered if, just maybe, Boris Johnson isn't really that bad after all. Have any of your other readers been momentarily swayed by the actions of the ex-Prime Minister in a dream?

Joe Smith, Exeter

* What a nice thought from Mr Smith. It seems the media are constantly giving our former PM a hard time simply because of the way he behaves. Write in with some of the nice things that Boris has done in your dreams and we'll redress the balance.

I'VE just watched a porn vid where the lead actor lifted the leading lady onto a wall-mounted wash basin in the bathroom before having sex. As a plumber, could I advise anyone thinking of doing the same to take care. These kinds of wash basins are not meant to take any great weight, and for reasons of safety, I would recommend only attempting this act on a pedestal-type basin.

Billy Whiffles, Tooting

MY friend and I have been having an argument, and we were hoping you could help settle it. I reckon that there are an infinite number of pairs of prime numbers that differ by two, but my friend asserts that there is a *finite* number of these prime pairs. Can you explain which of us is right, with diagrams where appropriate?

John Moynes, Dublin

* Sorry, John, we can't help you as we were off school the day they did Polignac's conjecture and infinite series prime pair progression in maths. Perhaps there is a mathematical genius Viz reader with a terrible haircut, appalling dress sense and no girl- or boyfriend who could help settle your argument.

WHY don't we hear swannee whistles any more? You used to hear them all the time in the 1970s, when a man's trousers fell down or when a woman driver accidentally reversed a car into a duck pond. Now that we have left the EU, it's about time we brought them back.

C Hawtrey, Deal

THEY say never put all your eggs in one basket. But what if you have only got one egg? I'd like to see the smartarse philosophers answer that one.

Jack Spratt, Stourbridge

STAR LETTER

I LOVE tricorn hats, the ones which were popular in the 18th century, and if I wore a hat, it would definitely be a tricorn. Unfortunately, however, I don't wear hats, so I guess I'll never get to wear a tricorn, which is a great shame.

Hampton Crumbs, Hull

I WAS just wondering if any of your readers could answer a question for me? We are all used to bikini-clad young ladies walking around the boxing ring holding up the number of the next round. But what happens to those who don't get a chance to go on? If, for instance, the bout finishes in the third round of a ten-round fight, do the other seven bikini-clad young ladies get paid, or do they just get their bus fare home? There's not much else going on in the world at the moment, so perhaps some MP could raise this in the house.

Gordon Bennet, Aukland

I HAVE been a reader of your magazine for over three decades now, having first come across *Viz* in about 1989. In fact, I've enjoyed it so much that I'm considering buying another copy very soon.

Dave Winter, Paris

WHY are priceless antiques like Ming vases and Fabergé eggs always made from really fragile materials like porcelain and bone china? If I was making stuff which was *that* valuable, I'd have the common sense to use something more durable, like tyre rubber or cement.

Ben Nunn, Caterham

I KEEP receiving random e-mails with photos of beautiful young girls telling me they find me attractive. All I can say is that I am not surprised. I've cut back on booze, narrowed the amphetamines down to weekends and I've got my own dartboard.

Les Lloyd, email

DESPITE developing thousands of miles apart, all civilisations eventually invented sausages, and they all contain either pork or beef. The evolution of *Homo sapiens* seems to have hit a brick wall with sausages, so I would like to suggest some new fillings like ducks, moles or jellyfish.

Mike Harris, Gourock

MY wife once shouted at my son for farting when he was actually on the toilet enjoying a shit. Have any of your readers experienced a more unreasonable admonishment for releasing an audible flatulisation?

Kevin Caswell-Jones, Gresham

IN response to your star letter (*page 32*), I was the individual who Mr Crisps spotted taking a dump on the morning that his Newcastle to London train passed Newark Northgate. I was unfortunately caught short after a rather heavy session on the real ale the preceding evening. It was not my intention to cause offence and I apologise unreservedly to Mr Crisps and all in First Class who had to witness myself pushing brown.

J Smotherbox, Newark

I CAN'T be alone in thinking that whilst Ming the Merciless's huge and ornate collar is impressive, it is also extremely impractical. I imagine that when he first started wearing it in the 1930s, it was to detract attention from his baldness. These days however, attitudes have changed and a completely bald head is considered fashionable and attractive. Perhaps it's time for Ming the Merciless to face up to his insecurities, lose the collar and learn to be accepted for the person that he is.

Phil Kitching, Isle of Jura

THESE bags of ice cubes need to have a 'use-by' date. I paid £1 for a Sainsbury's 'party pack' and the contents all turned to liquid after just one day in the cupboard. What a rip-off.

Neal Bircher, Ickenham

IMAGINE how disappointing it would be being American. Every Friday night when you ordered fish and chips, you'd get a juicy piece of fish and a pile of crisps. And they probably wouldn't even be salt and vinegar flavour, because according to my mate Tex, they don't do them.

Les Lard, Louth

the DICK PIC of DORIAN GRAY

WELL, SYBIL DEAREST, DOES MY PENIS PORTRAITURE PLEASE YOU?

GRACIOUS, MR. GRAY, BUT IT IS AS GNARLED AND SHRIVELLED AS A WIZENED OLD SLUG THAT HAS LIVED MUCH LONGER THAN IT EVER SHOULD!

I CAN'T believe there's so much mystery about how the ancient Egyptians built the pyramids. Surely they just made a square on the ground out of blocks, then put slightly smaller square of blocks on each layer as they went up? I sometimes wonder what we pay these boffins for.

Ian Wallaby, Spleen

I CAN'T help thinking that if Johnny Depp had married Thora Hird instead of Amber, he would have been a lot happier. Thora could have baked him Eccles cakes and, when the heady world of showbiz made him get above himself, she could have brought him down to earth by referring to it as 'a load of old stuff and nonsense' whilst dusting an aspidistra.

Mike Hayley, Penrith

HOW come some boys' names become girls' names just by adding the letter 'a' on the end, such as Paul, Carl, Daniel, and so on, whereas others don't, such as Les, Roy and Gary? There seems to be no rhyme nor reason. Whoever is in charge of these things wants to pull their finger out.

Flub, Musselburgh

ON a recent trip to a watery wildlife place, I noticed a heron, two swans, two oystercatchers, a crow and two seagulls, all within a very short distance of each other. Can anyone else recount a more diverse feathery gathering?

Dwayne Hickman, Telford

* *What is the greatest number of birds you have ever seen in the same place? And by that, we mean the greatest number of species, not the number of individual birds, so don't write in and say 5,000 pigeons in Trafalgar Square. We're not interested in the number of individual birds you have seen. Or indeed the number of species, come to think of it. In fact, let's just forget the whole thing.*

MY old granddad lost an eye in WW2, but he still kept his spirits up. He used to take his glass eye out and pretend he was looking up ladies' skirts. All harmless fun, but the modern 'snowflake' generation obviously took exception to his japes, and he was arrested for this and "other offences." Utterly ridiculous.

Howitt, Bedford

PEOPLE keep saying my cat Archie is majestic, and judging by this photograph, You would have to say they are correct. However, shortly after I took this picture, he started licking his own arsehole, which is far from majestic. I'd like to see our monarch do that.

Joel, email

PS. I wrote "our monarch" just in case there's a high profile death before this letter is published. But the point still stands - I suspect that neither The King nor Prince William could do it.

WHEN a friend of mine was thirteen, he got kicked in the bollocks by a classmate who went on to be a member of the Boomtown Rats. Have any of your readers ever been kicked in the bollocks at the age of thirteen by someone who went on to be a member of a not particularly memorable pop group?

John Moynes, Dublin

* *That's a rather narrow set of criteria, Mr Moynes. Could we perhaps widen it slightly by saying "…at any age" rather than limiting any anecdotes to when readers were thirteen?*

IF I had been the captain of the Titanic, I would have sailed *around* the iceberg. I mean, it's an *iceberg*, for fuck's sake.

John Moynes, Dublin

RECENTLY reading a book I discovered that Limfjord is a fjord which cuts across the north of Denmark, with its western entrance blocked by sandbanks. Geological studies have suggested it was, however, open "in about AD 1000-1100". When I was at school I was told my answers needed to be on the button, and in some cases I even had to show my working out. Battle of Hastings? About 1023-1092. 12 x 12? Just shy of 150. Come on scientists, show some pride.

Chloe Cardashian, Chelsmsfjord

I OFTEN say "I've got to see a pan about a log" when I need a turd. Has anyone said that? Just me, then?

TD Fitz Rovia, email

I SAW the film *The Incredible Shrinking Man* recently, and I'm afraid the science behind the premise is rather flawed. By the time he got to a few inches tall, he would have been torn to pieces by his grossly overpowered muscles. He would also be dead from being as dense as platinum. And this is not to mention that he would expire from hypothermia as his small surface-area-to-volume ratio would be insufficient to dissipate the massive amount of heat generated by his increased metabolism. Fighting spiders using a needle as a spear? I don't think so.

Bill Logical, Colchester

TWO wrongs don't make a right, they say. But any mathematician will tell you that two negatives make a positive. I think it's high time folk put less faith in this sort of old wives' tale and started using a bit more mathematical logic.

W Lineman, Manchester

AN ex-girlfriend of mine once had a threesome with the Chuckle Brothers years ago. Needless to say the phrase 'to me, to you' was used constantly throughout the whole seven-and-a-half minute encounter.

Gordon Bennett, Auckland

* *No, we're sorry, Mr Bennet, we simply don't believe that is true. And if you told us that Paul and Barry's ChuckleVision sidekicks The Patten Brothers joined in to make it a fivesome, and they kept shouting "Get out of it" and "No Slacking" at various points in the proceedings, we would be even less inclined to believe it.*

I WONDER if aliens have curtains. I would imagine that if their planet has 2 suns, they might never get any night time, so they would almost certainly have them. Whereas aliens on planets orbiting a dark star probably haven't got much use for drapery.

Mike Harris, Gourock

DO any readers know if it's safe to squirt whipped cream up your arse from one of them aerosol spray cans? I'm not intending to try it, I'm just asking for a friend.

Gerry Paton, London

VIRTUAL INSANITY!

ABBA support act malfunction leaves audience in shock

CONCERT-GOING ABBA fans were left in shock yesterday after the support act on the band's hi-tech hit 'Voyage' tour fell off the stage at the specially built 3000-capcity East London venue.

The two 20-foot robotic models of The Captain and Tennille, booked as the support for the computer-generated versions of the Swedish pop supergroup, had been warming up the capacity crowd with a selection of their hits.

However, during a rendition of *Love Will Keep Us Together*, a coupling link came loose, separating the metal husband-and-wife hit-makers from each other and sending them flailing into the crowd.

dancing

"It was absolutely terrifying," ABBA super-fan Sue Hexagon told reporters. "One minute people were singing and dancing, the next they were running for their lives."

"To be honest, the moment that the flatbed pulled the robot likenesses of The Captain and Tennille onto the stage, with their white, outsized grand piano and Hammond organ, my blood ran cold," she said. "Even in their dormant state, something about their scale and presence made me uneasy."

UNCHAINED MELODY: *Experts examine damage to the robotic duo's piano and stool.*

"However, once the servo motors kicked in and they started their jerky performance, I made a beeline for the bar at the back of the auditorium," she continued. "It just wasn't as polished as the technology used to bring 1970's ABBA back to the stage. It was more like a giant version one of those Sooty's Band puppet machines you used to get at the end of the pier."

mechanical

Concert organisers insisted that all necessary safety checks had been carried out on the mechanical *Do That To Me One More Time* duo prior to their performance.

"We'd run them through a couple of test songs; B-sides, mid-tempo numbers, that sort of thing, to make sure everything was working as it should," Geoff Egg, chief engineer for Egg's Animatronics and Salvage told us. "There were a couple of minor wobbles during *Lonely Nights (Angel Face)*

S.O.S: *Technical malfunction happened during Swedish superstars' hi-tech live show.*

where a bolt came out of Tennille, leaving her mouth stuck open, and The Captain's head turned 180 degrees on its axis, but we soon got it sorted, so we made the decision to let the show proceed as normal. We're as shocked as anyone. This is the first time they've come untethered from their ballast."

Amazingly, only two minor injuries were sustained during the incident, with one audience member spraining her wrist and another getting a papercut from a hastily dropped concert program.

pop

Police have issued a statement, warning the public to not attempt to confront the iron pop giants who, after leaving the venue by the service entrance, were last seen striding towards the Ford motor plant in Dagenham.

DJ '22

SATURDAY 2PM

SO WHERE'S YOUR PAL TODAY?

IT'S NOT LIKE HIM TO MISS HIS SATURDAY LUNCHTIME PINT.

APOLOGIES FOR MY TARDINESS, CASKETEERS!

ALAS, I WAS DELAYED DUE TO BEING FORCED TO COMPLY WITH THE DEMANDS OF MY EX-WIFE.

SHE WAS FOREVER ISSUING DEMANDS WHEN WE WERE MARRIED.

IT WAS ALWAYS "PUT THE BINS OUT" "PICK UP THAT BATHMAT", "WIPE THE TOILET SEAT"!

ONE MIGHT HAVE EXPECTED HER DIKTATS TO CEASE AFTER WE WERE DIVORCED, BUT IT SEEMS NOT!

SHE PHONED ME TWO HOURS AGO, JUST AS I WAS SETTLING DOWN TO MY BLU-RAY OF THE CLASSIC 1973 DOCTOR WHO EPISODE "THE MAGGOTS OF MERTHYR!"

AND THE CHORE SHE HAS ASSIGNED TO ME TODAY IS TO SPEND THE AFTERNOON LOOKING AFTER ...

HANG ABOUT! WHERE'S HE GOT TO?

OH THERE YOU ARE, PERTWEE — WELL COME IN THEN, SON!

DON'T DAWDLE IN THE DOORWAY, CHILD!

NOW SIT DOWN THERE AND PLAY QUIETLY WITH WHATEVER ELECTRONIC GIZMO YOU YOUNGSTERS FAVOUR NOWADAYS.

DADDY HAS GOT IMPORTANT MATTERS TO DISCUSS WITH HIS FRIENDS ...

... SUCH AS THE FULSOME, MALTY OVERTONES OF THIS RATHER IMPRESSIVE PINT OF DUNKY'S OWLD REGRETFUL ...

... A WELL-BALANCED RUBY-RED ALE WITH A CLEAN, BITTER AFTERTASTE. 5.4% ABV.

HOY, YOU KNOW THE RULES! NO CHILDREN ALLOWED IN THE BAR!

WHAT? BUT I ASSURE YOU, HE'LL BE NO TROUBLE ...

MAY I REMIND YOU THAT IT WAS YOU WHO ORGANISED THE PETITION TO MAKE THIS PUB A "CHILD-FREE ZONE."

"KEEP THE BEARD & SPIGOT SPROG-FREE"

TSK! YES, YES, VERY WELL ...

SUP UP YOUR PINTS, CASKETEERS! REGRETTABLY, WE ARE BEING FORCED TO DECAMP TO A ...UGH!... "FAMILY FRIENDLY" PUB!

COME ALONG, PERTWEE!

THESE ESTABLISHMENTS ARE USUALLY ANATHEMA TO WE AFICIONADOS OF THE TRADITIONAL ALEHOUSE.

THE JOLLY PIG

PUB RESTAURANT

FOOD SERVED ALL DAY

KIDS MEALS ½ PRICE

FAMILIES WELCOME

BUT NEEDS MUST WHEN THE EX-WIFE DECIDES TO RUIN ONE'S SATURDAY.

TUT TUT! IT IS JUST AS I FEARED ...

DAD...

A CHOICE OF FIZZY LAGER OR KEG BITTER, AND THE WHOLE PLACE REEKS OF SCAMPI AND CHIPS.

DAD, I NEED...

IT WOULD SEEM THAT GUINNESS IS OUR ONLY RECOURSE.

DAD!

THREE PINTS IF YOU PLEASE, AND A GLASS OF FANTA FOR THE CHILD.

OH FOR GOODNESS SAKE, PERTWEE, YOU SOUND JUST LIKE YOUR MOTHER! "I NEED, I NEED!"

WELL I HAVE NEEDS TOO, YOU KNOW — INCLUDING MY NEED TO ENJOY A CONVIVIAL DRINK WITH MY FRIENDS!

I WAS GOING TO SAY I NEED TO GO TO THE TOILET...

... BUT IT'S TOO LATE NOW.

THAT DOES IT! I GIVE UP!

HURL!

I CANNOT FULFILL MY ROLE AS LEADER OF THE CASKETEERS UNDER THESE INTOLERABLE CONDITIONS!

FORGIVE MY LACK OF JOVIAL REPARTEE, CASKETEERS...

I'M JUST GOING TO SIT HERE AND WAIT UNTIL FOUR O'CLOCK, WHEN MY TYRANNICAL EX-WIFE COMES TO COLLECT THE BOY.

SIP SIP!

AH YES, FANTA! A FULSOME ORANGEY AFTERTASTE, WITH MEDIUM MOUTHFEEL AND CARBONATED BUBBLES ON THE NOSE.

0% ABV.

IT IS REMINDFUL OF THE ORANGE SQUASH I SAMPLED AT THE FULCHESTER ROAD PRIMARY SCHOOL IN OCTOBER '19. THE DINNERLADY'S NAME WAS MRS FINCH.

Take a Shit

HEY! GO

ATTRACTIVE people are traditionally said to be 'blessed' with good looks. But could 'cursed' be a better way to describe their situation? For one drop-dead handsome Solihull man, the answer is a cut and dried 'yes.'

45-year-old Terry Freeview is living proof that being a highly attractive hunk can be a source of abject misery. And the former part-time wheelie-bin cleaning operative has now been **BANNED** from taking and picking up his daughter from school… and all because his potent blend of smouldering good looks and easy going charm were too much of a distraction for the mums at the school gates.

Speaking from the living room window of his bachelor pad bedsit, recovering alcoholic Freeview told reporters that he had received a letter from the headmistress of his daughter's school asking him not to approach any of the mums at the school gates. And Terry believes the reason for the ban is because he is drop-dead gorgeous.

"I know traditionally it's women who pick the kids up from school but I am unashamedly a feminist, and am only too keen to share all household

*As told to **Vaginia Discharge***

duties, regardless of outdated gender stereotypes," Terry told the *Dorridge and Bentley Heath Inquisitor.*

"Besides which I was never able to do the school run with any of my other kids due to being estranged from their rat-bag mothers," he added.

SCHOOL WALK ON THE WILD SIDE

The self proclaimed 'Best Dad Ever' started taking his daughter, 7-year-old Chelsea, to school at the beginning of term and things started positively enough.

"After good health, nothing is more important to me than education, and I was keen to do my bit by walking my daughter the half-mile to school each morning," he said. "I looked on it as an important bit of precious father and daughter time."

"Plus, it's one of the things they let you out of the house to do when you're wearing an ankle tag."

And it wasn't long before Freeview's clinically obese presence started making waves at his daughter's school gates.

Dad banned from school run because he's too handsome

Ladies' man: Terry Freeview believes his looks have led to him being issued an exclusion order at his daughter's school.

Street for the eyes: Heart-throb Terry's bedsit was only 15 minutes' walk from the yummy-mummies at the school gates.

"I've always had a way with the ladies, being what some might call an Adonis," he told the paper. "So I guess it was inevitable that when I rocked up at the school in my vest and tracky bottoms, I was going to set a few pulses racing. It's nature."

"My sweaty, brooding essence, coupled with my shoulder length hair, which is naturally oily and thinning in a masculine way, make me cat-nip for the local milfs," he confessed. "It's not something I can control."

"Putting a hunk like me amidst all those yummy-mummies was always going to be like throwing a string of sausages to a pack of starving, sex-crazed animals."

> *"It was like Beatle-mania, with me as John, Paul, George and Ringo all rolled into one."*

THEY LOVE ME, YEAH YEAH YEAH

At first things went well, and on the occasions when Freeview managed to get up in time to deliver Chelsea to the school gates, he made every effort to fit in with the other kids' mums.

"I like to be friendly and I've always believed in the psychological benefits that can be derived from a smile and a warm hello," he told the paper. "So I would target some of the younger, thinner, mums and do my bit to cheer them up with a few cheeky remarks, risqué jokes and lewd suggestions."

"As I'm sure you can imagine, this went down incredibly well."

According to thrice-bankrupt Freeview, the trouble was his interactions with the mothers in the schoolyard went down rather *too* well.

"You've got to believe me when I say this, I wasn't trying to break any hearts, but my raw animal magnetism clearly caused a stir amongst these red-blooded, nookie-mad females," he confirmed. "They couldn't help themselves."

"It was like Beatle-mania, with me as John, Paul, George and Ringo all rolled into one. Believe me, I'm not being big headed or anything when I say this, but whenever I strolled into the playground in a cloud of manly pheromones, I could feel the tension in the air as all those randy mums tried desperately to control themselves whilst in my company."

"It got so bad that lots of them tried to distance themselves from me by standing at the far end of the sports field. It was their futile attempt to quell the white-hot desire that I had clearly ignited within their collective nether regions," chronic halitosis sufferer Freeview said.

SCHOOL'S OUT FOREVER

And he believes that the warning letter from the headmistress came at the request of a group of mums to whom he would regularly chat at the school gates. "They were a really fit bunch, and every time I arrived, the conversation would immediately become fruity and sexually charged," he said. I can't help flirting. It's just the way I am.".

Too cool for school: The school that Terry can't believe he's been banned from and (inset) some of the mums distancing themselves from Terry to avoid his charms.

"I could tell that they were desperate to throw themselves at me; what red-blooded woman wouldn't be? But they were all married women, and they obviously didn't trust themselves when I was in the neighbourhood, so they asked the headmistress to save them from themselves."

Freeview considered the head's warning letter was not legally binding, and carried on with the important job of getting his daughter to and from school each day, when he remembered, and chatting with the mums. But when he was contacted by West Midlands police and served with a restraining order preventing him from being within 300 yards of the gates, he realised that the school had upped the ante.

"You could have knocked me down with a feather," he confessed. "When the order was served, I naturally assumed it was related to unpaid child maintenance as usual."

"When I saw it was actually due to the erotic effect I was having on the female parents I couldn't believe it. Since when is being impossibly attractive a crime? I'm clearly being victimised for my raw sex-appeal."

> "Since when is being attractive a crime? I'm clearly being victimised for my raw sex-appeal."

Since receiving the order, Freeview has been forced to lie in bed smoking and watching horse racing on the tv while his estranged wife Janice takes on the responsibility of doing the twice-daily school run.

"The trauma of this whole episode has drained me of all faith in the system and has left me unfit to continue in my search for employment," he said. "And I've a doctor's note to back that up."

And although he has lived with the curse of sexy good looks and animal magnetism all his adult life, leading to him being the subject of several restraining orders and criminal convictions, Freeview remains cautiously optimistic about the future. "I can only hope that one day we will all live to see more enlightened times, when a man's rampant sexual allure isn't the burden that mine has proven to be," he said.

SEX BOMBS AWAY!

SEXUALLY **attractive people have for centuries suffered at the hands of their affliction. But on some occasions, it is other people who fall foul of their allure.**

IN 1992, Right Said Fred frontman **RICHARD FAIRBRASS** was shopping in London when he witnessed a taxi pull out of Harewood Place into Oxford Street and run into a number 94 bus heading towards Acton Green. Nobody was injured in the collision, and the taxi driver was blamed for failing to check both ways before pulling out onto the thoroughfare. But it was accepted that Fairbrass's strong, sexual magnetism had distracted both of the drivers and according to insurers "had played no small part in the cause of the accident."

IN 2003, a light aircraft crashed on landing at Sacramento airport in California. The pilot, who survived the accident, had taken off from Fresno four hours earlier and had reported no problems during the flight and the black box recovered from the wreckage showed that all the plane's instrumentation was working. Air crash investigators concluded that the actor **BRAD PITT**, who was in the Sacramento departure lounge waiting for a connecting flight, was giving off such powerful sexual vibrations, that they interfered with the electromagnetic microwaves used by the aircraft's navigation system, causing it to lose the ability to calculate a safe flight path and altitude.

WHILST spending the day on South Beach, Miami, Hollywood A-lister **DAKOTA JOHNSON** was exuding such potent, sexual allure that she caused six young men nearby to begin showing off in the water. Whilst trying to impress the *Fifty Shades of Grey* star, the group got into difficulty in deep water. The men, all sophomores from the Florida State University, were eventually rescued by lifeguards. Arriving on the scene after the incident, Miami Police spoke to Johnson and warned her about the dangers of being extremely sexy and desirable in a public place.

TERROR AT 35,000 FEET

We are about the begin our descent into Bristol airport, so would all passengers please return to their seats and fasten their safety belts.

Beige Air flight BA301 was en route from Alicante to Bristol with 300 passengers on board, all of whom were on their way home after enjoying a SilverTours Over 70s holiday…

Could you sit down, please, sir? The captain has put the seatbelt sign on.

Aye, love. I've just got to go for a Jimmy Riddle. It's me prostrate, y' see.

You should go as well, Edna.

Could you sit down please, sir?

I will.

Eh!?! What's that, love?

Oh *MY GOD*! Both of the pilots have just died of heart attacks simultaneously. There's nobody at the controls…

…can anyone onboard fly a plane?

What's she on about?

I don't know. She mumbles, that one.

'Scuse me. Can I have another cup of tea, please?

Anybody? Can anybody fly a plane?

Aye, I can, love. I were in the RAF

Oh, thank God!

RAF!?! You weren't in the RAF.

I was. RAF Boulmer.

No, that was your Ken.

Was it?

It was. You were in the Navy.

Anybody? Can anybody fly a plane? *Anybody at all?*

Fly a plane?

Aye! I can. My grandson's got one of those computer game things where you land a plane, and I had a go on it once. I were very good, weren't I, Edna?

He were. He were very good.

Okay! Quickly. Come with me.

Not as good as me grandson, like. He were great. He's only seven

He's eight, Joe.

Please. Hurry.

He's not. He's seven.

He's eight.

She's wrong, you know. He's seven. It's Margaret's lad who's eight.

Miss… are you coming round with the trolley again?

I've got a picture of him in me wallet…

…that's him. Isn't he grand.

Quickly. Sit in the pilot's seat and put the headset on. Ground control will tell you exactly what to…

I'll just have a quick Jimmy Riddle, love. Goes straight through me, does tea.

What!?! *No!*

10 minutes later…

That's better. Takes a bit longer at my age.

Quick! In here.

Sit in the pilot's seat and put the headset on.

Eeeh! Look at all them buttons and dials…

'Undreds o' the buggers!

I'll 'ave t' get me glasses.

You're wearing them.

No, these are me readers… I need me lookers for this.

'Scuse me. Can I have a cup o' tea?

Where's the woman?

Eh!?! What!?! No, I don't work 'ere love.

She's up front wi' the dead pilots.

Eeeh! Y' can't even get a cup of tea.

What are you doin' up 'ere? I thought you were landin' the plane.

Aye! But I've just come back for…

Eeeh! I can't remember what I come back for now.

What was it?

I was in the driver's cab an' I thought I'd need something so I come back here to get it.

Now what was it?

No! It's gone. It'll come back to me.

Are they coming round wi' the trolley?

I don't know! The pilots are dead so they're just sortin' that out.

Eeh! I've only 'ad three cups. It's not good enough.

Roger, ground control. He's back. He's just been to get his glasses.

Glasses! That was it.

Where's the trolley? I need something sweet.

I don't know, love. I'm not one of the hostesses.

Eeh! They're always round wi' the trolley on EasyJet.

They do them big Kitkats

It was me glasses, Edna.

You've got them on.

No, these are me readers. I need me lookers.

'Scuse me. Could you put me coat in the locker… I put it on cos I thought we'd be down by now but we're not.

Aye. You don't want it on in here. You'll not feel the benefit.

Shortly…

Right. Where were we?

Sit here, and put these on.

Champion.

Hello!?!

Hello. Joe speaking.

Joe. This is ground control.

Hello ground control.

Okay, Joe… we've got this, me and you. Landing this plane is going to be a doddle. Just do exactly what I say, when I say it.

Aye. No problem.

Okay. Now look to your left, Joe, and you'll see a big dial… it looks like a clock… but it's telling you how high you are… can you see it?

Aye. Just about. It's a bit small.

Great. What's it reading?

It says 11000 and then the letter 'm'.

That's great, Joe, great. That means you're at 11 thousand meters.

Metres? What's that in feet and inches?

It doesn't matter, Joe. You've got to come down, so we need you to decrease your airspeed.

Right-ho.

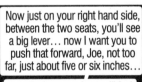

Now just on your right hand side, between the two seats, you'll see a big lever… now I want you to push that forward, Joe, not too far, just about five or six inches…

…and when you do, you'll feel the plane drop and the dial will start to move…

Now when it get to 6,000 metres, I want you to stop pushing the lever forward, okay?

Have you got that, Joe?

Joe!?!

Joe!?!

He's just gone for a Jimmy Riddle.

Are you coming round with the trolley again? I'm spitting feathers.

Next Week: *As Joe brings the plane towards the airport runway, he realises the numbers on the air speed indicator are too small, and he has to nip back to his seat to get his readers.*

Roger's PROFANISAURUS

All aboard the Sweary Express for a railway-related collection from Britain's favourite lexicon of profanity

Bakerloo breeze *1. n.* The pungent wind that precedes the London underground train moments before it exits the tunnel. *2. n.* The pungent *wind* that precedes the *cocoamotive* moments before it exits the *bonus tunnel*.

bangers and mash *1. n.* The flushed heaps of half-dissolved *bumwad*, human excrement, used *fanny nannies* and what-have-you which are often to be seen adorning the tracks at railway stations. Not, as a passenger, that you get the impression that anyone has ever managed to successfully flush a train toilet. *Rat's banquets, Radcliffe's sleepers. 2. n.* The contents of a well-used but badly flushed *bog*, the *bangers* being the *turds* and the mash being the *bumwad*. Usually found in the public conveniences of pubs, campsites and non-stop coaches to Spain. *"Cinders and ashes, Thomas, your coaches are a disgrace,' cried the Fat Controller. 'There are used tickets on the floor, soot all over the windows and Clarabelle's cludgy is full of bangers and mash."* (from *Thomas and the Dyno-Rod Man* by Rev W Awdrey).

Barber's Bridge *1. n.* A small town in Gloucestershire that was the site of the first intermediate station north of Gloucester on the old Ledbury & Gloucester Railway, as is well known. *2. n.* The small tuft of hair left on a lady's nethers after a *Brazilian* wax.

blood and custard *1. n.* Humorous, sex-case/train-spotter parlance for the cream and maroon livery in which British Railways coaching stock was painted in the 1950s and 1960s. *2. n.* The sort of curse that a soft pirate like Captain Pugwash might have uttered when he discovered that Cut-throat Jake had beaten him to the treasure of the San Fandango. *3. n.* The evidence left on the sheets after one has *done* it with a lady during her *unclean time*.

blow off steam *1. v.* Of a steam engine or highly strung person, to get rid of pent-up energy. *2. n.* To sound a high pressure fanfare on the *ragman's trumpet*.

Brownville *euph.* A *dump*. *'Must dash, your majesty. I've got to catch the last train to Brownville.'*

buffers *n.* A pair of large, solidly sprung buttocks. *'Sorry Kim. I can't get it any further in from here. I've hit the buffers.'*

bushey troughs *1. n.* Whence locomotives scooped up water into their tenders during the days of steam power. *2. n.* The deep, wet *bowers of pleasure* to be found on larger lasses.

camouflage fart *n.* A noisome *guff* dropped in a situation where there's no chance of it being detected, *eg*. On a farm, in an old folks' home, while changing a nappy or standing anywhere within fifty feet of the *bogs* on a Virgin train.

Chalfont Thunderer *1. n.* The sort of fictional steam train that might hurtle through a picturesque station run by Will Hay in *Oh Mr Porter*, while Graham Moffatt blows a whistle and Moore Marriott waves a little flag. *2. n.* A first class early morning *d'Oyly Carte* that chugs out of the *nipsy*, rattles the pots on the shelf and vibrates a fellow's *arse grapes*.

chuffage *n. coll.* A rats' *banquet, bangers and mash, Radcliffe's sleepers*. Railway track faecal detritus.

dead man's handle *1. n.* Safety cut-out switch on a piece of machinery, such as a train or industrial guillotine, which must be depressed in order for it to operate. *2. n.* A cheeky - not to mention borderline illegal - use of one's partner's *wanking spanner* while they are asleep in order to *make the bald man cry*. *3. n.* The life-saving "Stop" button on a DVD remote control, over which a gentleman's left thumb constantly hovers while he is enjoying an artistic videographic presentation.

double fare *n.* One whose fat *arse* takes up two seats on a train or bus. A *salad dodger, barge-arse, fat fuck.*

fiddle yard *1. n.* A concealed part of a model railway enthusiast's layout where he stores his toy trains and manipulates them away from the gaze of the general public. *2. n.* Another out-of-sight place where a model railway enthusiast manipulates things when he thinks nobody can see him.

flange squeal *1. n.* Ear-splitting, high-pitched noise that occurs when the wheels of railway rolling stock slip laterally on the rail when transiting a curve, due to the lack of a differential. *2. n.* Ear-splitting, high-pitched noise that occurs when large *member* slips into a *flange*, much to the delight of the lady concerned.

flying squatsman *euph.* One who has reached top speed in his desperate search for a *chod bin*. With all high pressure steam coming out his *arse*, and making chuff-chuff noises.

get off at Edge Hill *v.* To do a *coitus interruptus*, to withdraw before *spangling*. From Edge Hill, which is the last railway station before Liverpool Lime Street. Similarly *Haymarket* (Edinburgh), *Gateshead* (Newcastle), *Marsh Lane* (Leeds) *etc*.

guard's van *n.* When *pulling a train*, the least desirable position in the queue. The last *pink carriage* into *fanny* station. *'Bagsy I'm not in the guard's van fellas.'*

guard's whistle *n.* A series of shrill blasts warning that the *brown train* will shortly be leaving *arse station*. *'I've got to dash, your holiness. That's the guard's whistle. I'll give you a bell some time in the week, yeah?'*

honesty box bargain *n.* A *five fingered discount* available to the value-conscious shopper at railway station newsagents. Named after the express counter which used to be thoughtfully provided for the use of passengers who were in a hurry not to pay.

horror express *n.* Taken after a night of beer and fast food, a long journey on a train with no functioning toilet facilities - that is to say most trains. Named after the 1970s movie starring Peter Cushing, Christopher Lee and Telly Savalas. Us neither.

jazz drummer, go at it like a *sim.* When eating, to hunch over one's plate and shovel food into one's mouth at an unseemly speed, in a style reminiscent of Gene Krupa or Buddy Rich giving it *three cocks to the cunt*. *'Mate of mine says he saw John Prescott going at a big pork pie like a jazz drummer in the café at King's Cross Station.'*

lie-fi *n.* Free bus or train internet that simply doesn't work. See also *thinternet, fraudband*.

melting pot *1. n.* Blue Mink song from 1969, with a lyric they probably wouldn't include if they wrote it these days, referring to a huge crucible of sufficient capacity to render the world's population into a bubbling 310 million ton mass of hot blubber. *2. n.* A *chodbin* that hasn't been flushed for some considerable time, *eg.* On a train.

morning level crossing *euph.* The first *hit or miss* of the day. From the fact that you have to wait for the barrier to go down before you can proceed. Even though, on a real level crossing, you have to wait for the barrier to go up before you can proceed, obviously. Unless you're a train driver.

mudhole door *1. n.* The bottom of a steam locomotive boiler from where all the *shite* is riddled out from time to time. *2. n.* The *nipsy*.

next one's through the goods *exclam.* British Rail-based *farting* terminology, signifying that the next toot on the whistle heralds the arrival of the cargo.

next stop is Newark Castle, the *exclam.* Signifying the imminent arrival of a strong faecal smell. From the aroma experienced on the train when passing the sewage works just before Newark Castle station, which is typically strong enough to wake sleeping passengers,

profanisaurus@viz.co.uk

Roger's PROFANISAURUS
RAILWAY WORDSEARCH

THE human brain is a muscle, just like your biceps or abs. And just like any muscle, it needs to be exercised to prevent it from going flabby and putting on weight. So give your grey matter a proper workout with this *Roger's Railway Wordsearch*. The skill and mental dexterity needed to solve this complex lexicological puzzle is guaranteed to keep your brain active and alert. Hidden the wordsearch grid are all the entries in this Roger's Railway Profanisaurus collection. You know how it goes - they may read up, down or diagonally, backwards or forwards. And unlike other years, this year there is no free pen for completed entires, because we've given up the PO Box address after recieving about 10 letters a year, when the postman can be arsed to deliver them.

```
M Q R F E X D O K E M K J T V D G O P L Q E X F Y J U R W N L P H Y F S E J P R M L A
T A E H I V E M L F G O M D T C H K L P E G U A R D S W H I S T L E M L D X T E E F B
R M K F R D A M Y G E Q R M L S W E V H T K P O Y O M L O H D W T F G O P N X P M L E
A V D W J O D M L O T E N N E X T O N E S T H R O U G H T H E G O O D S M L E E K L A
F N G S Q T M L M Y O P U C I Z C R L U F D Q I H B M F R S O B M L R D G L P E D C O
E C M K L R A L E J Y F M D E N M L G T D S W Q I L M L Y G U A U M L D X E R L L P F
G A R E L P N H J Y C T P M L T G M K B T F H I P E M C B H P K X F N L B G Y S P O L
A O C G B E S M L T A R T M I B V L M L F V N K P F M D E X H E M L F N K F R Y M L Y
L B A E D A H R E S L R Y B T R C J E M L S D V Y A N J F T I R G S L E Y K P A M L I
F W A T B Y M F D S W D K O O L P G V T F B L P R K F E X V L L E K Y R B U W L T N
U E A O I B N M L F R W U K X W K H L P E L V R E E M L V T O O N V A F T S B L M E G
O J O F W T D B D X J U M L T N I A R T E L K C O C E H T S E O G E R E H T B I L O S
M S Z F H Y L N F C N P P F T V K T L B D E C M L D X C T E I B P N K F R H L A M T Q
A S R A B U E I M L F E T B Y I K W A K B G P R M C F R S T K R S A M L G E O R L R U
C M L T B F R W K M L Y Y B T L M L R K V C K U O L G R A M P E L M L T E N M U M O A
V N R E M F S Z P E L H T D B L M L F E E P K F Q S L T M F Q E T A M L S E O E L D T
B K T D X A F H K T A M L F E E B J L D C T M L H I S L F S W Z P N P B T X L M L B S
C A R G B F A V J L P J L G C D A U P G M L H M U Y P I P D W E L G P B T T L T L S M
L R Y E M L F E A C H P A E B L L Y U L D V I E A M L X N M Y C W E L P I S V O K P A
M U D H O L E D O O R J N Z I B T A S K L P F W A M F X R G M L T L L N B T W L B W N
Z G T I M L F C B J W I B A Z S R M L F C W L O T T M L F C B J A O G E E O L G V S R
E S E L M L F C X T L T R L D D L B H X A I E C E O R K L B D A P P E S F P L U G B X
M L F L A E F P S E T D T F S L R R C H A M L D X Z O A M B V U O L F L I P D A A R
M L D C X H P T H H R M Y V C B L U X R L M F V C O E E I E R T M U S C Y S L R R D Y
M F C B J L W T K I U L A M F C S R M M L F X F Y T W R P N P U L T R C S N B X S A E
B L O P T E N P H L L N L P F T W A C M L K F W P P K B M L D E E M L C Z E L B V D P
P K H X P W L T M S W A T R E S L H R E M F P E T A M S 2 D A P B F R R W P M D Z Y
L M F C O L E M D C H U P M R R M P U Z E R B T N K E E L F M L F X W S X A O P L H T
J A L D F H B F S P U E T E E M L S F P V B K S D M L T P O D E R S B M J R L B H P E
A E E B T M F R S B M L R H M H D R F L K F R W O E E S M E D T P R I F O K M L D C T
P N T U H J M D W L S T I F F A S A S I G N A L M A N S R A G I P J F E C P B M L E
O E S A Q U H B F S W O M L F R D W G M P E S E I E T A M L R D V D E W P A M L A E Y
F R E A P S M Y A T R L O M L F W Y E B S D L P N J Y M L R G C D J K P H S B S F T M
B T D P H I E B T N A E T D M C F T L P R A E L O E E L M E L B C F E O K T V H L T O
X A F H L T I G A L G B F E A M L T F N L A B V K H G A M F C B H I R I H L L G B P N
M F C B H P E H N V F E B E T N L O I M U T B K M D S N E D P Y E R M K G E P U J K O
M J C E I F T M L A Q P R M P F D A W U B V R B N I A G R A B X O B Y T S E N O H L C
M L C D W R E D T E L P G S B T R C M F C B U E I X L I E F T R L B C W P G T R M I E
C E L P E M L T F E R F P H A T A T U M L T H E R T X S M P E P B D T H P I D T M Y M
Z R T T M W S C P U H M T J A N M Y T S L B T D F E S E E X M L F C B H P E R Y E S U
O T T M F C B L P S R W H L I P D B L P T W S Z P H Y T P N R O H N I A R T L E M E I
B E M D C V H L P E S T L E F L G M V R Y A L B M L W R A P E S C A H P K J R H M Y M
W C H A L F O N T T H U N D E R E R A N D R R E F T E L U I M D R E S Y P U I S M T E
M E S E F Y I P M T P N F E I M L D E S R C I D L S N T D E L M P E R S W Y H U L E R
Z S E P L H Y F R T S W P E L M D R S E H M E R S E R R A C N O I T A V R E S B O L P
```

thus preventing them slumbering until Leicester.

numpty dumpty *n*. A person who manages to be both rotund and useless. An epithet coined by one or other of the sweary Scotch blokes in the film *In the Loop*. 'Hello, I'd like to buy a return ticket to London King's Cross, please.' 'Please hold the line while I put you through to the next available numpty dumpty.'

observation car *1. n*. On a scenic railway, a luxury train carriage with large windows. *2. n*. At a *dogging* site, a carload of non-participating voyeurs parked over to one side. Tea, coffee and cake may be served.

one on the down line *phr*. A railway industry term which track-workers use to inform each other of the approach of a fast-moving train or an imminent lavatory break during the working day.

pendolino *n*. An exceptionally large *brown trout*. Named after one of them technically advanced, state-of-the-art Class 390 tilting trains currently operated by Virgin Rail on their West Coast Main Line route, because "it doesn't go round the bends as well as it should and it makes you an hour late for work".

premium economy *n*. Guaranteeing oneself sole occupancy of a double seat on even the busiest of standard class train journeys by openly consuming a can of export-strength lager as the other passengers make their way up the aisle.

pull a train *v*. To take turns at *stirring the porridge*, to participate in a *gang bang*.

railway sleeper *n*. The largest, firmest and most angular *Thora* known to mankind, which makes a *dead otter* look like a minor *follow through*.

Rotherham railway station, wetter than *sim*. A topical reference to a ladyfriend who is in a heightened state of arousal, from February 2022 when the aforementioned station was submerged under floodwater. 'And I tell you something else, she came back from that Chippendales show wetter than Rotherham railway station. But enough about my weekend, let's play Popmaster.'

seven am angel *n*. When lighting an early morning *brown candle* while running out of time to catch a train, a benevolent *poo* that only requires only a couple of wipes. 'Please Lord, send me a seven am angel.'

shunt *1. v*. To shtup. *2. v*. To push, as opposed to pull, a train.

signalman's rag, stiff as a *sim*. A colourful turn of phrase dating from the days when a railway employee would spend all day alone with little to do except while away the hours frantically and repeatedly *polishing the brasswork* in his lonely box - a tradition still kept alive by volunteers at heritage railways throughout the country.

signalman's tea break *euph*. After the little white *jizz train* has passed, the necessary pause before the *big yellow express* can use the same bit of track. 'Can you use the downstairs bog, love? Only I'm trying to sluice the pipes in here but I'm on a two-fag signalman's tea break.'

take the A train *1. n*. Title of a jazz classic penned by Duke Ellington and Billy Strayhorn, which was famously covered by Dave Brubeck. *2. v*. To travel in the missus's *caboose, buffers permitting*.

there goes the cockle train *exclam. S. Aus*. Said after a voluble blast on the *guardsman's whistle*.

third rail, the *1. n*. Means of providing electricity to a railway locomotive or train via a rigid, semi-continuous conductor placed alongside or between the rails of the track. And if you wee on it, you'll die, and that's true. *2. n*. A particularly well-wrought *hard-on*. An impressive length *of pink steel*.

train horn *n*. A lady's party trick in which she firstly *drops a gut*, and then *drops her hat forwards* in quick succession, creating a tuneless, two-toned blast. Also known as a *Robson and Jerome*.

...money you continue to spend today...

...money you will spend in lonely solitude.

What... my wife will leave me...for good?

Yes. Unless you stop buying from the centre aisle at Lidl.

Make your decision Richard. And make it wisely.

I will spirit, but before I do... I must know one thing...

Ask, Richard.

Tell me some of the buys that are yet to come.

Well, in January we have airless paint sprayers for just £19.99, a light but sturdy chop saw stand for £39.99 and a selection of quality ski wear for all the family...

Oooh! That sounds good.

WELCOME, WEARY TRAVELLERS! COME YE' IN, PULL UP A PEW!

A DOUBLE ROOM WITH A CRIB, IS IT? NO PROBLEM!

WHILE YOUR LADY WIFE IS UPSTAIRS DROPPING THE SPROG, YOU WILL DOUBTLESS WISH TO FORTIFY YOURSELF WITH A BEVVY OR TWO.

ALLOW ME TO POUR YOU A FOAMING PINT OF OWLD JOSHUA'S TOOTING TRUMPET.

IT'S A WELL-BALANCED MALTY ALE WITH A HOPPY, BITTER FINISH .5·4% ABV.

AND WHILE YOU SUP, I WILL REGALE YOU WITH A FEW OF MY HILARIOUS DRINKING ANECDOTES.

I RECALL ONE AMUSING INCIDENT WHICH OCCURRED AT THE LEPER'S ARMS IN NAZARETH DURING THE GALILEE REAL ALE FESTIVAL IN MARCH OF 19 BC...

THE LANDLORD WAS A SPLENDID FELLOW NAMED BARRABUS, SON OF BETH-SHEBA...

MAYBE YOU HAVE A SHITTY OLD COW SHED OR SOMETHING THAT WE COULD SPEND THE NIGHT IN?

THE BEARD & SANDAL INN

ANYTHING WILL DO, REALLY.

Right! Now to melt these down into one monster Toffee Penny sweet

Shortly...

GUINNESS WORLD RECORDS

Ah! Here we are!

Guiness World Records HQ

Hello! I've come to claim the record for the world's biggest least favourite sweet.

My goodness... That Toffee Penny is indeed a record breaking least favourite sweet...

Wahay!

...Or at least it would have been five minutes ago...

HUNH!?!

...this boy has just come in with a 750kg Aniseed Liquorice Allsort.

Rats' cocks!

REET YUZ ARE, LADS! SEE YEEZ LOOZAS LATER.. SIDNEY SMUTT'S OFF TU GET A SMACKA ON THY FUCKIN' LIPS!

10!...9!...8!...7!...6!...5!

HOO, PET! IF ME LEFT LEG'S CHRISTMAS AN' ME RIGHT LEG'S NEW YEAZ, HOO D'YUZ FANCY SPENDIN' SOME TIME BETWEEN THE HOLIDEEZ?!

HEH-HEH! 'ERE WUZ GAN..!

4!...3!...2!...1!...

WALLOP!

HAPPY NEW YEAR!

WELL, Y'SORTAINLY GOT YUZ SMACKER ON THE LIPS, EH SID?

HO!HO!

GROAN!

109

Ignatius Manatee's Dixieland Jazz Band

110

MAJOR MISUNDERSTANDING

MICHAEL'S CYCLES

BRITAIN'S LIVELIEST BICYCLE AND PEDAL-PROPELLED WHEELED TRANSPORT FORUM, HOSTED BY WHAM! AND ALL THEM OTHER HITS SINGER GEORGE MICHAEL

Wotcha! The late **GEORGE MICHAEL**, here. You might know me as the sadly-missed lead singer of Wham! and all my solo hits, like *Patience (Pt. 2)*, *Cowboys and Angels* and *Kissing a Fool*. What you might not know is that, when I was alive, I *bloody* loved bicycles. All types of them; from way back in the days of Penny Farthings and Choppers, all the way up to modern times bikes. In fact, I loved bikes so much, you might have caught me *Spinning the Wheel* (the name of a song off of my 1996 album, *Older*) of an upside-down bicycle on my back lawn! And it seems like *Viz* readers can't get enough of these two-wheeled, self-propelled transportation devices either, as loads of you have *ridden* (written) in saying how much you *wheelie* (really) love them! So, without further ado it's time to crack open the mail sack and *get on your bikes!*

Fast love, George xx

I LOVE watching YouTube videos of stunt cyclists like Mat Hoffman and Danny MacAskill, jumping off enormous ramps and on-and-off walls and railings on their bikes without fear. However, I can't help but feel that these videos would be even more exciting if they'd pegged a playing card between the bike frame and back wheel before they set off, which would make a loud motorbike noise while they rode.

Edith Guffs, Reading

EVERYONE remembers the famous scene in *E.T. the Extra Terrestrial*, where the titular alien helps Elliot and his friends escape the federal agents by making their BMXs take-off and sail past the moon, or something. This is all very well, but don't forget that for the previous two-and-a-half minutes the lazy fucker had been sat on his arse in a cosy shopping basket on the front of Elliott's bike, wrapped in a blanket like the Queen of Sheba, doing fuck-all while Elliott and his mates pedalled their little hearts out to try and save him. Freewheeling little shit.

Adrian Manilow, Cardiff

THESE electric cycles are a great idea, being able to travel up to 40 miles before the power runs out. My Hoover only gets as far as the top of the stairs before I inadvertently yank the plug out of the socket.

Peter Repeater, Aberdeen

WHILE teaching my 4-year-old to cycle in the local park the other day, I quietly took the stabilisers off her bike before letting go of the saddle. Imagine my surprise when she not only cycled to the end of the main path, but also kept going - straight into the boating lake, splashing for a minute or two before doggy-paddling, lopsidedly to the shore. Thankfully, I had my smartphone on me and managed to film the whole thing. *Hilarious!*

Bob Egg, Cheshire

BIKE

FIND punctures quickly without needing to dunk your inner tube in a bowl of water by filling your tyres with cooked porridge instead of air and looking over your tyre for bits of milk or oats.

Edgar Golem, Wivenhoe

TIPS

I TOOK my grandson to the circus the other week, and we saw a clown riding a bicycle with only one wheel. The next day whilst shopping in town, I saw an old lady riding a bicycle with three wheels. Then yesterday at the seaside, I saw a family riding along the promenade on a four wheeled bike. Where is this madness going to end?

Ada Bearsbum, Widnes

'YOU'D look sweet upon the seat of a bicycle built for two', the famous song goes, but if it was being sung about a two-seater Penny Farthing, this would result in a two-level saddle arrangement with the singer either leering directly at the back of Daisy's arse, or Daisy sat downwind of the singer's backside. *Absolutely disgraceful.*

Mrs. F Rump, Devizes

BIKE

SAVE money on expensive bicycle bells by simply shouting "Get out of my way, I haven't got a bell!" at anyone who gets in your way while cycling.

Mrs G. Jpeg, Herts

TIPS

I BOUGHT an exercise bike a few years back in an attempt to get fit, but ever since the day I purchased it, it's remained folded up in the cupboard as I've never learned to ride a bike and am frightened of falling off.

Ian Oatmeal, Redditch

RED LIGHT SPELLS *DANGER!*

THERE IS nothing more infuriating than seeing a cyclists brazenly drive through a set of red traffic lights. Many of these people think the Highway Code applies only to drivers and that cyclists can behave any way they please. But why shouldn't they? Should cyclists be allowed to jump red lights? We went on the streets to find out what *YOU* think.

...TRAFFIC LIGHTS are paid for and maintained by the vehicle tax paid by drivers. I'm a cyclist and I don't own a car and so, since I'm not paying for the traffic lights, why on earth should I have to obey them? I say let the car owners pay for their own lights.

Tobamoray Winks, vegan

...AS LONG as there's nothing coming the other way, I can't see any harm in cyclists jumping red lights. It all helps keep traffic moving.

Charles Rhomboid, accountant

...YES, THEY ruddy well should have to stop at red lights like everybody else. And if they jump them, they should have their tyres popped by the police and be put on the sex offenders' register.

Ada Vitriol, pensioner

...A LOT of these cyclists simply mount the pavement when they come to a traffic light. If they put a small traffic light on the pavement as well, that would stop these two-wheeled menaces in their tracks.

Doris Lisk, shop worker

...IF A cyclist is physically able to jump a red light, then fair play to them. Providing they land well away from the road and moving vehicles, preferably in the cycle lane, then I don't really see what all the fuss is about.

Tom Ballsup, plasterer

BIKE BLOOPERS IN THE MOVIES

Two-wheeled cinematic gaffes with celluloid cycling supremo *Mark Commode*

◇ **IN THE** children's film *BMX Bandits* (1983), **NICOLE KIDMAN**'s character does a series of BMX 'free-style' stunts on a ramp to impress her friends. However, when she goes up the ramp her watch shows the time as 2.58pm, yet on the way down it shows 2.59pm, suggesting that she would have been airborne for a *full minute!*

◇ **IN ALAN PARKER**'s film *Bugsy Malone*, set in depression-era New York, the child actors ride around in pedal-powered bicycle 'cars'. These were actually pointless, since the film was actually shot in the mid 1970s, by which point the characters would have been old enough to drive actual cars.

◇ **IN A** famous scene in *Butch Cassidy and the Sundance Kid* (1969) **PAUL NEWMAN** and **KATHARINE ROSS** ride around on a bicycle to **BURT BACHARACH** and **HAL DAVID**'s classic song *Raindrops Keep Falling On My Head*. However, throughout the 3-minute sequence not a drop of rain can be seen on screen. In fact, it looks *sunny!*

◇ **IN VITTORIO DE SICA**'s 1948 Italian neorealist classic, *The Bicycle Thief*, **LAMBERTO MAGGIORANI** plays the desperate father Enzo Staiola, on a search for his stolen bicycle, without which he will lose his job, taking his family into destitution. However, throughout the film, the actor constantly mispronounces the word bicycle as 'biciclette'

More bicycling blunders next time, you pedal-crazy pedants! *Keep on Cyclin', Mark xx*

Who's in the Saddle?

USING YOUR skill and judgement and the three clues below, can you identify which Doctor Whos are going out for a ride through time and space on the Trardris - the Doctor's famous three-seated trandem?

Clues:

A: It *whit-take-'er* quite a while to cycle around the Universe by herself, but thankfully this Doctor Who has two friends helping her out!

B: Good *day!-Vid* you like to ride to Mars and back with this Doctor Who? Lis-*'ten ant'* look out for our clues, or he could be tricky to identify!

C: This Doctor Who might suggest visiting his Aunt Sally, *pert-wee*'d be surprised if you guessed who was *J-on* the final saddle without a little help from us!

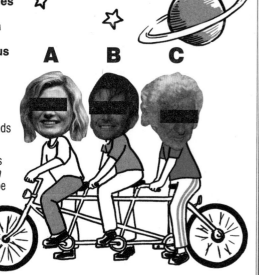

ANSWERS: *The three Doctor Whos are A:* JODIE WHITTAKER, B: DAVID TENNANT *and C:* JON PERTWEE.

ON YER BIKE!

Your bicycle questions answered by Dr Heinz Wheelz

Dear Heinz,

I KNOW what the wheels are for on a bike, and understand what the brakes do but I've often wondered what the large metal tubular structure between the wheels and under the saddle is for? Every bike seems to have one but I simply can't work out what its purpose is. Is it possible to remove this at all? It just gets in the way when I try and climb on.

Mrs J. Whitepube, Herts

*Unfortunately not! What you're describing is the bicycle's frame and, although seemingly useless, this is what holds all the component parts of your bicycle together. You can remove it if you wish using special tools, but just make sure that you replace it every time that you want to use your bicycle or you'd find your daily cycle to be a bit of a grind!

Dear Heinz,

WHILE I was cycling to work the other day, my chain came off the main pedal gear causing my pedals to spin wildly and my feet to slip off the pedals. When I got off the bike I noticed that the chain had covered the bottom of my trousers in thick, black grease. Is there an easy way to remove this grease from my clothing?

Mr H. Thefonz, Carlisle

*It's a little-known fact but, like using white wine to remove red wine stains, applying a small amount of white grease, such as lard or congealed chicken fat, should conceal the offending stain. It will also cover-up the taste of chain lube.

Dear Heinz,

HOW do the gears on a bike work?

Mr K. Under, Neath

*No idea, sorry.

Have YOU got a question about bicycles and stuff for Dr. Heinz? If so, write in to the usual address: Viz Comic, PO Box 841, Whitley Bay, NE26 9EQ. Don't forget to mark your envelope 'I've got a question about bicycles and stuff for Dr. Heinz.'

WHEEL OF FORTUNE

How many words of three letters or more can you make by using the letters shown between the bicycle wheel spokes? You mustn't use any letter more than once. And can you find the special 7-letter word hidden within our special *Wheel of Fortune?*

Score:
10 words or more – *Well done!*
20 words or more – *Well done!!*
30 words or more – *Well done!!!*

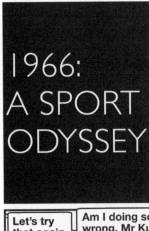

1966: A SPORT ODYSSEY

July 1965

He's got –

Some people are on the pitch, they think it's all over.

It is now, it's four!

Cut.

Let's try that again.

Am I doing something wrong, Mr Kubrick?

No Geoff, you're doing great work, *great work*, I really mean that.

I'd just like to see you try it once more.

We've tried it *once more* about a hundred times! *What do you think you'll see on the 101st?!*

I don't know, Bobby.

And that's the point.

I *don't* know. But I *want* to know. Don't you?

Some weeks later

Cut.

Again.

The following day

Cut.

Again.

A fortnight later

Cut. Make-up please.

Stop *crying* Your Majesty.

May 1966

Cut.

Marvellous work, Nobby, *marvellous.* I'm moved.

But let's try that just once more.

I'm bloody knackered Mr Kubrick.

I know, that's your truth. Use it. *I need it.*

Places everyone.

Cut.

Again.

The following week

Cut.

Again.

Once more please, Nobby.

He's exhausted you pillock!

I know that Gordon. *You* know that. But do the audience?

Sorry to interrupt Mr Kubrick, but there's an urgent call for you – they say they're the CIA!

Speaking. Oh. *What?!* Why?

I see.

Yes. BBC Lime Grove, Studio G, 5pm. I'll need three patsies, two cameras, and a shitting elephant which will take direction.

No. I'll take care of the keeper.

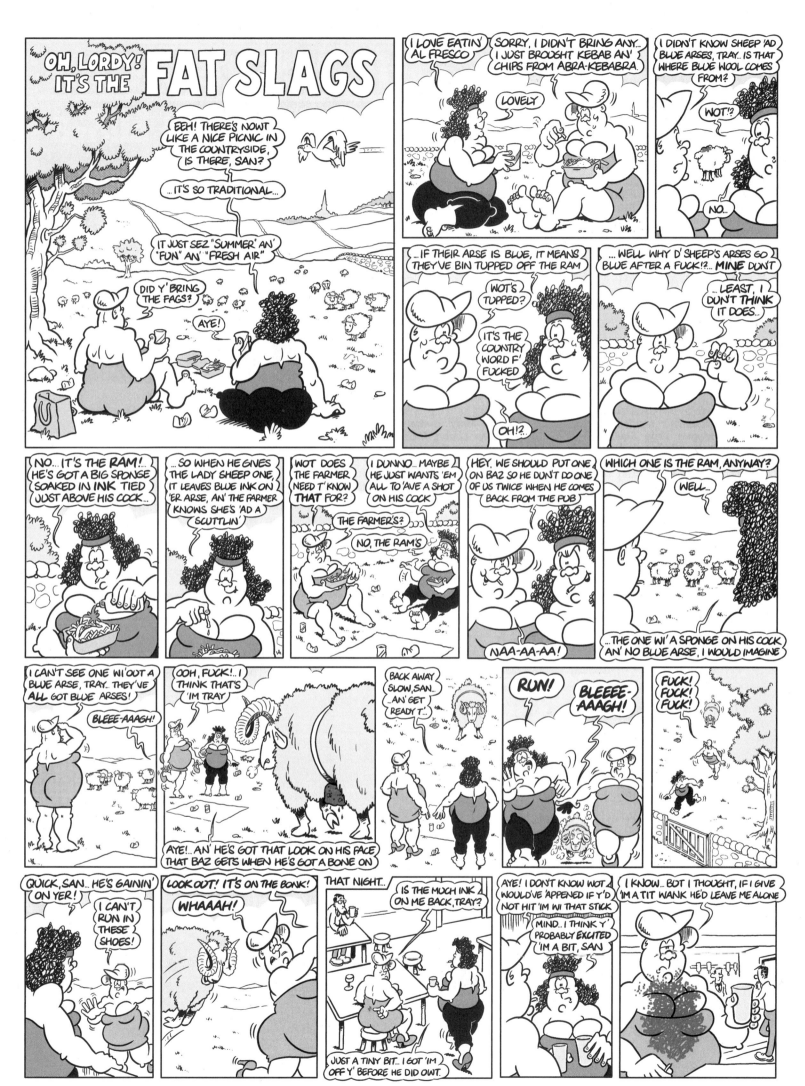

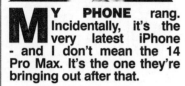

PIERCE DORGAN

The End of an EIIR-a

MY PHONE rang. Incidentally, it's the very latest iPhone - and I don't mean the 14 Pro Max. It's the one they're bringing out after that.

Two after that*, actually, and you can't buy it in the shops because they haven't released it yet. It's on 10G, so it even works on a different system with five more Gs than anyone else's phone. That's according to my very good friends *Buzz Aldrin*, *Andi Peters*, *Lulu* and *Denis Law*. *Actually, three.

My gold iPhone 18 had indeed rung at the wrong time, as I was at that moment in the middle of an exclusive birthday party. A selection of my very closest personal friends, including *Megan Thee Stallion*, *Clive Tyldesley*, *Professor Brian Cox*, *Joan Armatrading* and *Little Jimmy Krankie* were giving me 'the bumps' at the Ritz.

I had also called room service up to my private suite, and ordered several crates of really expensive Champagne, as well as a dozen really big trays of truffle vol-au-vents - a favourite of many of my closest friends such as *Steven Spielberg*, *Anton du Beke*, *Gyles Brandreth*, *Diana Ross and the Supremes*, *Glen Matlock* and *Mike Yarwood*.

"Aren't you going to answer it, Piers?" enquired *Joe Bugner*, *Elton John*, *Tess Daly*, *Freddie 'Parrot-face' Davies* and *King Juan Carlos*, hearing my phone ringing. "It might be imporant." "No, *Joe*, *Elton*, *Tess*, *Freddie* and *King*," I replied. "I think I'll just let it go to voicemail."

With hindsight, I suppose I should of answered it, but I didn't want to interrupt a party with such an impressive rollcall of famous guests picked from amongst my oldest and dearest celebrity friends, including *Jennifer Aniston*, *Todd Carty*, *Buster Bloodvessel*, *Angela Merkel* and *Whoopi Goldberg*.

Not to mention *Mary Berry*, *Lionel Ritchie*, *Peter Simon*, *The Pope*, *Placido Domingo*, *Dermot O'Leary*, *Tom Cruise* and *Monty Don*, who are also some of my very dearest pals who I really do know and have definitely met.

Before I knew it, it was time for my birthday cake - which had been made specially for me by my very close friends *Denzel Washington*, *Billy Dainty*, *Stella McCartney*, *Paolo Nutini*, *Timothy West* and *Ralph Lauren*. My great pals *Dickie Bird*, *Sadie Frost*, *Stephen King*, *Art Garfunkel* and *Warwick Davies* wheeled it over on a trolley and I blew out the candles. "Make a wish!" cried *Handy Andy*, *Tim Berners-Lee*, *Torvill and Dean*, *Yoko Ono* and *Kurt Angle*.

I closed my eyes and made a wish. Incidentally, it wasn't a wish for more viewers for my extremely successful television show, which I know for a fact is watched by a huge number of people including *Gwen Stefani*, *William Roache*, *Cardi B*, *Barry Gibb*, *Harrison Ford*, *Bez*, *Erykah Badu*, *Peter Purves* and many dozens more.

But when I finally opened my eyes and checked my phone, I saw that I had texts from *The Three Degrees*, *Twiggy*, *David Beckham*, *Angela Rippon* and *GG Allin* telling me that the Queen had died, which was very sad. Incidentally, the first call I mentioned was from *Prince (now King) Charles*, who said I was the first person he'd told.

© Pierce Dorgan 2022

...AS YOU CAN SEE, THE BEERS AND ALES ARE ARRANGED AROUND THE SIDES OF THE MARQUEE ALPHABETICALLY...

8 ACE.

TONY PARSEHOLE

The second Elizabethan Age is at an end, and a new Charlesian Age begins

WHEN I HEARD the news that Her Royal Majesty Queen Elizabeth the Queen of England had died, I wept.

I wept and I wept and I wept.

I wept real tears. Not like the crocodile tears I wept for celebrities. These were real tears. British tears. Red, white and blue tears.

For the Queen was mother to this nation, and we loved her as much – if not even a little bit more – than our own mothers. And when she passed away at the age of (writing this in 2017 so drop age in here) at her beloved (drop in castle or palace where she carked it) a little piece of all of us died with her.

Yes, she lived a life of great privilege.

A life of influence.

A life of *(can't think add another thing here – rule of three)*

But those things came at a price. A heavy price. A very heavy price. For hers was also a life of great responsibility.

A life of duty.

A life of *(add another – rule of three again)*

And her passing sees the end of an age; the second Elizabethan age.

And it heralds in the Charlesian age. For she has done her ultimate duty in producing an hair in whose hands this great country will be safe in the years, decades and centuries yet to come.

But producing an hair in whose hands this great country will be safe in the years, decades and centuries yet to come was just one of the ways our beloved Queen served this country. There were many others.

Many, many others.

So many, it is impossible to count *(speaking of counting, that's 257 words. Over half way)*.

But after (subs insert how long) years on the throne, her duties are now at an end. She can finally hang up her crown, lay down her septer, and join her beloved husband, the Prince of Edinburgh, in that great palace in the sky.

And her funeral was a great occasion. And I don't mean great as in fantastic.

No. I mean great as in important. For at that funeral, we came together. We watched together. We wept together.

We wept and we wept and we wept together. As a nation. As a realm. As a country. Four countries, actually. England, Scotland, Wales and Ireland. *(Northern Ireland, actually, which is better because that's two words.)*

Seventy million bereaved people weeping in unison. Each one of

her subjects from the UK *(and that stands for the United Kingdom, so that's two as well)* mourned the loss of our majesty. A loss which we will never get over.

But as we mourned, yet at the same time did we celebrate. We celebrated her life as the figurehead of the UK (come to think of it it stands for the United Kingdom of Great Britain and Northern Ireland, so that's 8, plus another 8 for when I used it before) and the work she did and the legacy she left. A legacy that will forever there thats 500 inv enc.

HANDEL'S WATER MUSIC

ST/DJ '22

1727: THE LONDON HOME OF G.F. HANDEL.

WUNDERBAR!

I HAFF NEARLY FINISHED COMPOSING ZE ANTHEM FOR ZE CORONATION OF KING GEORGE II AT VESTMINSTER ABBEY ZIS AFTERNOON!

GEORGIE, LOOK WHAT I'VE FOUND IN THE ATTIC...

NICHT NOW, MOTHER! I'M VERY BUSY!

BUT GEORGIE, IT'S ALL YOUR OLD CHILDHOOD TOYS!

HMM...

LOOK, HERE'S THE MUSIC BOX YOU HAD AS A TODDLER!

WE GAVE IT TO YOU WHEN YOU WERE POTTY-TRAINING...

YOU USED TO SIT ON YOUR LITTLE POTTY HAVING A WEE-WEE WHILE YOU PLAYED WITH YOUR MUSIC BOX.

SEE - IT STILL WORKS!

TINKLE TINKLE TINKLE TONK...

DO YOU REMEMBER THE TUNE, GEORGIE?

TINKLE TINKLE TINKLE TONK

HIMMEL!

SCUTTLE

ZAT MUSIC IS GIVING ME A SUDDEN DESPERATE URGE TO URINATE!

AW, THAT'S SO SWEET, GEORGIE!

GASP!

AFTER ALL THESE YEARS YOU MUST STILL SUBCONSCIOUSLY ASSOCIATE THE MUSIC BOX TUNE WITH GOING FOR A WEE-WEE!

GIVE ME ZAT MUSIC BOX!

SNATCH!

I AM NO LONGER A TODDLER, MOTHER — ICH BIN A HIGHLY RESPECTED COMPOSER OF OPERAS AND ORATORIOS!

SEE, I PUT ALL ZIS CHILDHOOD NONSENSE BEHIND ME!

FLING!

ZERE! IT HAS GONE FOREVER!

THOSE PARROTS ARE A CORONATION GIFT FOR THE NEW KING!

PARROT DELIVERIES

TAKE THEM TO WESTMINSTER ABBEY IMMEDIATELY!

TINKLE TINKLE TINKLE TONK

PARROT DELIVERIES

NOW IF YOU DON'T MIND MOTHER, I VILL TAKE MY COMPOSITION TO VESTMINSTER ABBEY, VHERE ZE KING AWAITS ME!

AH HANDEL! I TRUST YOU HAVE COMPOSED A ROUSING ANTHEM FOR MY CORONATION!

INDEED I HAFF YOUR MAJESTY!

WESTMINSTER ABBEY

PLEASE EXCUSE ALL THESE PARROTS FLYING AROUND THE ABBEY.

THEY WERE A CORONATION PRESENT.

TINKLE TINKLE TINKLE TONK

TINKLE TINKLE TINKLE TONK

TINKLE TINKLE TINKLE TONK

I WONDER WHERE THEY ALL PICKED UP THAT LITTLE TUNE...?

EXCUSE ME, YOUR MAJESTY!

I MUST JUST... ERM... RUN A SOUND CHECK FOR THE CORONATION ANTHEM!

GASP! I'LL HAVE TO SLASH INTO ZE RECENTLY BUILT TOMB OF SIR ISAAC NEWTON!

HERE LIES SIR ISAAC NEWTON 1643–1727

I'M SURE SIR ISAAC VOULD UNDERSTAND ZE GRAVITY OF MY PREDICAMENT!

I MUST STOP ZOSE PARROTS SINGING ZAT TUNE!

ZIS EXTRA-STICKY GERMAN BLACK FOREST GATEAU SHOULD DO ZE TRICK... HERE, BIRDIES!

AND

GMMF!

MMF!

HO HO!

ZAT STICKY CAKE HAS GUMMED ZERE BEAKS SHUT!

UND JUST IN TIME — ZE CORONATION ANTHEM IS DUE TO START!

COO-EE, GEORGIE! LOOK WHAT ELSE I FOUND IN THE ATTIC!

NOT NOW, MOTHER!

I JUST WANTED TO SHOW HIM THE SQUEAKY RUBBER PIG HE HAD WHEN HE WAS A TODDLER...

HE USED TO PLAY WITH IT WHEN HE WAS SAT ON HIS POTTY HAVING A POO...

A-VUN, A-TWO, A VUN TWO THREE...

SQUEAK! SQUEAK!

BTTTHHRRRP!

HIMMEL!

I HAFF DONE A POO-POO IN MY PANTS!

118

BAXTER BASICS MP

...I WOULD LIKE TO MAKE IT CLEAR THAT WHEN I ATTENDED WHAT I UNDERSTOOD TO BE A WORK-RELATED MEETING IN MY OFFICE DURING LOCKDOWN, I WAS UNAWARE THAT IT WAS IN FACT A DRUG-FUELLED SEX ORGY...

I ONLY INJECTED CRACK COCAINE INTO THE SHAFT AND GLANS OF MY PENIS BECAUSE MY STAFF AND I HAD BEEN WORKING PARTICULARLY LONG HOURS DURING THE PANDEMIC...

INDEED, I ONLY REMAINED AT THE ORGY FOR A FEW MINUTES OR 11 HOURS IN ORDER TO THANK MY STAFF FOR THEIR HARD WORK AND COMMITMENT...

...AND TO TAKE PART IN WHAT I BELIEVED AT THE TIME TO BE AN IMPORTANT DEPARTMENTAL MEETING ABOUT THE REQUISITION OF MUCH-NEEDED PPE...

...A MEETING THAT I SUBSEQUENTLY DISCOVERED WAS IN FACT A FIVE-WAY SADO-MASOCHISTIC ANAL GANG-BANG AND BUKKAKE CUM-BATH...

WILL YOU BE RESIGNING, MR BASICS?

WE'LL HAVE TO WAIT AND SEE WHAT IT SAYS IN THE OFFICIAL REPORT THAT EXONERATES ME.

...BUT OF COURSE I REGRET IF ANYONE FEELS THAT MISTAKES OR MISJUDGEMENTS MAY APPEAR TO HAVE BEEN MADE BY OTHER PEOPLE IN MY DEPARTMENT...NOT ME.

THAT WENT VERY WELL, I THOUGHT, BAXTER...

hmm?

I THINK YOU'RE OFF THE HOOK.

A POLICEMAN TO SEE YOU, MINISTER...

I WONDER WHAT HE WANTS

I'D LIKE TO TALK TO YOU ABOUT THE STABBED AND STRANGLED NAKED WOMAN FOUND BEHIND YOUR FILING CABINET THIS AFTERNOON...

BELIEVE ME, OFFICER, I'D LIKE TO HELP YOU IF I COULD...

...UNFORTUNATELY, IT IS NOT POSSIBLE FOR YOU TO INVESTIGATE CRIMES THAT MIGHT HAPPENED IN THE PAST, IS IT..?

ERM...

...SUFFICE IT TO SAY, I FOLLOWED MINISTERIAL GUIDANCE AT ALL TIMES. NOW, IF YOU'D EXCUSE ME, I HAVE IMPORTANT WORK TO ATTEND TO.

ERM...?!

THANK-YOU FOR YOUR HELP, MINISTER.

SLAM!

ANY TIME...

CRUMBS, BAXTER! I CAN'T HELP THINKING THAT THIS NEW SCANDAL MIGHT ADVERSELY AFFECT YOUR PARTY LEADERSHIP HOPES..!

...I MEAN IF IT GETS INTO THE PAPERS...

NO CHANCE.

...THE RED-TOPS ARE BACKING ME FOR NUMBER 10 ALL THE WAY..!

AS LONG AS I KEEP THEIR AGENDA IN MIND WHEN I'M FORMULATING MY POLICIES, MY CAMPAIGN WILL HAVE THEIR FULL SUPPORT.

...IN FACT, I'M GOING TO OFFICIALLY LAUNCH MY BID AT A PRESS CONFERENCE THIS AFTERNOON..!

SO...

...LET ME MAKE IT CLEAR - THERE MAY HAVE BEEN LEAKS ABOUT INAPPROPRIATE BEHAVIOUR IN MY OFFICE, BUT THAT IS GOING TO STOP RIGHT NOW...

...THERE IS IMPORTANT WORK TO DO..!

BIG SMILE AND SOME TITS OVER HERE FOR THE SUN, MR BASICS..!

FUCK THE BBC!

ON page 99 of this book, Billy Whiffles from Tooting wrote that he had watched a pornographic film in which a lady was lifted onto a wall-mounted bathroom wash-basin for sex. Mr Whiffles suggested that such an act would be dangerous due to the weight and warned against it. However, I work for a leading distributor of kitchen, bedroom and bathroom products, and can confirm that, assuming the cabinet was fixed to an outside wall, a suitable bracket was used (the Camar 807 02 E1 RV for example), and weight was distributed fairly evenly, then they should be okay up to a weight of approximately 150kg, providing they're not too enthusiastic when the chap gets to the vinegar strokes.

David Milner, Durham

THE people who roll toilet rolls up in the factories must be very good at it. Every time I drop one, (a toilet roll that is, not a fart), it always takes me about 2 hours to roll it back, and it's never as good.

Stanley Stickbrick, Ulverston

LIKE most people at the moment, my gas and electricity bills are sky high. I for one am certainly intending to use as much as I can in order to get my money's worth.

Jane Hoole Garner, St Ives

THE actions of the French police at the recent Champions League final were not only disproportionate and shameful, but they were also completely counter-productive. If anyone is going to Paris in the near future, could they have a word with the police and tell them that it's *bees* that calm down when you douse them with smoke. Football fans tend to get a bit more upset.

Hampton Peasgood, Tooting

YOU would think an omniscient Creator might have handed down the odd commandment about stuff that is actually a problem, like racism. Then again He invented those worms that swim up your cock, so what do I know?

Palmer Vjorhend, Portstewart

MY mate told me he couldn't wait to see the new *Top Gun* movie, but then I caught him sat down in a tent outside the cinema on Friday evening doing exactly that. Why do the British set themselves up for failure with such unachievable statements?

TKP, Newport

STAR LETTER

AFTER the country waited so long for the Sue Gray report, I can't help thinking that the Government should have asked my wife's friends to compile it. Whenever I misbehave on a night out, she has a full dossier of eyewitness accounts and incriminating photos stored on her mobile before I've even managed to stagger through the front door.

Steve Crouch, P'borough

I RECENTLY bought a new laptop which, to my surprise, was made by HP. This must be a really progressive company to diversify from producing baked beans, soup and tomato sauce to making computers. Their competitors should take a leaf out of HP's book and get busy. Maybe we could see new gadgets like a Fray Bentos Fitbit, Batchelors Bluetooth Earbuds or even a Mr Kipling Raspberry Smartphone.

Heinz Doofenshmirtz, email

IN Stephen King's *Pet Sematary*, Dr Louis Creed buries his cat and it comes back all evil. If I did the same I honestly wouldn't know the difference because my cat is already a massive cunt.

Joe Hartshorn, Grassmoor

IN her 1981 disco classic *Pull Up to the Bumper*, Grace Jones encourages listeners to "Pull up to the bumper in your long black limousine". Surely Ms Jones is aware that even at 20 mph, a safe stopping distance of 40 feet should be maintained, and even if the car in front is parked, you should allow ample room for it to manoeuvre out of its position. Pulling up to the bumper is, therefore, either selfish or even dangerous. That said, my mate Dave reckons she's singing about shagging, not driving.

Jim P, Ramsbottom

I HAVE a friend who takes photos of train spotters, making him a train spotter spotter. So I took a photo of him, making me a train spotter spotter spotter. Anybody want to take a photo of me and jump on this bandwagon?

Aaron, Halifax

WHENEVER I watch a funny video on YouTube, it always seems to say 'try not to laugh' in the title. Isn't that supposed to be the whole point?

Jack Spratt, Stourbridge

NOW It turns out that dinosaurs never actually existed. Honestly. You couldn't make it up.

TC Rusling, email

I'VE just got the Crack Whore Jack Pencil strip in *Viz* issue 219. Fuck me, am I thick or what?

Gas Fires, Manchester

✱ *Well, since that issue came out in October 2012, you are certainly a little slow on the uptake, Mr Fires. But like fine wine, that cartoon strip will have matured with age and so ironically, you will have enjoyed it more than someone who read it fresh off the press.*

HOW on earth did Hadrian's Wall keep anyone from invading England? I've been up there and seen it and it's only about two feet high in most places and with gaps all over the shop. I was easily able to cross over it, so the Scots must have been a right soft bunch if it kept them out.

Ben Nunn, Caterham

I'M no scientist, but I reckon they didn't think the CERN Particle Accelerator through properly. The particles can't be going that fast, as the accelerator is a circle, and they must be cornering all the time. The Channel Tunnel would be much better because it's nice and straight, so the particles could get a bit of speed up. It would also make it easier to collide particles because, without corners, they could see the other ones coming and head for each other. Obviously they would have to wait for any trains to get out the way before they pulled the trigger, but I'm sure that's no biggie.

Rigsby, London

I AM sending this email from Buckingham Palace, where I am currently at a Royal Garden Party. Have any of your readers ever written such an unimpressive letter from such an illustrious location?

Jack Orchel, email

TOP TIPs

PRETEND you are in a sitcom by keeping a completely straight face whenever your friends say something funny and taking a long pause before you reply to allow for canned laughter.

Dave Turton, Doncaster

LOST your car keys? Simply pull a plastic panel off of your steering column, connect together the first 2 wires that pop out and off you go, just like in the films.

Chingfordrob, Chingford

ITALIAN bakers. Increase the load-bearing capacity of your breadsticks by baking a few lengths of spaghetti into each one as a sort of 'pasta rebar'.

Mark Glover, Coventry

PARENTS. Teach your child to count up to four by giving them a packet of McCoy ridge cut crisps.

Smiffy, Mansfield

BUS drivers. Align your career trajectory with that of a professional footballer by stopping driving buses at 34, and making your living talking about driving buses for the rest of your life.

Eldon Furse, email

VISIT the Blackpool Illuminations when it's raining so the reflections in the wet road make it appear that there are twice as many lights.

Julian, York

SAVE money on expensive electric toothbrushes by sellotaping a regular toothbrush to your washing machine and offering your mouth up to it during the spin cycle.

Kevin Caswell-Jones, Gresford

toptips@viz.co.uk

I REALLY don't understand why F1 drivers use those cheap tyres that only last half an hour before they need changing. I pay about £100 a tyre and haven't changed mine for over a year. With all that sponsorship money floating about in F1, you'd think they would spend a bit more. Buy cheap, buy twice, they say.

Chris Jacob, Wetherby

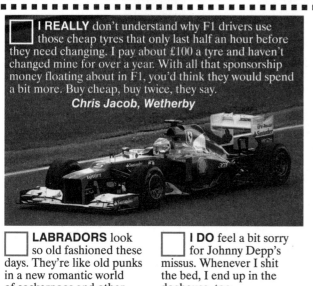

LABRADORS look so old fashioned these days. They're like old punks in a new romantic world of cockerpoos and other designer shit machines.

Stuie, Bunny

I HAD an idea for a cookery programme recently where Bear Grylls cooks mammals of the family *Ursidae*, using downwards radiated heat from a flat, horizontal element or flame. However, I am struggling to think of a title. Can your readers help?

Eldon Furse, email

MY cousin's son started his new job as a BT technician about 6 months ago, and he spends most of the working day up telegraph poles on housing estates. But in all that time he hasn't once seen a pair of MILF tits, or a couple going at it in their bedroom. What is the country coming to? It's not the job he signed up for.

Theodore Firedoor, Chipping Norton

ISN'T it odd that secret agent 007 never seems to experience any toilet trouble whilst chasing criminal masterminds abroad? I only have to hop over the English Channel and within 48hrs it's like the start of a pigeon race in my bathroom. I'm hoping for a bit more realism in the next instalment.

Del Le-Belli, Barrow

WE'RE always hearing nonsense about the Iron Age and the Bronze Age but what about good old brass? Come on brass, have an Age!

Mathew Shepherd, Derby

IF anyone from Cadbury's is reading this, the 'Dairy' in Dairy Milk is sort of implied. It would be a bit fucking weird if the Friesians were just donating the milk of their own volition.

Shenkin Arsecandle, Llaregyb

I DO feel a bit sorry for Johnny Depp's missus. Whenever I shit the bed, I end up in the doghouse, too.

Rick Pistol, email

NAPOLEON once famously asked of a new general in his army "I know he's good, but is he lucky?" Well, if that general had been Spawny Get from the pages of *Viz*, the answer would have been an unequivocal 'yes'. I'm not sure what the point of this letter is, but still, it just goes to show, eh?

Dylan White, St Ives

WHATEVER happened to TV detector vans? As a child, I remember the acute fear that one might drive slowly down our street, call at our house and take my parents away, even though we had a colour TV licence at the time. It would be lovely to see the traditional British TV detector van grace our streets once again so, come on BBC. Keep us on our toes and run heritage TV detection van services when we least expect it!

Prescot Cables, Leeds

CAN anyone name something that can be described as 'pert' other than a woman's breasts or buttocks? I can't. Doubtless this is another word that will be abolished by the so-called 'woke' brigade sooner or later. I advise all your male readers to make good use of it while they still can.

Wo-Nchu Taikmitu, Funky Town

AFTER watching several episodes of *Gardener's World*, it has left me wondering if Monty Don's dogs ever have a shit or lick their bollocks, or is it just clever editing?

Jack Spratt, Stourbridge

I JUST saw a newspaper headline reading "Mum Guilty of Murder!" But when I rang my dad up, he said she was sitting in the garden and he didn't know anything about it.

Nick Haskell, Adelaide

AFTER going in a pass-thru dishwasher whilst tied to a stretcher for a bet, I was permanently blinded and had to endure months of skin grafts. They say, "What doesn't kill you makes you stronger," but I can definitely say I am a frail shadow of the person I was before the experience.

Kelvin Griffith, Nuneaton

DURING the Second World War, Elizabeth Windsor worked as an ambulance mechanic, but by 1952 she was the Queen. So if you're stuck in a dead end job, just remember that young lady and reach for the stars.

Frank Discussion, Orkney

YOU can use your mobile phone as a torch, but you can't use your torch as a mobile phone. Yet both are battery-powered instruments. Once again it's one rule for one thing and one rule for another.

Nevets Nannarb, Southport

I FOLLOWED the advice of one of your Top Tips about sliding a tenner into your funeral suit so that the next time you wear it at a funeral you find it and get a nice surprise. Well I just put the suit on for a funeral I am attending this morning and, Hey presto! A crisp tenner! Unfortunately it was one of the old paper ones which are no longer legal tender, so my joy was short-lived. Thanks a lot for kicking a man when he's down.

Matty O'Toole, Chewton Mendip

WHATEVER happened to castor oil? In the comics of the 1970s, kids were regularly punished with a spoonful of the stuff, yet today it's simply never mentioned. Come on, comic publishers, bring back castor oil.

Doug Roberts, Sompting

IF the makers of Astroturf wanted to make their artificial, plastic grass even more realistic, they should start selling accessories such as artificial, plastic dog poo which they could call Astroturd. Yet again it's left to the likes of me to come up with these initiatives because these 'so-called' marketing boffins don't even care.

Jimmy Changa, Chive

MY wife and I had an argument recently whilst *Ant & Dec's Saturday Night Takeaway* happened to be on the TV. Have any other readers had an already miserable situation compounded in a similar way?

Eldon Furse, email

TRAVELLING LIGHT

IT'S OFTEN said that when packing for a holiday, you should take half as many clothes and twice as much money. *But what else should you pack? Is there something that YOU always take with you when you go away? We asked some celebs what things they simply could not travel without.*

Ian Dunt, *i columnist*

I LOVE fucking off for a couple of weeks' hols, but the wine abroad is weak as vicars' piss and tastes like fucking shite, so I never go away without a dozen bottles of my favourite plonk from my local Booze Buster. Of course, with fucking airport restrictions, you're not allowed to take any bastard liquid airside, so I have to neck the fucking lot before going through cunting security.

Katie Hopkins, *gobshite*

AS A professional vile columnist, vitriolic words are the tools of my trade, and so whenever I go on holiday, I always take a simple notepad and pen with me. Then, if I'm relaxing on the beach and I think of something spiteful to say about disabled people, or if I'm in a restaurant and I come up with some poisonous comment about gays, I simply jot them down.

Benedict Cumberbatch, *actor*

WHENEVER I go abroad on holiday, I always take an egg harp with me. They don't have them anywhere but the UK, and I can't stand slicing boiled eggs with a knife. It's something about how the hard yolk smears on the blade that makes me go a bit tizicky. I don't actually eat boiled egg sandwiches, but you never know when someone you are holidaying with might like one.

Clive Myrie, *news anchor*

OFTEN, holidays fail to live up to our expectations and we don't have as good a time as we had hoped. So I always pack a portable CD player and an Ed Sheeran CD in my luggage. That way, if I'm feeling a little down because the weather's not much good or the hotel isn't up to scratch, I just think how much worse it would be if I put that CD on and listened to it, and that cheers me up a little bit.

OPERATION LEO
The exciting story of courage, cunning and a big cat that turned the tide of war!

IN 1940, after the Allied evacuation of Dunkirk, advantage lay with the Axis powers. The popular song *Hitler has only got one ball* had become tired and was losing its effectiveness as a weapon against the Führer. The tyrannical dictator was emboldened, and it was decided that a new source of ridicule was needed to defeat the evil Third Reich.

IN WHITEHALL, Prime Minister Winston Churchill gathered his war cabinet to discuss the pressing problem of coming up with a devastating new song with which to taunt Hitler and bring him back down to size. After many hours of work, many discarded ideas and many cups of tea, a possible solution was postulated.

CODE-BREAKERS at Bletchley Park had intercepted a conversation between two German officers in which one recalled a story he had heard. Apparently, as a young boy, Adolf Hitler had been to Berlin zoo where he had fallen into the lion enclosure. He was rescued, but it had left him with a lifelong fear of lions. Could this fact be used to the Allies' advantage?

WHAT IF a lion could be smuggled into the Berghof, the Führer's retreat in the Bavarian Alps? Coming face to face with his darkest fear, Hitler would immediately soil his trousers on the spot. A new version of the song - *Hitler, has gone and shit his pants, You can smell it, the other side of France* - sung to the same tune, would soon sweep across Britain!

BUT GETTING a fully grown lion into one of the most fortified buildings in Europe would be no easy task. Any such animal approaching the gate would be shot on sight by the *Sturmabteilung*, the Führer's crack team of bodyguards. But then, Churchill himself came up with a brilliant idea… *what if the lion were disguised as one of the Sturmabteilung?*

THE SEARCH was on for a suitable animal. Many zoos offered their beasts for the noble cause, but none were suitable as every one of them walked on all fours. A bodyguard approaching the Führer in such a manner might arouse suspicion. No, the animal had to be able to walk on its hind legs… and there was only one place where such an animal existed.

SULTAN WAS a 5-year-old Asiatic lion who had performed all his life at Stromboli's Circus, and one of his tricks was walking on his hind legs. The ringmaster was only too pleased to help the country in a time of war, so it was arranged that Sultan would be delivered to a military airbase at a secret location to be prepared for his mission.

SCIENTISTS SHOT the animal with a tranquilizer dart, and recorded how long the 500lb beast remained unconscious. The plan was to drug the animal to make it drowsy, but still able to walk. As the effects of the drug wore off and in the Führer's presence, the beast would become fully conscious and ferocious. Timing and dosage were critical.

AT LAST, British intelligence working behind enemy lines in Germany reported that Hitler had gone to his mountain retreat for the weekend. Sultan was drugged and dressed in a specially made *Sturmabteilung* uniform. A military transport plane was arranged, false papers were produced and transport to the Berghof was arranged. The mission was on.

THE DROWSY lion drifted safely to earth. On the ground, the reconnaissance team disguised as German peasants loaded the King of the Jungle onto a truck and began the drive to the Berghof. This was the most perilous part of the plan - if they were stopped, they would have difficulty explaining away a Sturmabteilung officer in a cage in their truck.

THE DISGUISE worked like a charm. The two guards were completely unaware of Sultan's real identity as he was greeted with a cheery "Seig Heil!" High on his balcony and wearing a pair of white tennis slacks, the genocidal despot watched as the new guard arrived. Hitler was unconcerned, and completely unaware of the horror that lay in store.

RECOVERED FROM his anaesthetic, Sultan let out a roar that echoed round the mountains. Terrified, Hitler lost control of his bowels, which loosed themselves into the arse of his white slacks and all down the back of his legs. His mission completed, the big cat leapt from the balcony and disappeared into the Bavarian forest.

A FEW hours later, Sultan was aboard a Bristol Buckingham transport aircraft high in the skies above Bavaria, drowsy from an intricately calculated dose of tranquilizer. The team on board the aircraft got the signal from the team on the ground. It was all systems go as the massive tail door slowly dropped open.

OUT OF SIGHT of the guards, Sultan, ripped to his feline tits, was helped out of the truck. With his tail tucked down his trousers, he began walking on his hind legs towards the gates of the Berghof. The plan had worked like clockwork so far, but at this point it was out of the team's hands. The success of the mission now lay in Sultan's paws.

SULTAN MADE his way through the castle towards the balcony where Hitler was enjoying the scenery. Just as planned, the drugs were now beginning to wear off. The big cat began to make a low grumbling sound as he gradually regained his senses. The Führer knew something was wrong as he saw the Sturmabteilung officer approach.

HITLER HAS gone and shit his pants was soon being sung throughout the land. The Führer was humiliated as the song of his trouser accident spread across the globe. It was the beginning of the end for the Third Reich, and unable to live with the shame, Hitler shot himself in the head and then set himself on fire in 1945.

Your Sex Life in the Afterlife

Psychic Sex advice with Doris Stokes

Dear Doris,

I RECENTLY went on the ouija board, and I started talking to somebody whose name began with B. We got along great and I've contacted him many times since. But recently when I've gone on the ouija and asked if there's anybody there, there isn't. Last week I could only contact somebody beginning with a J or a K, and somebody who had died in a car accident – but when I asked if there was anybody there beginning with B, the glass never moved. I'm worried that he might be seeing somebody else on the other side and I don't know what to do.

Doris says... Relationships fail, and it's often the fault of neither party. And it's nice when break-ups are done properly – with dignity, in person and with both parties agreeing to go their separate ways amicably. But these days, it seems that simply ignoring your former partner with no explanation is the norm. Being 'ghosted' – in your case literally – is never a pleasant experience, but you must put it behind you and move on. There are plenty more fish in the sea, and plenty more spirits in the astral plane.

Dear Doris,

I HAVE recently met someone on the ouija board and our messages to each other have become increasingly flirtatious. Recently he began sending sexually overt messages. First, he asked me to do the seances topless, and then last week he asked me if I would sit on the board while he controlled the upturned glass. He knows that I am married but I feel under pressure to fulfil his requests. I feel really guilty about it, but I can't give it up because of the thrill it gives me every time. Life in the bedroom has become dull and the flirtation makes me feel wanted as I did at the beginning of my marriage. Is this a bit of harmless fun, or should I tell the spirit I can no longer communicate with him?

Doris says... Forbidden relationships with ghosts can be exciting at first, especially when you have been out of the dating scene for some time. But you must remember that sex via the ouija board is still sex and you must ask yourself whether it is worth risking your marriage for the sake of a bit of fun. And remember, the person you met may not be as he describes himself, or may be communicating with a number of different women at the same time. If your sex life has become dull, perhaps consider asking your partner what he would like, or experiment with a bit of role-playing to spice things up.

Dear Doris,

I'VE been seeing a gentleman in spirit world for two months, and everything has been going well. But last week, we went out to a restaurant and things went a bit wrong. I set the ouija board up on the table and read the menu out and he moved the glass to 'Yes' when I got to the dish he wanted. But when the food arrived – sirloin steak with chips – he didn't touch it. It was the most expensive thing on the menu and the waiter took it back and threw it away. And I'm not so old-fashioned that I think the gentleman should pay, but when the bill came, he never even offered to go halves on it. Should I confront him about it?

Doris says... There may have been a reason why he didn't touch his meal. Perhaps he didn't like the look of it, or perhaps his spiritual energy wasn't strong enough to move the knife and fork. Similarly with him not offering to pay. He may simply have forgotten his wallet, or maybe there isn't money in spirit world. Whatever the reason, you shouldn't confront him over the ouija board. Wait until you die and have a talk with him face to face.

SID the SEXIST

THE TRUTH IS OUT THERE!

Jilted stargazer seeks answers in Celestial Realm

THE JAMES WEBB space telescope successfully launched by NASA in 2021 is already looking further than ever into the hidden corners of the cosmos. The data relayed back to earth by the high-tech billion dollar instrument will give scientists fresh information about the origins of the universe. But one amateur astronomer from West Yorkshire hopes that the space boffins in America will allow HIM to have a shot on the orbiting observatory's controls to save his marriage.

Guttering salesman Frank Wetherby, 49, has always been interested in what lies beyond our readily visible environment. Despite living in the centre of Huddersfield, an area not famed for astronomical research due to light pollution, Frank spends many hours each night scanning the skies on the lookout for comets, planets and meteors through his binoculars.

all-sorts

"You can see all-sorts if you know where to look," he told his local paper the *Huddersfield Taint and Freckle*. "You can often see Mars, Pluto or the Milky Way just next to the upstairs windows of the flats by the pound shop, especially the third floor where that young couple has just moved in."

But a recent fall from a ladder followed by a night in a police cell has threatened to bring Wetherby's 30-year marriage an abrupt end. And he told the paper he now hopes the boffins at NASA will help him set the record straight.

"There was a bit of a misunderstanding one night when I was trying to get a look at the rings of Saturn through my binoculars," he said. "It's thousands of miles away,

ON THE LOOKOUT: 49 year-old guttering salesman Frank is scouring the heavens for proof of his innocence.

so I was trying to get a bit closer to it by going up a ladder that I'd propped up against my neighbour's back wall by the bathroom."

"Unfortunately, she saw me and screamed, probably thinking I was a peeping Tom or something. I tried to explain that I was just doing some planetary research, but before I could say anything, her husband came in the bathroom and shoved me off the ladder."

A bruised Wetherby was put on the sex offenders' register and sentenced to 200 hours community service. But worse than the conviction, his wife Marge threw him out of the family home.

"The fact that the missus didn't believe me, and thought that I was up the ladder peeping at the bird next door, was the most hurtful part," he said. "She's believed me on every other occasion like this, so I don't know what was different this time."

heavenly

Now Wetherby is pinning his hopes on the US space agency coming to his rescue and convincing

his wife that the only heavenly bodies he was looking at up his ladder were planetary ones in the far reaches of the solar system.

"The James Webb space telescope is able to detect light which left the farthest reaches of the universe billions of years ago," Wetherby told the paper. "And when space boffins mentioned being able to see back in time to what happened just after the Big Bang, it got me thinking."

"If it could look back twelve billion years to the beginnings of the universe, it could easily look back to that August bank holiday when I was up the ladder," he said.

And Wetherby hopes that NASA bigwigs will let him use the $10billion orbiting observatory to prove to his wife that he was looking towards the heavens and not into his neighbour's bathroom window.

"When the picture from NASA comes in, Marge will see for herself that when I was up the ladder, I was looking up towards Saturn all the time, except for the few minutes I was trying to steady myself at the top and by necessity facing the window," he said.

And Wetherby vowed that he is quite willing to put his hand in his

pocket and pay for the loan of the high-tech space eyeglass himself.

"I've got a pension pot from an office job I did for a year after leaving school," he said. "I'm sure that will buy me enough time on the telescope to discover and film the confirmatory waves of light before they disappear into the ether."

bingo

And the amateur star gazer believes it will be good publicity for the space agency to help him prove his innocence.

"People are always banging on about how expensive astronomy is and what little relevance it has to everyday life," he said. "What better use is there for the most expensive space telescope ever than to scour the extremes of an ever-expanding universe in search of the fast-receding images of me not spying on my neighbour's tits?"

"The proof will be irrefutable and she'll have to take me back. You can't argue with science."

"And if she still doesn't believe me, perhaps I could use it to see her being scuttled the Christmas before last by him from the post office in his flat with the curtains open when she told me she was at the bingo," he added.

I-SPY WITH MY SKY EYE: Wetherby hopes NASA's cutting-edge James Webb telescope may help save his marriage.

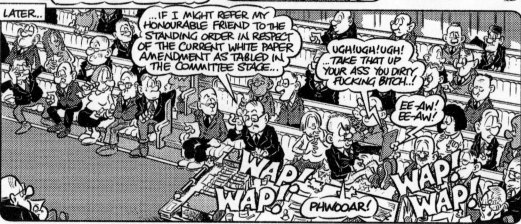

one Day at the CAR HIRE

You wait here, love, I'll go and pick up the car.

Okay. Quick as you can.

ARVIS CAR HIRE

Good morning sir, how can I help you?

I've got a car booked. The name's Evans.

Ah yes, here we go… a two door Fiat 500.

What!? No… it was a people carrier. A Renault Espace.

Yes, but our T's and C's make it clear that it's a Renault Espace *or similar*.

Well yes, but an Espace is nothing like a Fiat 500.

Yes it is, sir.

But I've got three kids and four suitcases. And a buggy.

Then you'll need to hire roof bars, sir. That's £48 for the week.

Plus a £20 fitting charge. And a £20 removal charge.

What?

And would you like to take out fully comprehensive insurance, sir?

I've done it. I've already took it out and paid for it online.

No, you've paid for the comprehensive insurance, sir. I'm talking about the *fully* comprehensive insurance.

What's the difference?

Well, one is more fully comprehensive than the other.

Eh!?!

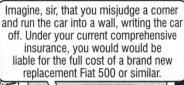

Imagine, sir, that you misjudge a corner and run the car into a wall, writing the car off. Under your current comprehensive insurance, you would would be liable for the full cost of a brand new replacement Fiat 500 or similar.

Or similar?

Yes. Like a Renault Espace…

But under our fully comprehensive insurance plan, you would have nothing at all to pay.

How much is it?

An extra £48, sir.

Okay, I'll have it.

And would you like alloy wheel damage waiver?

No, sir.

What!?! Wouldn't alloy wheels be included in the fully comprehensive insurance?

Alright then.

Shortly…

Here's your Renault Espace or similar, sir. Have a good holiday.

It hasn't got alloy wheels.

That's right, sir. Only the Espace has alloy wheels.

Excuse me… there's a scratch on the boot. Can I register that?

Oh!?! Let me see.

No need, sir, it's a superficial scratch, sir… If you can't feel it with a fingernail, we do not deem it a scratch.

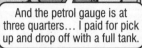

And the petrol gauge is at three quarters… I paid for pick up and drop off with a full tank.

That's a rough guide, sir, it's all within reason.

Eventually…

Have a good holiday, sir… see you in a week.

A week later…

Hello sir, welcome back.

Here you go. Ta.

Thank you very much, sir… I'll just carry out the return check.

Oh, dear! There's a scratch here, I'm afraid.

That was there when I picked it up.

Did you register it?

You said there were no need…

…you said it were superficial.

No, I can feel it with my fingernail.

I've got fully comp insurance anyway.

Fully comp doesn't cover scratches, I'm afraid.

And the petrol tank is only 98% full…

…we'll have to charge you a full tank, plus refuelling surcharge…

SPLATCH OF THE DAY!

MOTD Lineker soils himself a second time

MORE THAN THREE DECADES after his on-field toilet accident at the 1990 World Cup, former England captain turned TV pundit *Gary Lineker* has soiled himself live on TV for a second time filming an episode of *Match of the Day!*

The football legend famously defecated in his shorts after going in for a tackle during a televised game against Ireland. The TV cameras caught the striker dragging his buttocks along the grass in an attempt to wipe them clean of the offending foulage.

But as if one embarrassing incident like this were not bad enough, the unlucky former England front man has done the same thing again, this time on the Beeb's flagship Saturday night football show.

fouling

Lineker was discussing the Everton and Nottingham Forest clash with fellow presenters Alan Shearer and Micah Richards when TV viewers heard a loud rasping sound from his trousers as he leaned forward to emphasise a point.

"It was clear on the studio floor what had happened," said one BBC camera operator who wished to remain anonymous. "Alan and Micah both clocked it and there was a little embarrassed silence."

Showing the same professionalism off the field as on, the co-hosts carried on with the post-match analysis

A VIZ SOILED KEKSCLUSIVE!

between themselves, giving Lineker time to sort himself out.

"Poor Gary was dragging himself slowly sideways in his chair whilst the other presenters were keeping things going for the cameras," the source continued. "But after a few minutes, it was clear that the show could not continue."

dribble

TV executives took the decision to pull the programme, telling viewers that there was a technical fault, and that normal service would be resumed as soon as possible. However, after five minutes the show was abandoned and an episode of *Dad's Army* was broadcast in its place.

On Sunday morning, the *Match of the Day* production team issued an apology on its official Twitter account, saying that one of the presenters had been taken ill, but reassuring viewers that the individual concerned had made a full recovery.

The BBC refused to give details

EXTRA TIME: *Lineker shat himself on live broadcast.*

about the incident, citing the privacy of the presenter, but images of Lineker's MOTD chair being burnt in a skip behind Salford's Media City studio quickly circulated on social media.

And on Monday, Lineker himself put an end to speculation by apologising himself on his social media platforms.

"I would like to apologise to all MOTD viewers who witnessed me once again soiling myself on camera. The combination of my leaning forward to make a point in the discussion and a three-day old

prawn salad took a grim toll," he told his 10million followers.

And fans were pleased to learn that, although embarrassed, he had not lost his sense of humour. "I would like to promise that this will not happen again, but time has proven that to be a promise I am incapable of keeping," he quipped.

skid

However, the episode has once again led to calls for the BBC to curb what many people see as Lineker's excessive salary, reputed to be in the region of £2.5million per year.

"For that amount of cash, you'd expect him to use a toilet," said one correspondent to Samira Ahmed's *Newswatch* programme.

However, *MOTD* producers yesterday issued a short statement saying that it now considered the matter closed.

"Gary has apologised and we have drawn a line under the matter," they said.

"And although this was an unfortunate incident, we would like to remind viewers that the vast majority of live broadcasts on the BBC end without anyone soiling themselves."

WE ARE IN a dystopian future. A future where the rule of law is nothing but a distant memory, a sick joke from before the Apocalypse. Life is cheap in the fortified citadel that was once New York's Madison Avenue, where renegade creatives continue to work as advertising executives, desperately fighting rival agencies to secure the next big ad contract...

...Advertising executive Max Draper pitches his latest 30-sheet panel to renegade clients from a steel-clad fortress beyond the Wastelands...

Here it is, gentlemen. O[...] final visual for your ne[...] billboard campaign...

MAD MEN MAX

It better be good, Draper... We've had a meeting with Cutler Gleason and Skullcrusher... and you got a lot to beat.

I'm sure we have... CGS are a good agency. They can speak to those who buy your product...

...but at RDST, we speak to those who don't.

Fuck those who don't!

Well, with respect Mr Humungus...

...you should fuck those who do.

HUNH!?!

They're by your side like a loyal wife. They'll cook your dinner and keep your home till the day they die. You can afford to say fuck them...

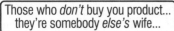

Those who don't buy you product... they're somebody else's wife...

...we want to have an affair with them... and this will let them know we are interested.

WOW!

Yes... Yes... I like it. You got the contract, Draper.

Great!

Where do you want us to put it?

At the crossroads... outside the Fortress of Fire.

What?!...in the Wastelands!?! But that's madness...!

...we'd have to drive the billboard through the Valley of Annihilation!

That's the most lawless territory in the Forbidden Sector!

Joan's right! The valley is crawling with road pirates! No-one's ever made it through there alive... least of all in a 100-ton mobile billboard rig.

It's a suicide mission!...

...I won't do it!

Oh you'll do it, Draper...

...you'll get that 30-sheet billboard up outside the Fortress of Fire before sundown tonight...

...or you'll never see Joan alive again!

Heh-heh!

So...

Don't worry, Joan... I'm coming.

WHUP! WHUP! WHUP!

VROOOM!

WHOOOOO!

YOUR NAME HERE
Call ROCKATANSKY, DRAPER
STERLING & TOECUTTER

RAAAAAGH!

As Max's truck carrying the 30-sheet billboard neared the Forbidden Sector, the other ad execs in the convoy began turning back...

This is as far as we go, Max! Fuel's getting low and I'm pitching a new Playtex campaign at two!

VROOOM!

The mobile billboard hurtled between the sheer rock walls of the Valley of Annihilation... and Max had an eerie sense that he was being watched...

Death to the incomer!

Looks like I've got company.

WOO!

RAARGH!

Time to light up a Lucky Strike...

SMASH!

AAARGH!

PETROL

FLICK!

...and get toasted.

KA-BOOM!

And...

Welcome to the Fortress of Fire, Draper...

...glad you could make it!...

WELCOME TO THE FORTRESS of FIRE

WOAH!

Genius!

YOU ONLY GET AN OO WITH Ty·Phoo

Max! You came for me!

Oh, Max... I... love you!

Love!?!...

Joan... what you call love was invented by guys like me to sell you nylons.

131

THE GREAT VIZ LOCH NESS MONST

FOR OVER 100 years people have argued over the existence of a mysterious monster inhabiting Loch Ness in the Scottish Highlands, with only hearsay and blurred photographs for evidence. For less time – but almost as long – people have argued about whether King Edward VIII should have abdicated in 1936 in order to marry his true love, American divorcee Wallis Simpson; a move which not only led to him becoming the shortest-serving UK monarch, but also left the throne open to his brother George VI and his wife the Queen Mother. In order to clear this issue up once and for all, we put the following question to some of today's top stars:

"Does the Loch Ness Monster actually exist or should King Edward VIII have abdicated?"

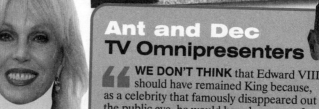

Joanna Lumley
National Treasure

❝ NO MATTER how fantastical it may seem, one cannot ignore the fact that the abdication of Edward VIII took place in 1936, *just 2 years* after Colonel Robert Wilson developed his celebrated black-and-white photograph of the Loch Ness monster. I often find myself fancifully wondering whether – had that disputed sighting of the amphibious beastie not of taken place – things may of turned out differently and Edward VIII might of stayed king. And then again, I think he probably wouldn't of. ❞

Ant and Dec
TV Omnipresenters

❝ WE DON'T THINK that Edward VIII should have remained King because, as a celebrity that famously disappeared out of the public eye, he would have been a perfect candidate to appear on *I'm A Celebrity, Get Me Out Of Here!* We could film the series in the ruin of Urquhart Castle on the shore of Loch Ness and get him to eat Nessie as part of an eating challenge, which would have proved once-and-for-all the existence of the monster. Although, thinking about it realistically, even if Edward hadn't died in 1972, he'd be 128 years-old now which would make for quite distressing viewing. Especially if he made it through to the Celebrity Cyclone. ❞

Gary Barlow
Take That Man

❝ SOMETHING NOT many fans know about me is that I'm Loch Ness Monster-mad! I've got a huge poster of Nessie sellotaped to my lounge wall at home with "I Want To Believe (in the Loch Ness Monster)" written along the bottom in red marker pen. Also, the Take That song *Patience* was written about the patience that's required if you want to see the Loch Ness monster in actual life. Although I've spent hours sat on the side of the loch with my binos, I've yet to see her in the flesh. I do believe Nessie's a 'her' because of the name Nessie, which is possibly short for 'Vanessie', and sounds like a girl's name, I'd put good money on her existing. What was the other question? ❞

Will Smith
Irascible Oscar Winner

❝ I RECENTLY FOUND myself in a spot of hot water after I got up on stage at the Oscars and slapped Chris Rock across the chops. Viewers thought it was because he'd been cheeking my missus (her out of a couple of them *Matrix* films) but our on-stage barney was actually the culmination of a long-running disagreement between us about the Loch Ness Monster and the Windsors. I maintain that Nessie is actually a floating log and Wallis Simpson had secret vagina-tightening surgery to allow her to be successfully penetrated by the Duke's freakishly small penis, whilst Rock believes – quite wrongly – that the monster is a plesiosaurus and Mrs Simpson was actually a man in drag. ❞

Justin Welby
Archbishop of Canterbury

❝ WHAT IF the "monster" is nothing more than a distraction, something to get us looking in the wrong direction while the Duke of Windsor and Mrs Simpson steal treasure they've found in an abandoned goldmine buried deep under Urquhart Castle on the banks of Loch Ness? I bet that if we caught Nessie and pulled off her mask, we'd find the former King Edward VIII inside, operating a miniature submarine whilst Wallis Simpson drives a truck full of illicit gold bars down the A82 to be melted down in Inverness. At which point the pair might complain that their plan would have succeeded if it hadn't been for that meddling prelate and his suffragan bishops. And then I would go back to Lambeth Palace for a slap-up feed. ❞

R AND DUKE OF WINDSOR DEBATE

Mick Hucknall
Red Singer

I DON'T SEE HOW anybody in their right minds could think that the Loch Ness Monster doesn't exist, bearing in mind the wealth of grainy-yet-blurred black-and-white photographic evidence supporting it. However, after a cursory Google search I cannot find any photographic evidence of Edward VIII swimming with his neck, head and crown emerging from the murky depths of Loch Ness, and therefore have to assume that he never existed, let alone abdicated. I'm happy to change my opinion on this should any out-of-focus telephoto shots of this event ever come to light.

Jeremy Clarkson
Petrolmouth Motorhead

AFTER WE'D FILMED our episode of *The Grand Tour* in Loch Ness, a handful of production assistants wrote in to online forums to suggest to the show's fans that they may have briefly spotted Nessie emerging from the loch on the large video screen behind us at the end of the show. This was of course CGI trickery, but it does make me wonder whether nascent computer graphics technology could have been employed back in 1936 to create a primitive, valve-powered version of King Edward VIII. This 'steampunk' King could then have taken on all of the day-to-day responsibilities of the monarch, while the then Duke of Windsor swanned off to France with scandalous divorcee Wallis Simpson.

Dr Ben Goldacre
Epidemiologst

ALTHOUGH IT WOULD seem easy to rule out the existence of the Loch Ness Monster it's entirely possible that, if she did exist, Nessie could easily survive to a grand old age on a simple diet of the fish that populate the Loch, such as pike, eels and salmon, *which she would probably down in one gulp!* This is a diet similar to that which Edward VIII would have enjoyed during state banquets, had he not abdicated. Instead, the throne went to his brother, Prince Albert, later King George VI, who passed on the task of eating fish at state banquets in one gulp to his wife, the Queen Mother, with mixed results.

Dwayne Johnson
Movie Rock

IT'S COMMON KNOWLEDGE that I'm a huge fan of your English Scotchland and its many famous monsters, like The Lizard o' th' Loch and Bravenessie. However it's not so well known that I also love abdications, especially regal ones. In fact, for many years I've been looking to make a blockbuster movie where I play King Edward VIII and, after blowing up the English throne, I travel to Scotchland with my one true love, Mrs Simpsons, to play golf. That's as far as I've got with the plot for the moment, but I can guarantee it'll feature at least one scene where I hang from the landing skids of a crashing helicopter, whilst repeatedly kicking a water dinosaur in the plums.

Cat Bin Woman
Feline Disposal Operative

EDWARD'S ROMANCE with Mrs Simpson is always said to be the greatest romance of all time, as he "gave up everything" for the woman he loved. But after he abdicated, the Duke of Windsor spent the rest of his life farting about in free castles at the British taxpayer's expense, exactly the same as he would have done if he was still the king. Every picture I've seen of him, he's playing golf on some exclusive course, sat on a verandah in the Bahamas sipping a cocktail, swimming in the Med or getting out of a Rolls-Royce in a bow tie while someone bows at him. And don't get me started on the Loch Ness Monster. If that thing came near me, I'd just lob it in a wheelie bin.

Nicholas Witchell
BBC Royal Correspondent

SPEAKING AS the country's leading expert about both the royals *and* the Loch Ness Monster, I would have to say that her majesty really is so marvellous and wonderful that it doesn't bear thinking about her not being the Queen. If I imagine for just a moment a world without Elizabeth Windsor as our gracious and regal head of state, I break down in floods of tears. If she were to celebrate her forthcoming Platinum Jubilee by riding on Nessie's back the full length of her kingdom, waving at her people as she made her gloriously regal way around the country, I would probably go off in my pants.

NEXT WEEK: The Stars debate time travel and murdering baby Hitler

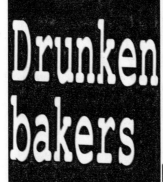

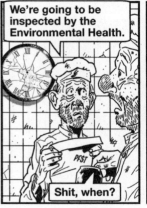

NOBBY'S PILES

...WELL MR GILES... AFTER LOOKING AT THE RESULTS OF YOUR LATEST ROUND OF ARSE TESTS, I'M PLEASED TO TELL YOU THAT YOUR HAEMORRHOIDS ARE NO LONGER GALLOPING...

WOW!

...THAT'S EXCELLENT NEWS, DOCTOR!

...IN FACT, I'M TAKING YOU OFF THE PANEL!

AT LAST!

IT MEANS I CAN FINALLY GET THE JOB I'VE ALWAYS DREAMED ABOUT WITHOUT WORRYING THAT I'LL INADVERTENTLY AGGRAVATE MY ARSEGRAPES!

Harley Street Private Bumgrapes Clinic

THAT'S MARVELLOUS NOBBY!

NEXT DAY...

STUDIO 3
STUDIO 2

PLYWOOD STUDIOS

STUNTMEN WANTED for JAMES BOND FILM Apply Within

...OKAY, NOBBY, WHEN I SHOUT "ACTION!", DRIVE THE CAR UP THE RAMP AND DO A BARREL-ROLL ACROSS THIS CROCODILE-INFESTED RIVER!

RIGHT YOU ARE MR BROCCOLI!

...AAAND... ACTION!

VROOM!

HMM... I THINK I MIGHT HAVE FORGOTTEN TO DO UP MY SEATBELT...

GAAH! ME FARMERS!

CUT!

≥ GROAN! ≤

DON'T WORRY, NOBBY... WE'LL SOON GET YOU PATCHED UP FOR YOUR NEXT SCENE...

FIRST AID

SHORTLY...

...AAAND... ACTION! CUE THE CIRCULAR SAW!

WHIRR!

...NOW, I'M JUST CHECKING... WE DID REMEMBER TO PUT THE RUBBER BLADE IN THE CIRCULAR SAW, DIDN'T WE..?

ERM...

YAAARGH! ME JOHNNY FUCKING GILES!!

...AND CUT!

007 SOUND STAGE

LATER...

...OKAY, NOBBY... IN THIS SCENE YOU'VE GOT TO SKI OFF THIS PRECIPICE AND DROP ONTO THE CRASHMAT!

LEAVE IT TO ME MR BROCCOLI!

PROPS DEPARTMENT

DID HE JUST SAY GET THE BIG CRASHMAT OUT?

NO. I THINK HE SAID "SPIKY ALPINE SCENERY"!

...AAAND... ACTION!

GAAAAAA!

...AAND CUT!

AT THE OSCARS...

...AND THE ACADEMY AWARD FOR BEST STUNT PERFORMER IN A MAIN-STREAM CINEMA RELEASE GOES TO...

...NOBBY GILES FOR "FOR YOUR DIES ONLY"...

...PERHAPS YOU'D LIKE TO SAY A FEW WORDS TO THE MANY MILLIONS OF PEOPLE WATCHING LIVE AROUND THE WORLD...

WOO-OOAH..!

GAAAH!

ME POOR FUCKING RINGPIECE!

The Pole Vaulting Vicar of St Fiacra's

A True Tale of Wartime Bravery

THE CHURCH of St Fiacra's in Barnchester was like many other village churches in England in 1941. But the vicar was certainly not like any other vicar. Because Father Tommy Tipper was the British and Commonwealth record holder in the athletic discipline of the Pole Vault.

It was a beautiful Sunday afternoon, and the entire village had turned out to enjoy the St Fiacra's church fete...

My, that looks a splendid cake, doesn't it, Mrs Antrobus.

It is, Father... I think it must be three and a half pounds at least.

Oh, I think it might be more than that, Edna

Yes... I guessed 7 pounds 3 ounces.

Help! Help!

Did you hear that, Mrs Roper?

I did, Father... it sounds like somebody is in trouble.

Help!

Where is it coming from? ...I can't see anyone...

LOOK!

My word! It's a golden eagle...

Yes! And it has two children in its talons.

SCREEEK! SCREEEK!

Help!

Sob! Sob!

Look! It's taking them to the steeple!

Good Lord!

Can you go and rescue them, Father?

I'm afraid not, we've lost the key to the tower door...

...nobody has been up there for years.

Should we call the fire brigade?

No! All the tenders have gone to London to deal with the Blitz!

There's no time anyway...

...the eagle is a bird of prey... a raptor...

SCREE-EEEK!

Sob!

...it will tear those children to pieces and feed them to its young... we may already be too late.

Wait a minute... you're the British and Commonwealth pole vault champion, Father... Could you not vault up there and rescue them?

I don't know... my personal best is 19 feet 3 inches...

...the base of the spire must be 60 feet high

But you must try, Father..

You're right... I'll get my vaulting poles from the rectory.

Within minutes, Father Tommy had modified his poles, and as the fete-goers clapped rhythmical encouragement, the elite athlete vicar prepared to make the jump of his lifetime...

CLAP!... CLAP!...

CLAP!... CLAP!... CLAP!... CLAP!... CLAP!...

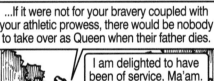

The End

THE VIZ CROWN COURT

THE criminal case you are about to read is fictional, but the proceedings are authentic. Consider the evidence set out before you carefully, because YOU are the jury, and your verdict will determine whether or not justice is done...

Will the defendant please rise..?

James Arthur Chippercock, you are charged that on 30th July 2021, during a funeral service in St Barnabus's Church, Fulchester, you performed a sex act upon yourself in the rear pew whilst watching pornographic material on your mobile phone, contrary to the public decency act...

How do you plead?

Not guilty.

Call the first witness.

Miss Ursula Summers QC begins the case for the prosecution by calling to the witness stand Mrs Mary Housewhite, the church warden on the day in question...

Mrs Housewhite, do you remember what you saw at the funeral service on July 30th last year?

Remember?... I doubt I will ever forget. It makes me sick to my stomach to think about it.

Could you describe what you saw to the court?

The reverend had just given the Eulogy for the departed, a beautiful and moving speech, and I walked to the back of the church to get the plate for the offerings...

...and that's when I saw him... sitting in the back pew...

Saw who, Mrs Housewhite?

Him! Him in the dock... watching pornography on his phone... the filthy beast.

What else was he doing, Mrs Housewhite?

He was... he was... fondling...

Go on...

...Fondling... fondling his...

BLOOOAGH!

BLOOOAGH!

I think the court knows what you mean, Mrs Housewhite...

...no further questions, your ladyship.

Mr Easter Bartlett QC begins his cross examination for the defence...

Mrs Housewhite... you allege that Mr Chippercock was watching pornography on his phone.

Yes. Yes, he was. Absolute filth.

And do you watch a lot of pornography yourself, Mrs Housewhite?

What!?! Certainly *NOT!*... I have never watched any pornography in my life.

Oh!?...

Then how do you know that what the defendant was watching was pornography?...

What!?!

How do you know he was not watching a *German Arthouse Film*... a movie exploring the complex nature of the relationships between two women and six men in a hotel room?

Well.. I...

Rather distasteful to be watching any film at a funeral, I admit...

...distasteful... but not illegal...

No further questions.

Next, IT expert Tom Charlton is called to give evidence for the prosecution.

Mr Charlton, you have been able to gain access to the web traffic that passed through the IP address corresponding to St Barnabus's church on the day in question, have you not?

I have.

It's Only Grock and Droll

Doctor I'm very depressed.

You should go and see the great clown Grock.

Man's a genius! Laugh-a-minute, more, *and* he's in town right now!

Bound to cheer you up, bound to!

Sob! Oh doctor...

What's wrong?

I am Grock.

Oh my God!!

Really?!

Weep. Yes.

I love your stuff!

Tim? You will *never* guess who I've got in the surgery.

Only bloody Grock!

No, straight up!

No that *is* him.

Well he doesn't wear the make-up offstage, does he?

But – why would he lie?

Say something funny.

Help me.

Ha ha!

Dark.

BRICK TEASE

BLOCKHEAD: *Lego release model of man purchasing new Lego kit.*

THE MAKERS of the ever-popular Lego building bricks delighted fans across the world today by announcing their next release: a model of a middle-aged man buying Lego sets on the internet.

According to the company's website, the 1,250-piece model comprises a desk, an office chair, a PC and a middle aged man in black rimmed glasses clicking 'BUY' on a Lego *Ghostbusters* Fire Station set.

audience

"We've done a lot of good kits in the past, but this one really speaks to our company's core audience: middle-aged men who really want to build a Lego model of the fire station out of Ghostbusters," said the Danish company's CEO Kurt Hammar.

BRICKSCLUSIVE!

"The detail on the new set is remarkable," he continued. "The blend of black and grey bricks which make up the man's clothes shows he got in from his office job two hours ago and hasn't changed yet. And his hunched posture perfectly conveys his desperate desire to drop £450 on a toy fire station full of ghosts."

tragic

Promotional material on the Lego website adds that a number

Lego fans go wild for new set

of options will be available, giving fans the chance to build the stubbly middle-aged man spending a range of amounts from £250 up to £500 on a whole variety of kits, including the cave from *The Goonies*, the school room from *The Breakfast Club* and Number Johnny Five off *Short Circuit*.

And Hammar said that the toy giant had some equally exciting kits planned for the future. "We've already got our next couple of

sets in the pipeline," he said. "A 3,000-piece model of the middle-aged man building the Ghostbusters fire station while his children play in the sun outside will be on sale in the summer," he added.

"And I predict the best selling toy next Christmas will be our stunning 4,000-piece set depicting the man's wife leaving him and taking the kids after discovering he has spent the equivalent of a month's mortgage payment buying himself a toy fire station," he added.

141

LetteRbOCKs

letters@viz.co.uk

ST★R LETTER

DO we burn calories when we let rip, I wonder? I regularly bottom blast and I'm as trim as was when I was 20. My wife, however, thinks guffing is disgusting, never letting one go, and she has really filled out over the years.

Gaz Trump, Windermere

WITH all the worry about obesity, petrol shortages and global warming, how come more people aren't getting around town using their old space hoppers? Come on, Britain. Let's put the fun back into shopping.

Dominic Twose, L'ton Spa

FORMER Prime Minister Boris Johnson has been criticised for meeting an ex-KGB agent without his officials present when he was foreign secretary. But I don't think there was ever any security threat. The meeting took place at a Bunga Bunga party in an Italian castle with loads of booze, drugs and prostitutes, for heaven's sake. They weren't going to be standing around talking about work.

Hector Popkiss, Luton

I'D just like to remind any of your readers from the Skipton area that my ex-wife Barbara is a bloody liar.

Dougie Fourpence, Skipton

∗ That may be so, Mr Fourpence, but in the interest of balance it is important that we give your ex-wife the right of reply. If the former Mrs Fourpence would like to write in and give her version of the situation, we will happily print it. Not that you can believe a bloody word she says, mind, from what we hear.

WHY do Gucci sell sunglasses in their British shops for £400 a pair, and yet they charge just £5 a pair when you buy them off one of those blokes on the beach in Spain? This blatant price inequality is exactly the reason we left the EU.

Ian Webb, Bury St Edmunds

I GOT a smart meter installed yesterday, and now I can see how much energy I'm using it's going to change my life. I've already stopped boiling the kettle for fun when I don't even want a cup of tea.

Pete Beat, Newcastle upon Tyne

IT'S all very well Jesus turning water into wine in the Bible, but when I set up a still in my garage to make my own booze, I get the council and the old bill knocking at my door. And this Jesus bloke is supposed to be an example to us all, according to the Archbishop of Canterbury.

Iain Devenney, Abingdon

I WAS going to write to *The Fortean Times* to tell them about some ghosts and UFOs I saw in my back garden the other week. But then I remembered I was off my nut on LSD at the time so thought I'd tell you instead.

Big Jon, Alloa

I NOTICE that scientists haven't discovered any new species of elephant in the last 22 years. There have just been the same two species for as long as I can remember. This strikes me as a bit lazy, as elephants are really big so they should be easy to discover. Come on science nerds, get elephant-spotting.

John Moynes, Dublin

WHY is it that women with itchy fannies can buy Vagisil, but there is no equivalent product for men? Quite frankly, I could do with applying a squirt of 'Bollosil' to my nuts most mornings. If sex equality is to mean anything, it has to work both ways.

Richard Swipe, email

PEOPLE with poor memories often say that they would forget their head if it wasn't screwed on. I have to laugh whenever I hear this phrase, as I was created from a variety of body parts in a German castle, and my head is held on with bolts.

F Monster, Bavaria

WHO do NASA think they are, trying to pass off colour photos from their James Webb telescope? They tell us that they show distant galaxies and light from 13 billion years ago, but everyone knows that photos were in black and white up until about 1950. Or sepia at best. Another instance of fake news.

Andy Huntingdon, Chorlton-cum-Hardy

I REFER to Mr Smotherbox's apology (*page 98*) to the First Class train passengers who witnessed him taking a dump near Newark Northgate. I was also on that fateful journey and had to watch Mr Smotherbox's call to stool, albeit from Second Class. As usual, it's apologies for those in First Class and a total neglect for the feelings of the other passengers. Whatever happened to 'levelling up'?

Laurence Mackay, email

SO what if Tory MP Andrea Jenkyns gave people the middle finger outside Downing Street the other week? As a Member of Parliament, she effectively works for the people of Great Britain, and if you can't tell your boss to fuck off now and again, it's a poor tale.

Tommy Golightly, Bradford

HOW come balding men don't wear toupées anymore? Nowadays, the follically-challenged all seem to shave their heads in an effort to look hard or 'trendy'. Come on slap-heads, dust off those syrups and cover up your shiny nuts.

Prince Asbo, Folkestone

LOOKING on Google maps, I see that West Grinstead is over 25 miles from East Grinstead. Surely, this makes Grinstead the 2nd biggest city in the UK, but I've never met anyone from there.

Ampersand Smorgasbord, Bude

HOW do dead people know when to turn up to a seance? Do mediums have a way of broadcasting into the ether for spirits to be in the pub at a certain time and date as there's going to be a chance to connect to the living? And, if so, surely the estimated 100 billion people who have died since Earth began can't all be crammed into the back room of The Red Lion just in case someone they know shows up.

Johnny T, Kirkcaldy

WHATEVER happened to stilted CEOs doing their own TV adverts? It's a long time since we cringed through the likes of Fred 'Book Early' Pontin, or those regional carpet shop owners with all the acting talent of a plank. Come on CEOs, do some adverts and get the nation's toes curling again.

Eldon Furse, email

COP 26

DING-A-LING-A-LING-A-LING!

EVENING ALL.

DO YOU MIND STOPPING FOR A MINUTE, SIR? THIS LOOKS HIGHLY IRREGULAR.

'ELLO, 'ELLO, 'ELLO, WHAT'S ALL THIS THEN?

JUST AS I THOUGHT. YOU'RE USING PLASTIC BAGS!
TSK! TSK!

DO YOU HAVE ANY IDEA HOW LONG IT TAKES A PLASTIC BAG TO DEGRADE IN A LANDFILL?

1,000 YEARS!

AND EVEN THEN THEY RELEASE HARMFUL MICROPLASTICS INTO THE ENVIRONMENT!

THERE'S JUST NO EXCUSE THESE DAYS, THERE ARE SO MANY OTHER ALTERNATIVES. JUTE, CANVAS, PAPER, COTTON...

HERE, USE THESE! ECO-FRIENDLY! AND YOU CAN USE THEM AGAIN THE NEXT TIME YOU'RE OUT.

NOW, ON YOUR WAY WITH YOU.
GOOD DAY, SIR.

BUT THEN... CRASH!
'ELLO, 'ELLO, 'ELLO, WHAT'S ALL THIS NOW?

EXCUSE ME, SIR... HAVE YOU EVER CONSIDERED CHANGING TO A HYBRID, OR EVEN A FULLY ELECTRIC VEHICLE FOR YOUR RAM-RAIDING?
SWAG FOR LIFE
JEWELLERY SHOP

ToP TIPS

MEN. Wear a Playtex girdle in public to help prevent embarrassing, involuntary erections. Unless the thought of wearing the girdle causes arousal, in which case this won't work.

Gerry Paton, London

SAVE money on expensive draught excluders by having your butler lie across the gap at the bottom of your drawing room door.

Jacob Rees-Mogg, Somerset

CROOKS. If a combination lock is proving hard to crack, try the number 9406. It's a 1 in 9999 shot, but you never know, it might just work.

D Williams, Donegal

SKIERS. Always keep a hot sausage in your pocket so search dogs can find you quicker in the event of an avalanche.

Nick Clarkson, Aberdeen

DOG poo bag manufacturers. Give your bags a camouflage design so that they don't seem obvious when filled with dog shite and thrown into a hedge.

Simon Burdett, Chesterfield

GIVE burglars a taste of their own medicine by breaking into your local prison and shitting on the ping pong table.

Kevin Caswell-Jones, Gresford

toptips@viz.co.uk

LAST month, a friend of mine was doing 55 in a 30 zone when his wheel clipped a kerb and he drove into a pillar box. As a result he was given 6 points on his licence. Now, I've not driven into a pillar box and yet I've never been awarded any points. If you ask me, the DVLA are just encouraging bad driving.

Terry Wilson, Lindfield

THE way the delinquent rabbits in the Peter Rabbit stories respectively refer to the farmer as 'Mr McGregor' is completely unrealistic. Since they spend all day trespassing on his land and stealing his property, it is much more likely they would call him 'That Cunt McGregor' or even 'paedo-McGreg', regardless of his actual sexual proclivities.

Andrew McGuigan, Blaydon

THIS afternoon I thought I'd go down to the lake to paint some watercolours of crested grebes. Then I remembered that I don't live anywhere near a lake. To make matters worse, I know fuck-all about birds and wouldn't know a crested grebe if it pecked me on the arse. And I'm rubbish at painting, so I went for a few pints instead.

Ben Nunn, Caterham

I'M fed up to the back teeth of hearing Chaka Khan claim that "I'm every woman." I'm pretty sure that I'm not Chaka Khan, and Mrs Harris next door with the purple rinse is definitely not her. And that's just two for starters.

Jane Hoole Garner, St Ives

MANY people say Saturn is their favourite planet because of its beautiful rings. But if you take them away, Saturn just looks like any other planet. It seems to me Prof. Brian Cox and his cronies have got a nice little scam going there.

Gary Ireland, Tauranga

NOW that a litre of petrol is more expensive than a litre of cola, isn't it about time that we started using fizzy pop in our cars? Come on, boffins. Sort it out!

David Fiddes, Reading

YOU hardly ever see people polishing apples on their sleeves before they eat them any more. Whatever happened to standards in this country? Come on apple-eaters, have a bit of pride.

Jonathon Snodgiblet, Snodland

SUMMER is here and, as seems to be increasingly the case, my house is full of flies. This makes me wonder, when did spiders stop catching them? Are Gen Z spiders just lazy snowflakes? I shouldn't have to bend over backwards to keep flies away, keeping all my windows shut in this stifling heat, or cleaning the bog twice a year. Come on spiders, do your job.

Henry T, Derby

I'D love to get my name in *The Guinness Book of Records* for that thing were they stack up dominoes and knock them over, but frankly it looks like a lot of work and to be honest, I simply can't be arsed.

Les Lloyd, email

ARCH Brexiteer Jacob Rees-Mogg said that our ability to display the emergency exit signs in the Dartford Tunnel in yards rather than metres is a real, although 'rather trivial' benefit of our leaving the EU. But I don't think it's rather trivial at all. Being able to write "Exit 100 yds" instead of "Exit 100m" and moving the sign a few feet one way or another is well worth all the turmoil of the last eight years.

Billy Gammon, Leeds

I WAS just looking at Google Earth, and I noticed that Red Square in Moscow isn't really square, but more a sort of rectangle. It's just another thing Putin and his cronies have been lying to us about for years.

Iain McKellan, Dundee

I'M no tennis fan but, after watching a bit of Wimbledon, surely it would be much easier for everyone if they removed the net. It just seems to get in the way most of the time.

Stu Mandry, Droitwich Spa

MY neighbour would always say "there are no flies on me." But by the time his relatives kicked his front door in after he carked it in his armchair last summer, I think he'd rather lost that argument.

Eldon Furse, email

WHEN going through my emails, I was intrigued by one with the subject line *'Sleep with a Milf in your area tonight'*. I was thrilled and looked forward to filling my boots with a sexy milf. So you can imagine my disappointment when I noticed that the email had actually arrived in my inbox the day before, and this golden opportunity had been lost forever.

Ray, Prestwich

USAIN Bolt says he dreamt of running the 100 metres in under 9.5 seconds. Well last night I dreamt that I ran it in under 8 seconds, so it looks like I win that one.

Ian Webb, Bury St Edmunds

I RECENTLY discovered that the English equivalent of the christian name Vladimir is Robert, so I've started referring to the Russian President as Bobby Putin. It makes him sound far less sinister and aggressive. In fact it makes him sound soft as shit really.

Vladimir Charlton, Manchester

WHY on earth do people get arse sweats? What possible benefits do sweat glands around the arse have? Come on Darwin, answer me that one.

Phil, Bedford

Drunken bakers

DOUBLE-BARRELLED TOP

Indoor League career change for Minister

MPS ARE USED are used to colleagues announcing their retirement in order to spend more time with their family or go to prison. But members from both sides of the House were left stunned this week after the member for Somerset North – Jacob Rees-Mogg – announced he is leaving the world of politics in order to pursue a career in PROFESSIONAL DARTS. And what's more, the Minister for Brexit Opportunities made the decision after receiving divine instruction from GOD!

Despite having absolutely no experience in the working class pub game, a bullish Rees-Mogg, 52, announced his decision outside his West Harptree home. "I had just returned home from the Commons and instead of selecting the BBC Parliament channel, Nanny inadvertently tuned into Sky Sports, who were showing the World Darts Championship at the time," he told Sky's Beth Rigby.

"I have eschewed public houses my entire life as I understand they are frightfully common, so this was literally the first time I have ever been exposed to darts," he said. "I found the game awfully exciting. The audience were evidently somewhat inebriated, and one of the protagonists, a Mr Edward "Ted" Hankey, began talking about whether he or the Devil was in charge."

"I was in no doubt that this was a sign from Our Lord Jesus Christ that this was

the direction he wanted my life to take," said Mr Rees-Mogg.

toff

The Eton-educated former leader of the house said it was not only the prospect of doing God's bidding and competing at the highest level that was attractive. He is also looking upon a late-blooming professional darts career as a chance to let his hair down.

"Ancient traditions of etiquette often render the Palace of Westminster quite a stuffy environment, but Hankey and his ilk are evidently able to call the dartboard a cunt with impunity," he said.

"Were I to use such inflamatory language in the chamber, calling the leader of the opposition a cunt, for example, it is likely that I would be sanctioned by the Speaker for the use of unparliamentary language, and I would be invited to

JOLLY OCHE STICKS: *Rees-Mogg (inset) to pursue darts career.*

withdraw my statement," he added.

Despite never having thrown a dart in his life, Rees-Mogg's upbringing has given him such self-confidence that he believes he will be crowned PDC World Champion within three years.

"I also intend to be the first former Leader of the House to record a televised nine dart finish, and perhaps the only one to defecate in the shoe of Dutch maestro Raymond Van Barnevald," he said.

Rees-Mogg has commissioned a team of Savile Row tailors to produce a flamboyant, loose-fitting, double-breasted darts top in Tory blue to wear on stage. And

the pantomine toff has been developing his own obligatory nickname of the sort all professional darts players adopt. High in the running are 'Jacob "The Power" Rees-Mogg,' 'The Somerset Tsunami' and 'Rex Telorum,' which is 'King of Darts' in Latin.

podex

And despite never having won so much as a goldfish at a funfair, the Brexit-bonkers streak of piss is unconcerned that his fellow competitors have reached the pinnacle of their careers after many years of dedicated practice at the oche.

"If my opponent wins, I shall simply assert that he most certainly did not in a really plummy voice and claim the victory for myself thusly," he said in a voice that made it sound a bit like he was yawning.

Rees-Mogg is expected to make his first appearance in a ranking event this weekend at the Sheffield Arena. And Professional Darts Corporation Chairman Eddie Hearn welcomed his decision to join the sport's pro ranks.

"The lad is pure box office," said Hearn. "Very little needed changing to prepare for his arrival, apart from ensuring an adequate supply of Pimms, having a solid gold oche installed on the floor and converting the numbers on the board to roman numerals."

SPOILT BASTARD

CHECKERS MATE!

Old Favourite Crowned King of the Christmas Gift Hit Parade

CHAIRMAN OF THE BOARD: *Toy shop owner Duckworth (left) and this year's must-have Christmas toy, draughts (inset above).*

PANICKED PARENTS punching, kicking and biting each other in shops while on the hunt for that latest must-have toy is a festive tradition as old as plastic toys themselves. Whether it's Cabbage Patch Dolls, Tracey Island or Cuddle-Me Evel Knievel, every year there's one plaything that gets normally rational people behaving like deranged animals. But you might be surprised to learn that the top toy filling stockings this year has been around for longer than Christmas itself - the humble game of *draughts!*

"Who's have thought that in these days of Playstations, Nintendos and Game Boys, a square of cardboard and 32 plastic discs would be my best seller?" says Derbyshire toy shop owner Donald Duckworth. "I've never known anything like it. Mind you, I haven't been in the toy game all that long."

Duckworth, owner of The Fun Hole, between Fags-U-Like and Barrels a-Weigh in Alfreton's bus-station precinct, says that the draughts sets are flying over his counter as quickly as he can lay hands on them.

"My wife Doreen got back from the wholesalers with a thousand sets last Monday because they were discontinued stock and they were going cheap," he told us. "I have to admit that I lost my temper and called her a stupid cow, asking what she thought we were going to do with a thousand draughts sets."

"I told her nobody wanted old fashioned board games these days, and that she had just thrown 500 quid down the drain," he said. "But I've ended up eating my words."

EXCLUSIVE!

According to Duckworth, word got round the town that The Fun Hole was selling draught sets for just £1.99, and people quickly started to come in and snap them up.

"I couldn't keep pace with the sales," he told us. "We had to have a queuing system in the shop. I was knocking them out faster than Doreen could carry them in from the van."

digestive

Such is the level of draughtsmania that has swept Alfreton, that Duckworth has been forced to limit the number of sets that any one customer can buy. "For the sake of fairness, I have limited it to twenty sets per person," he said.

Alfreton's very own 'Mr Toys', whose imaginative Christmas window displays have become a cherished traditional fixture on the town's festive calendar since

his shop opened in 2020, puts the popularity of his draughts sets down to economic factors.

"Nobody's got two ha'pennies to scratch their arse with this year," he told the *Alfreton Ocarina and Crumhorn*. "Parents certainly haven't got the money for expensive electronic toys, and even if they did, they couldn't afford the leccy to run the bloody things off."

convoy

But Duckworth expects that youth of today, raised on the dazzlingly sophisticated, fast-paced immersive computer games, will be charmed and delighted by the simplicity of the ancient board game. "The beauty of draughts is that no two games are the same," he said. "Using the 8 by 8 square board and pieces, it's possible to play literally hundreds of different games, if not thousands."

Duckworth also warned parents in the market for a draughts set not to make their purchase anywhere other than his own shop. "There

are a lot of cheap sets from China on the market which are extremely dangerous," he said.

"The plastic they are made from is poisonous and there's been reports that the boards are prone to spontaneous combustion," he said. "You don't want to make a leap in the dark with your child's safety."

"With my sets, you know that for £1.99, you're getting a quality product with safe plastic and a board that won't go up in flames unless you put a match to it."

And Duckworth advised parents to get to The Fun Hole quickly if they want to avoid tears and disappointment on Christmas morning. "I've got a few boxes left, but they are selling fast," he warned. "And for a limited time, I'm lifting the twenty box maximum purchase."

"Between now and Christmas Eve, customers can buy as many draughts sets as they like," he said. "And I'll do them for £1.50 a go if they take more than 50 off my hands."

DRAUGHTS THROUGHOUT HISTORY

3000BC Draughts is thought to have been invented in Mesopotamia sometime in the third century. Archaeologists have discovered an 8x8 square papyrus board, along with 32 small bone discs, half of them painted black, in the burial chamber of the tomb of King Messanepada. It is thought that the draught-mad monarch took the set to his grave so that he could play his favourite game in the afterlife. The tomb also contained the remains of 100 slaves who were killed so as he had somebody to play against in spirit world.

335AD The Romans brought draughts to Europe from their conquests in Asia, and the craze for the game quickly spread throughout the Empire. Simple wooden boards and counters have been discovered as far apart as Hadrian's Wall in the north and Hierasycaminus in the south. And when the Emperor Constantine the Great converted the Roman Empire to Christianity, the must-have toy at the very first Christmas in 335AD was a draughts set.

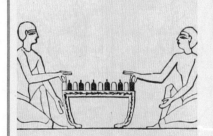

Allsorts of Fun!

IF YOU ARE hoping to buy your son or daughter a draughts set this Christmas, you might have to be patient, or lucky, or both. Because stocks of the traditional board game are extremely low and where they can be found, the queues of anxious parents waiting to snap them up are extremely long.

But don't worry, because a perfectly good draughts set can be made simply and cheaply by anyone, using using nothing more exotic than a box of Liquorice Allsorts. So if your little ones have put a draughts set at the top of their list to Santa Claus, and you can't find one for love nor money in the shops, *don't panic!* Here's how to make the perfect set to keep them enthralled. What's more, they can turn it back into a bag of delicious sweets once they're fed up with playing the – admittedly – rather dull game.

Instructions

Fig 1. Take an empty cornflakes packet and cut a square from the back or front.

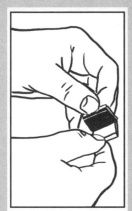

Fig 2. Take several of the black and white cubic Allsorts and peel apart the white fondant and black liquorice layers.

Fig 3. When you have 32 of each, arrange them into a chequerboard pattern on your cardboard square, fixing them down with thick glue made from icing sugar and water.

Fig 4. Take 12 each of the round, yellow and round, pink coconut Allsorts with a liquorice centre to use as your draughts.

Fig 5. When you become bored after two games, peel the chequerboard squares from the cardboard, and stick them back together using more icing sugar glue.

Fig 6. Pop them back in the Liquorice Allsorts bag with your 24 Allsorts draughts.

1037 It is known that the Vikings of Scandinavia relaxed after a day of violent raiding, pillaging and plundering by playing a game of draughts. When walrus ivory chessmen were discovered on the Isle of Lewis in 1831, a small draught counter, made of the same material, was found along with them. Archaeologists believe that the chess set's Viking owner must have lost one of his prawns and was using a draughts piece instead, showing that draughts was regularly being played amongst the warlike Nordic people.

1145 Up to the 11th century, draughts was a game to play at home. But in the 12th century, as European merchants and traders embarked on long journeys, sets of 'travel draughts' became popular, with small pegs in the counters and holes on the board to keep the pieces in place. One version, popular with rich travellers was played on a metal board with bone counters containing a small piece of magnetised iron. This 'Lodestone Draughts' allowed the game to be played on ships in the roughest of seas, and in carriages traversing the bumpiest of roads.

1601 Draughts was introduced to Britain more than 400 years ago, when buccaneer Sir Francis Dingwall brought an ebony and ivory set back from a holiday in Antwerp and presented it to the decapitation-mad monarch Elizabeth I. The Virgin Queen was enchanted with the game, and decreed that every English household should obtain a draughts set and play for two hours daily, on pain of death! Amazingly, we are all still required to play our daily two hours of draughts, as this law has never been officially repealed from the statute. But don't worry, it is not now enforced, and the last Briton to be executed under this law was hanged way back in 1954.

1969 Towards the end of the last century, man finally left the Earth and set foot on our nearest planetary neighbour, the Moon. Fearing that there wouldn't be much to do during their 21 hours on the lunar surface, astronaut Edwin 'Buzz' Aldrin asked NASA bosses if he could take a draughts set along to relieve boredom. However, it was feared that small plastic discs floating around the Eagle Lunar Module may cause problems, and a magnetic set could not be used as the magnetic fields the counters possessed would interfere with the craft's telemetric communication systems. The request was denied by the launch control team at Cape Canaveral, and Aldrin took a set of golf clubs instead.

The Pies of Living Crisis

THE BOTTOM INSPECTORS in... ON THE BUTTOCKS

YOUR STOOLS MAY RUN, BUT YOU CAN'T HIDE, BECAUSE THERE'S NO ESCAPE FROM...

NEXT WEEK - SOYLENT BROWN!

GIVE IT A REST!

WE HAVE often heard people say that it is better to give than to receive. In *Acts* chapter 20 verse 35 of The New Testament, the apostle Paul quotes Jesus as saying exactly that, and for over 2000 years it has been taken as gospel. But now a major scientific study at Bristol University has concluded that the Son of Man was *wrong*, and receiving is considerably better than giving.

The study looked at the relative happiness of 1340 participants who took part in the research. "The subjects were randomly divided into two groups, A and B," said Dr Marius Gormenghast of the university's Department of Psychology.

"Group A were given a Playstation 5, an iPhone14 and a £250 Amazon gift card, which they were then instructed to give to someone in group B for keeps," said Dr Gormenghast.

questionnaires

Both groups were then asked to fill out questionnaires about their current state of happiness. And according the researchers, the results were remarkable.

EXCLUSIVE!

"Those in group B – the ones who received the high-tech gizmos and cash – were on average 94% happier than those in group A," he said. "That is a significant difference, and it turns everything we previously thought we knew about the psychology of giving on its head."

The findings have particular significance at this time of year, when we traditionally assume that presenting loved ones with Christmas gifts will bring us more joy than it brings them. The study shows this theory to be woefully

Scientific study finds Bible verse WRONG!

inaccurate, and Gormanghast believes that we may now have to rethink the festive gift-giving process completely.

"What this study has conclusively shown is that if you have bought a present for somebody, you're not going to be as happy as that person is once you've given it to them," he said. "They are going to be happier than you are, and by some considerable margin, especially if it's a really expensive, high-tech item."

crisis

The report has caused unease in the retail sector as shop owners, already struggling under the cost of living crisis, fear that gift-buying may become a thing of the past if people realise the scientific truth.

GIVE IT A BREAK! *Receiving considerably better than giving.*

"This December was already shaping up to be the worst on record for shop owners," said Avis Catspaw, chair of the Consortium of British Retailers. "Now it's scientifically proven that gift-giving is substantially inferior to gift-receiving, I think this could spell the end for a lot of high street businesses."

And she made this plea to anyone thinking of cancelling their Christmas shopping plans in the light of the report. "Why not buy all your presents for everyone this Christmas as usual, and then keep them all yourself?"

149

Snowplougher

THAT WINTER the snow came hard. And it stayed for days. For the 683 souls aboard the 14:30 from Kings Cross to Edinburgh, this train was all that stood between them and the icy discomfort of the coldest snap since 2017. But all was not well, and disharmony was about to break out on the train they called **Snowplougher**... *10 carriages long.*

Blimey, this journey seems to have been going on forever.

Yeah. And having the heating broke doesn't help.

SCREEEEEEECH!

Eh!?!... What's going on? We're stopping.

BING! BONG!

Good afternoon, this is your train manager. Unfortunately there is a snow drift on the line ahead which is being cleared...

...I've been told we will be on our way in about twenty minutes.

BING! BONG!

Oh, dear!

Good afternoon, this is your catering manager speaking...

...I would like to remind First Class passengers that we will be providing a complimentary 'at seat' service of hot and cold meals from the James Martin Yorkshire Pride gourmet menu...

There you are, sir... Yorkshire cheddar ciabatta with balsamic fig relish.

Thank you.

...Standard Class passengers can purchase hot and cold drinks and crisps from the trolley.

I'll get us both a drink.

Excuse me... could we have two cups of tea and two bags of crisps, please?

Sorry, we've run out of crisps.

Oh! Just the tea, then, please.

No hot drinks, either... we might stock up when we get to Berwick... possibly.

What do you mean, no hot drinks? There's got to be.

The only hot drinks are in First Class, and they are reserved for the first class passengers.

Can I just buy one cup of tea for my wife?... she's pregnant.

No. Now if you'll excuse me I've got to get up train to help serve the James Martin meals.

Hey! That's not good enough.

Yeah! We need a cup of tea, too!

That's right... I'm going up to First Class to buy some tea and crisps...

... WHO'S WITH ME!?!

YEAH!

One train!

ONE TRAIN!

One train!

ONE TRAIN!

Miss Wardell... the tail end... they're revolting... they're marching up to First Class to buy cups of tea...

I tried to stop them, but...

Thank you, Kevin. I shall sort it out.

Mr Osweiller... would you disable the door to standard class, please?

Certainly, Miss Wardell. Is everything okay?

Ladies and gentlemen, some Standard Class passengers have broken out of their carriage and are on their way to First Class to buy tea…

What!?!

But we've bought First Class tickets… that's our tea.

Please remain calm, we have the situation under control…

BANG! BANG!

They're here, Miss Wardell.

Leave it to me, Mr Osweiller.

BANG!

BANG!

This is a First Class carriage. Would you all please return to your seats, or you will be charged an upgrade on your ticket.

What are we going to do? We might be stuck here for twenty minutes… and I'm spitting feathers.

Don't worry. I have an idea.

Get ready to rush in when I open the door.

What!?! You can't go out there… it's madness.

Well what's the alternative? To spend the rest of the journey as a second class citizen while a handful of passengers get complimentary James Martin snacks?

We are ALL passengers… ONE TRAIN… remember!

HNNNNG!

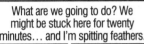

Don't worry, madam, that door is capable of holding back the rowdiest tail end ticket holder.

I'm very glad to hear it.

Another cinnamon swirl, or perhaps a James Martin chocolate fudge brownie?

CRASH!!!!

SCREAM!

Come on, everybody…

….keep seated lady… we don't want any trouble…

…we just want to buy some tea…

DOOR ISOLATION

…And it is OUR TEA to buy. For too long have some of you sat around with your extra leg room in well-upholstered seats enjoying complimentary James Martin cuisine while we are herded together with nothing to eat since Newark Northgate…

… but no longer! From now until Edinburgh Waverley, there will be only one class on this train…

ONE TRAIN!… ONE CLASS!

Mr Wilford… they've broken through…

…First Class is compromised.

Don't worry, Ruth… order will be restored…

I'm sending…

… Big Bob!

Oh, thank goodness.

And…

Right! let's start punching some fucking Second Class tickets…

Next week:
Big Bob restores order in First Class, but Andre and Pike take Mr Osweiller hostage and demand 100 individually wrapped James Martin lemon curd muffins be sent down-train to the tail.

151

It was the sitcom of the century, running to 10 seasons, 236 episodes, translated into 438 languages and aired in 1746 countries. It made household names of its six stars and had celebrities clamouring to appear in cameo roles. It's *FRIENDS*, and chances are you've watched every episode a hundred times over. You're familiar with what goes on on-screen, but what happens when the filming and the laughter tracks stop? How much do you actually know about Rachel, Monica, Phoebe, Joey, Chandler and Ross, played by the American actors Jennifer Aniston, Courteney Cox, Lisa Krudow, Matt LeBlanc, Matthew Perry and David Schwimmer? Wonder no longer as we give you...

21 THINGS YOU NEVER KNEW ABOUT F·R·I·E·N·D·S

1 THROUGHOUT its run, a dazzling selection of celebrities took the opportunity to play cameo roles in the top-rated sitcom, including *Magnum*'s Tom Selleck, balloon-crazed billionaire Richard Branson, drug-addled funnyman Charlie Sheen and 'toe-job' royal Sarah Ferguson.

2 DAVID SCHWIMMER and Jennifer Aniston have become synonymous with their *Friends* characters, but they were not the director's first choice to play the parts. The role of Ross Geller was intially offered to Clint Eastwood, but it was thought that the *Dirty Harry* actor was too old to make the character work. And the director's first choice to play Rachel Green was British mass murderer Rose West who was keen to play the part, but it was decided that serving a life sentence in Durham prison would be too problematic to the filming schedule.

3 IF YOU KNEW how many viewers tuned in for the 2021 *Friends* cast "reunion" hosted by big-boned Brit James Corden, dividing that number by 90,000 would give you the number of Wembley Stadiums full of people who watched the show.

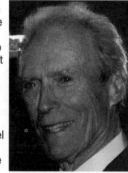

4 IF YOU TOOK all the numbers from 1 to 24, then cubed them and added them together ($1^3+2^3+3^3...+24^3$), the total would be 90,000 – exactly the number of people who would fit into Wembley Stadium!

5 RUNNING at 24 minutes each, it would take almost four days to watch all 236 episodes of *Friends* back to back. That's enough time to master four musical instruments using the method described in the successful *Play in a Day* series of books.

6 THE WORD "Friends" obeys the schoolboy spelling rule of "i before e except after c". However, the word "neighbours" - which describes Joey and Chandler's relationship with Monica, Rachel and Phoebe - does not.

7 OTHER COMMON words that flaunt this vowel arrangement directive include "eight," "sleigh," "beige" and "foreign."

8 *FRIENDS* is enjoyed all over the world, but the show is known by different names. The Dutch watch *Vrienden*, the Finns love *Ystävät*, whilst *Vinir* is one of the most popular shows on Icelandic TV. However, the Germans have two words for Friends, depending on whether they are masculine or feminine. Consequently, in Germany, the show is called *Freunde und Freundinnen*.

9 THE SCRIPT for each 24-minute episode contains an average of 3252 words. So the entire 236 episode run features around 767,472 words. As there are only 171,476 words in the English language, this means that each word is repeated around 4.475 times.

10 3.475 TIMES, actually, since the first time a word is used, it is not a repeat.

11 WHILST THE THREE female stars may get along fine on the show, in real life, they simply cannot agree on the best perfume. Lisa Krudow loves the scent of Bvlgari pour Femme, whilst Courteney Cox plumps for Jour de Fête by L'Artisan Parfumeur. But failing to find any perfumes she liked, Jennifer Aniston created her own signature scent, Beachscape, which has top notes of sea and sand, middle notes of wildflowers and fresh fruits, all brought together with woody, herbal base notes.

12 WHEN she's not wearing Beachscape, she likes to wear another of her signature scents, Near Dusk, with its top notes of coconut, pink pepper and nectarine, middle notes of jasmine, peony and orange blossom, complimenting the base notes of musk, vanilla and white amber.

13 AND WHEN she isn't wearing Beachscape or Near Dusk, she likes the top notes of smoketree and white pepper, middle notes of jasmine and gardenia, and the base notes of sandalwood, white musk and amber which are found in her third signature scent, Solstice Bloom.

14 ROSS and Monica's mother Judy was played by British actress Christina Pickles, who by strange coincidence is the sister of plain-speaking 1990s Yorkshire judge James Pickles. You couldn't make it up!

15 ALTHOUGH we haven't checked, it is highly likely that Television X has made a porn film called *Friends with Benefits*, loosely based on the show, featuring 3 women in wigs doing appalling American accents having sex with three blokes on a settee in the cameraman's house.

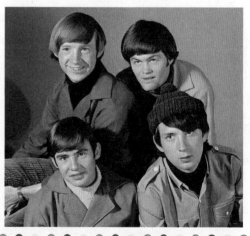

18 FOR THE FIRST series of *Friends*, the cast were paid the US national minimum wage of $8.21 per hour, meaning they each took home just $3.28 for every 24 minute episode. But as the popularity of the show increased, the cast were able to name their price, and by the tenth series, they were each banking around $4x10^8 after tax for every show.

19 SAFETY was always the number one priority when filming, and a fire drill would be carried out on set every Friday at 11:00am. Shooting would be halted as the entire cast, crew and live studio audience filed out the Warner Brothers' Burbank Studio and gathered at the fire assembly point in the car park. After 5 minutes the chief safety officer would allow everyone back in and filming would start up again. It is thought that these weekly fire drills account for the many continuity errors in the show.

20 IN EPISODE 2 of season 8, "The One with the Red Sweater," eagle-eyed viewers will have noticed that Joey has no lines whatsoever, and only appears on screen with his back to the camera. That's because on the day of filming, actor Matt LeBlanc woke up with terrible diarrhoea and had to call in sick. The tightness of the shooting schedule meant that filming had to go ahead without him. As LeBlanc sat at home squirting fizzy gravy out his arse, writers on set quickly changed the script and one of the studio runners, who was the same height and build as LeBlanc, stepped in to play his character.

21 MUCH of the show takes place in Central Perk, a trendy West Village coffee shop where the gang chat and jest over freshly brewed coffee. But the beverage they sip on set isn't actually coffee at all – it's tea with a little bit of bovril mixed in to darken it up, an old Hollywood trick to make it look like they are drinking a rich roast Americano.

16 MANY PEOPLE have commented how the *Friends* theme song *I'll Be There For You* by The Rembrandts, sounds very similar to The Monkees' version of *Pleasant Valley Sunday*. But music experts have dismissed suggestions that there was any copyright infringement involved. "When writing a piece of music, you only have 7 notes to choose from, A, B, C, D, E, F and G, so you are bound to get some songs sounding like others," said The Guildhall School of Music's Professor Ichabod Crumhorn.

17 CHRISTINA and James's uncle was veteran British actor Wilfred Pickles, who appearaed with actor Duggie Brown in the 1972 movie *For the Love of Ada*. What *Friends* viewers probably didn't realise was that Duggie's sister was *Coronation Street* battleaxe Lynne Perrie, who once licked a male stripper's Charlie on live telly.

A PLAGUE ON ALL YOUR HOUSES!

Accident sends Sheffield back to the dark ages

SHEFFIELD City Council was yesterday struggling to contain an outbreak of a medieval disease after workmen unwittingly unearthed a 12th century apothecary.

A long-reach excavator working on the A6178 relief road at Brinsworth broke open the site, discharging a cloud of gas into the atmosphere. Shortly afterwards, local residents complained of dizzyness, watering eyes and an imbalance of the humours.

Shefffield's Chief Medical Officer Dr Ken Sowerbury, who spent the day at the scene, explained the need for a careful and measured response to a range of symptoms not seen since the reign of Henry II. "I've selected a team of physicians, wise women and priests," he told the *Carbrook and Tinsley Speculum*.

"Thankfully, there was a carefully preserved copy of *Bald's Leechbook* in the rare books section of Grimesthorpe Library, and this has been invaluable in diagnosing and treating many of the maladies presented by local residents," Dr Sowerbury added.

Maureen Crumbs, manager of Tinsley Fire Surrounds, told how she became ill just minutes after the accident. "Ever since breathing the noxious humours, I've had a surfeit of black bile," she said. "The district nurse tasted my urine and purged me with an elixir of henbane and wormwood but it's troubled my spleen something awful."

"I'm still not right. I've been melancholic all afternoon and can no longer find my passion for fire surrounds."

loganberry

According to Dr Sowerbury, following the science is the only way to get through this medieval plague. He told the newspaper: "*Handel's Magikle Almanac* is very clear on the subject. We must stay indoors, close our windows and take a tincture of loganberry and quicksilver."

"Any lesions that form on the skin can be treated with a poultice of wild swine lard, celandine and red nettle. Simply boil these together until they be like gruel," he advised.

However, sticking to medical

PLAGUE AWAY: *Excavations mistakenly unearth medieval plague.*

advice has proved difficult as many residents found sourcing such obscure ingredients a challenge in the 21st century. Sheffield City Council updated its website to direct anxious residents to their nearest local apothecary, *Widow Brown's Most Excellent Chemikal Tretements* in Darnall.

Secretary of State for Health Sajid Javid says his department is continuing to monitor the situation. "Our advice is simple. Wash your hands for as long as it takes to sing the *Te Deum* twice, and make sure you cover your face with a fragrant nosegay in the shape of a bird's beak," he said.

He also advised that people maintained a safe distance from others of one perch (approximately 2.5 rods).

And the minister warned that anyone who developed symptoms, including developing buboes or agues, must self isolate. "Paint a red 'X' on your door and stay inside until all the symptoms have gone," he said.

"If your condition worsens, consult a barber surgeon who can apply leeches, trepan your skull or cup some blood."

"And of course, in an emergency, don't hesitate to go straight to Saint Sebastian's shrine at the Basilica Apostolorum in Rome and pray for atonement," Mr Javid added.

mr. LOGIC

HE'S AN ACUTE LOCALISED BODILY SMART IN THE RECTAL AREA.

...WELL, IT'S LOVELY OF YOU TO COME ROUND, LAWRENCE. HOW'S YOUR CUP OF TEA..?

≥SLOOP!≤

IT'S A MORE OR LESS ACCEPTABLE INFUSION OF *Camellia sinensis* WITH MILK AND TWO SUGARS... CURRENTLY AT A TEMPERATURE OF APPROXIMATELY 56° CELSIUS...

...329 KELVIN.

WELL THAT'S NICE.

IT IS THE BOILING POINT OF ACETONE.

ANYWAY, I MUST BE GOING. IT'S 'ONLY CONNECT' AND MY FAVOURITE TEAM THE DATA WIZARDS ARE ON.

OOH..! BEFORE YOU GO...

...WILL YOU POP ROUND AND MOW THE LAWN FOR ME SOME TIME?

...IT'S GETTING A BIT LONG.

OF COURSE.

LATER...

...Hmm... NOW TO COMMENCE ASSESSING THE OPTIMUM TOPOLOGICAL APPROACH FOR MOWING NAN'S LAWN IN THE MOST EFFICIENT MANNER...

...IT'S A COMPLEX GRAPH THEORY PROBLEM WHICH WILL ENTAIL A SUBSTANTIAL SERIES OF EXPERIMENTAL ITERATIONS TO SOLVE.

MONTHS LATER...

...I'VE GOT IT! AN OPTIMISED MINIMUM WASTAGE STRATAGEM!

NAN WILL BE SO EXCITED!

GILBERT RATCHET

SUNDAY MORNING

I'M OFF TO CHURCH, READERS!

STAY-AWAKE-O-MATIC EYELID CLAMP

CHURCH →

AND I'VE INVENTED THIS DEVICE TO HELP ME KEEP MY EYES OPEN DURING THE VICAR'S HOUR-LONG SERMON.

I'M AFRAID THERE WILL BE NO CHURCH SERVICE TODAY, GILBERT.

ST PREPUCE'S PARISH CHURCH

APART FROM YOU, NONE OF MY CONGREGATION HAS TURNED UP!

ALL THAT GOD AND JESUS STUFF IS OLD HAT, VICAR!

SCIENTIFIC INSTITUTE

MARVEL AT THE WONDERS OF SCIENCE

WE ALL GO TO THE NEW SCIENTIFIC INSTITUTE OVER THE ROAD ON A SUNDAY INSTEAD, NOWADAYS.

...YES, THANKS TO MODERN SCIENCE YOU CAN NOW REMOTELY SWITCH ON YOUR ELECTRIC TOOTHBRUSH USING AN APP ON YOUR MOBILE PHONE!

OOOOH! AAAHH!

MARVEL AT THE WONDERS OF SCIENCE

TCHOH!

NOT TO WORRY, VICAR!

WE JUST NEED TO MAKE THOSE OLD BIDDIES LOSE THEIR FAITH IN SCIENCE, AND THEY'LL COME FLOCKING BACK TO YOUR CHURCH!

I'VE CONSTRUCTED THIS RAMPAGING ROBOT WITH LASER BEAM EYES WHICH WILL DESTROY HUMAN CIVILISATION

ZAP!

BLEEP KILL!

THAT SHOULD TEACH YOUR PARISHIONERS THAT TECHNOLOGICAL PROGRESS DOES NOT NECESSARILY IMPROVE OUR LIVES!

RARGH!

HELP! THAT ROBOT WILL KILL US ALL!

ZAP!

IT WAS FOOLISH OF US TO PUT OUR TRUST IN SCIENCE!

THEN WHY NOT PUT YOUR TRUST IN RELIGION, INSTEAD?

ST PREPUCE'S PARISH CHURCH

IF YOU'D CARE TO STEP INTO MY CHURCH, I HAVE PREPARED A SERMON ON ST PAUL'S EPISTLE TO THE APPALACHIANS.

OH, ORGANISED RELIGION DOESN'T REALLY APPEAL TO US.

ST PREPUCE'S PARISH CHURCH

WE WOULD PREFER TO EMBARK UPON A PERSONAL VOYAGE OF SPIRITUAL SELF-DISCOVERY.

NO PROBLEM, LADIES!

"LIVE IN THE NOW TO BECOME YOUR ETERNAL SELF."

I'VE BUILT THIS FACEBOOK-MEME-O-MATIC WHICH WILL BRING YOU PROFOUNDLY INSPIRATIONAL THOUGHTS OF A SPIRITUAL NATURE.

"LET THE VIBRATION OF YOUR BEING BECOME AS ONE WITH THE ENERGIES OF THE COSMOS."

OH, THAT'S SO TRUE, ISN'T IT?

"LIVE, LAUGH LOVE."

HOW IS THAT HIPPY-DIPPY CLAPTRAP SUPPOSED TO HELP ME GET MORE PUNTERS INTO MY CHURCH, GILBERT?

DON'T WORRY VICAR — I'LL GRADUALLY START INTRODUCING REFERENCES TO GOD AND JESUS INTO THE INSPIRATIONAL QUOTES!

HUG A TREE

YOU ARE STARDUST

GO TO CHURCH

YOU'LL BE GETTING BUMS ON PEWS FOR YOUR SUNDAY SERMONS IN NO TIME!

WAKE UP! THE SECRET WORLD GOVERNMENT ARE USING 5G TECHNOLOGY TO CONTROL YOUR MINDS!

ILLUMINATI

DO THE RESEARCH

OH, THAT'S SO TRUE, ISN'T IT?

HUNH?

OH CRIKEY! THE ALGORITHM HAS MADE MY FACEBOOK-MEME-O-MATIC SHIFT FROM HIPPY SPIRITUALITY TO BATSHIT CONSPIRACY BOLLOCKS!

BILL GATES 666

VACCINES MAKE YOUR COCK DROP OFF!

IT'S THE JEWS, YOU KNOW!

MEANWHILE, UP IN THE SKY

GOD

IT'S A LOVELY DAY, SO I THOUGHT I'D POP DOWN TO EARTH AND SEE HOW MY CREATION IS GETTING ON.

WHAT'S THAT BIG CLOUD MOVING ACROSS THE SKY?

THAT'S NOT A CLOUD — IT'S A GIANT CHEMTRAIL MADE OF MIND-CONTROL GAS, CONCOCTED BY THE ROTHSCHILDS!

DESTROY THE CHEMTRAIL!

PELT IT WITH HEALING CRYSTALS TO NEUTRALISE ITS MALIGN ENERGIES!

GOD

OUCH! OOYAH! GERROF!

GURR! HOW DARE MANKIND THROW STONES AT ME?!

GOD

RUMBLE OF THUNDER

I CAN FEEL A BIT OF PROPER OLD TESTAMENT STYLE SMITING COMING ON!

TAKE THAT, YOU FUCKERS!

KAPOW!

HELP! GOD HAS GONE ALL WRATHFUL!

ST PREPUCE'S PARISH CHURCH

QUICK! INTO THE CHURCH TO PRAY FOR HIS MERCY!

NICE ONE GILBERT! MY CHURCH HAS GOT A FULL CONGREGATION NOW!

TREMBLE

PLEASE ACCEPT THIS PLATEFUL OF JAM AND CREAM COMMUNION WAFERS, AS A REWARD!

SLURPEROONIE!

HISTORY REPEATS ITSELF
New C4 show to recreate life of Tudor Queen

THE LAST few years have seen a new approach to the portrayal of history on TV. Long gone are programmes featuring stuffy academics bombarding us with facts and dates, droning on about which Pope excommunicated which king, or who fought in which battle against who. Now, so-called 'immersive history' shows such as *Living in the Past*, *The 1940s House* and *Back In Time* bring bygone times to life by getting people to live as our ancestors did, experiencing history through their eyes.

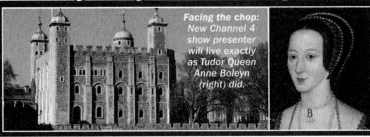

Facing the chop: New Channel 4 show presenter will live exactly as Tudor Queen Anne Boleyn (right) did.

And a new Channel 4 show will use this immersive technique to explore what life would have been like for Tudor Queen Anne Boleyn, as a modern-day subject spends 6 weeks wearing the same clothes, eating the same food and passing the time exactly as the second wife of Henry VIII did.

"This is the best way to fully understand what life would have been like for Anne in Tudor England," said the show's producer Crispin Bellsend.

"The history books can tell us what clothes Anne wore, but they can't tell us what she felt like after wearing them for a day. That's why this living history show is so important," he added. "It will bring the past to life."

And he was keen to point out that

EXCLUSIVE!

the presenter would not be putting her comfy clothes back on and heading back to her hotel for dinner in the restaurant after a day's filming.

tudor

"Anne would not have been whisked off to sleep on a memory foam mattress at the end of the day, so our 'Queen' will sleep on a reproduction of the exact bed that Anne slept on at Hampton Court," he said. "Only by her spending twenty-four hours a day living in the same conditions as the real Queen did can our viewers get an authentic feel for what life was like for Anne."

And as well as eating the same food and wearing the same clothes as Anne, in order to see what life for the

Queen in the 17th century was really like, the presenter will be forced to have sex with an obese man with ulcerated legs.

"We can only imagine what it must have been like for a young woman to go through this humiliating act with a sweating, cankerous, twenty-stone man ten years her senior," said Bellsend. "By actually doing it, our subject will experience the grotesque horror of Anne's situation at first hand."

The show is set to run to 6 episodes, with each one looking at a different aspect of the Queen's life. The final episode will see the show's presenter executed in the grounds of the Tower of London.

"Anne's failure to produce a male heir was the sole reason for her

being put to death," said Bellsend. "It is hard to imagine the terror she must have felt as she was led to the headsman's block."

"But when the French executioner's sword comes down on our modern day Anne's neck, she will really get a feel for what it must have been like for the real Anne on that fateful May morning in 1536."

Channel 4 have put out a call for applicants to take part in the project and will be holding auditions in the spring.

"Henry was not the only womanising monarch, and we're also thinking about doing a series on royal mistresses, so we're interested in hearing from women with big tits who own a basket of oranges," Bellend added.

LIGHTS OUT!

Blackpool Mayor proposes second carnival of light

THE POPULAR seaside town of Blackpool is planning to cut its energy consumption this year by having a grand *SWITCH OFF* of its iconic illuminations – *just a couple of hours after they've been switched on!*

The illuminations, a popular fixture along Blackpool's Golden Mile for almost 150 years, encapsulate the extravagant, colourful charm of the traditional British seaside holiday. However in recent years, money-saving measures have seen the illuminations' traditional filament lightbulbs replaced with more cost-effective LED equivalents.

Blackpool's ebullient Mayor, Athelstan Popkiss, believes that, although this measure has significantly cut the cost of keeping the promenade lit over the darker winter months, even more could be done to save money.

"The annual switch-on of Blackpool's illuminations is such a huge event, that I thought why not follow it a couple of hours later with a bigger, better switching-off celebration?" said Popkiss at a press conference in the Winter Gardens. "It would be a real boost for the local area to have two celebrations in one day."

suggest

The mayor went on to suggest that the switching-on of the lights could serve as a build-up to the more impressive switching-off ceremony.

"If we downgraded the level of the first star who came to switch the lights on, someone like Naughty Boy

EXCLUSIVE!

off of *I'm A Celebrity*, we could get some excitement going by promising somebody bigger, like Joe Swash, to switch them off again," he said. "I reckon we could probably get both of them for less than Peter Andre."

jeroboam

And the mayor had ideas about saving even more money on the spectacle. "We traditionally get the crowd to count down from ten before we light the seafront up," he said. "If we get them to count down from a hundred, that's ninety seconds of leccy we've saved."

"Then, as soon as the lights go on, we'll get them to start counting down from 7200 for the turn-off," he continued. "Can you imagine the excitement that would build up over the two hours until Joe Swash plunged the Golden Mile back into darkness? It would be wild."

But not everyone is convinced that the Mayor's proposals are as cost-effective as they could be. Local councillor Evelyn Knievelyn believes that even more money could be saved by simply moving the ceremony to 2am.

MOST ILLUMINATING: *Mayor Popkiss (right) plans to ramp up excitement in Blackpool with two light ceremonies in one evening.*

"There's no denying that lighting the Golden Mile for just 2 hours a year will bring Blackpool's electricity bill right down," Knievelyn explained. "But if we kicked off the celebrations when everyone was asleep, then there'd be no need to switch them on at all since everyone would have their eyes closed."

"Then, when everyone woke up in the morning, they would think we had

switched the lights on and off again while they were asleep," she continued. "We could probably dispense with the booking cost for the celebrities too, since they'd probably also be asleep. It's a win-win situation."

"The only thing we'd need to make sure of is that we whispered the countdowns, so as not to wake anyone up," Knievelyn added, as an afterthought.

THE STARS' ★ ★ £NERGY-SAVING TIPS

WITH energy prices through the roof, we're all looking for new and inventive ways to cut down on our energy usage. Turning off unused lights and switching the television off at the plug are well-known energy saving tips, but modern Britain has become so reliant on its electricity and gas supplies that it's not easy to cut back without making even larger lifestyle changes. We asked some A-list celebrities for their energy-saving tips.

Jeremy Clarkson

WHEN I FIRST got wind that the energy prices were going up, I decided to go entirely off-grid by connecting a couple of jump leads between the main fuse board of my Chipping Norton mansion and the battery of my Range Rover Autobiography V8. Now I just run the Rover's engine 24/7 and use the electricity from that. If I need to put a washload on, I just use longer jump leads and do donuts in the garden until after the spin cycle's finished. If the tank's running low on petrol I make the short trip to the local Shell garage in my other Range Rover, fill up a few petrol cans and then come home and top it up.

Ray Mears

LIVING OFF-GRID in my tent made out of animal skins and twigs you would think that I'd find it hard to save any money on heating or electricity. But it's a little-known fact that I actually possess the world's longest four-plug mains extension cable – 500 miles long! Whenever I do one of my survival shows, I always plug a few appliances into it so that I can have some home comforts with me in the wild, like a dishwasher, range cooker, 70" OLED television and one of those laser light show karaoke machines. If I did have to tighten my belt, I'd probably unplug the karaoke machine.

Katie Hopkins

I'M NOT GOING to cut back on my energy usage, because the rising cost of energy doesn't worry me in the least. If gas and energy prices go up, I'll simply write more poisonous, vitriolic columns in the press in order to pay the bills. And if things really did get expensive, I could always launch a subscription-only, hate-filled-bile-spewing blog, and that would tide me over until the current crisis comes to an end.

Noel Edmonds

I DON'T NEED to save any money during the energy crisis since my entire house is powered by my own positive mental energy. It is said that some people light up a room when they enter it, and I do - quite literally! In fact, my positive mental energy is so powerful that I have to add 'resistance' in the form of more layers of clothing to avoid blowing up smaller electrical items like smartphones and beard tidiers. For more power-hungry appliances like kettles and 3-bar heaters, I just remove all my clothes, which is handy as it gets pretty cold in the nip and I can sit by the fire and warm my bits by the element.

IT'S THE GREAT BRITISH BLOW-OFF!

Tell Putin to shove his gas up his arse and blow the top off the energy cap

I'M PUMPING MY WAY TO A BETTER BRITAIN!

BRITAIN is a nation in crisis. The ever-rising 'cap' on energy prices means that many thousands of Britons are facing a winter where they'll have to make the hard choice between food or heating. By reducing the amount of natural gas his country supplies to the West, Russian Premier Vladimir Putin has got Europe over an oil barrel, driving wholesale prices for the dwindling natural resource through the roof.

But it's not just gas that's been affected by greedy Vlad the Bad. The UK is also heavily dependent on natural gas to generate electricity for its homes and businesses, which has led to our Great British Electricity Supply being hit by the catastrophic price hikes, too.

But don't worry. Your ever-resourceful *Viz* is launching a campaign to help our great nation during this time of crisis, and let Putin know we don't need his stinking gas! We're asking our big-farted *Viz* readers to go off-grid and generate *their own natural gas* to help heat and power our country once again. And it's *so* easy! Just a few small changes to your diet will help make **BIG** savings on your monthly fuel bills. Just follow the simply instructions on the right.

To help speed the process along, fill in our handy termination of service letter below with your details and post it to your energy supplier and you'll be off-grid in no time!

1. Using the handy chart below, eat the recommended food for the amount of power required.

2. Pre-stretch a pack of party balloons. Save hard-to-inflate long, corkscrew ones for emergency use only.

3. Connect a balloon to one end of a length of garden hose and stick the other end up your arse

4. Carefully fill the balloon before tying the end. Store filled balloons away from naked flames.

5. Disconnect your gas supply at the meter and connect a full, fart-filled balloon to your household gas pipe.

6. For electrical appliances, fit a gas-powered electricity generator to your fuse board.

Energy output kWh		Dietary Input	Balloons
1 x 18w LED lightbulb for an hour / 1 x charging smartphone overnight	**0.018 KWh**	1 x 400g can of butterbeans in their brine	🎈
Boiling kettle: one cup of tea	**0.043 KWh**	1 x Family-sized jar of pickled onions (with vinegar)	🎈🎈🎈
Washing machine: full load 90 degree boil wash	**3.000 KWh**	Asparagus, sprout and artichoke gratin x 4 servings with three pints of homebrew IPA	🎈 x 166

Termination of service letter

To .... ,

Please cut my home electricity ☐ and gas ☐ supply off right away (*tick applicable*)

From .... (*insert date*), onwards, I will be entirely self-sufficient by powering my home using my family's own natural gas.

You are welcome to purchase any excess gas produced by me at the cost of £........................... per balloon.

Signed ....

(*The homeowner*)

DUAL GRUEL ENERGY

With The Naked Secretary of State for Business, Energy and Industrial Strategy, Jacob Rees-Mogg

Salvete servi!

Although my strict diet of swan foie gras and quinoa produces a refined, steady supply of flatulence, I occasionally slum it with simpler fare such as this cheap-as-*frixum capsicum annuum* gruel recipe.

Gruel is a proper tasty mouthful – a bit like porridge – and for not very much *pecunia*, it will get you chuffing your way to cheaper fuel bills!

Simply follow the recipe below and with a little practice you'll be knocking this cheeky morsel up in no time, not only giving yourself a warm gruel glow inside, but also producing enough bottom *flatus* to power your household for days on end.

Recipe

First grab yourself a handful of our old *amica*, Mr. Oatmeal, and chuck him in a saucepan from a height whilst doing that twiddly thing with your fingers so some of it falls on the floor and countertop. *Bishus, bashus, boshium!*

Next, turn on the tap and glug out a pint or so of lovely *aqua* into a measuring vas. Splosh a little bit into the pan, mixing with the oatmeal to make a paste. Then huzz the rest in and stir. *Felix diebus!*

Turn on the calor and boil the mixture for 10 minutes or so until cooked through. Add salt to taste and tuck in! *Pulchra jubbly!*

Turbo-charge your gruel at any point during cooking by adding mushy peas, cabbage, overripe bananas or figs.

Crypto Nige

Happy birthday, Dad.

Oh, and I popped a bit of something in the card for you...

Fulchester Cemetery

Fulchester Retirement Repository

What's this?

A screenshot of the transaction.

I've bought you fifty quid's worth of crypto!

Of what?

Cryptocurrency! Blimey Dad, I explained the *whole* thing last week. And the week before!

It's all I ever talk about!

So... Can I spend this in a shop?

Of course not!

You hold it - *and watch it soar!*

I'd rather have it in brass, if that's alright.

It's *better* than brass! You probably earned another fiver on it in the time it took to open the envelope!

It's yours for forty quid.

Dad, I'm trying to *help* you -

- crypto is the future! Sooner or later you'll *have* to get on board.

No I won't.

I can't be arsed.

Looks nice out... *Twenty.* Twenty pounds, cash.

Later

Alright John.

Hey, alright Nige. Long time no see.

How you keeping?

Great, you? How's your crypto portfolio doing?

I...

Haven't a clue what you're on about.

You are *kidding!* You *seriously* ain't heard of cryptocurrency?!

Nah, I've heard of it.

Sounds like a *right* load of dodgy old bollocks.

I don't really understand even what it is, let alone how it bloody works.

Arf!

It's a piece of piss!

Basically, investors like me and, er, that Elon Musk, buy in at one price...

Then the value goes up and up!

What's all that *blockchain* thing then?

Well, it's kind of like... Er...

Sort of a... *Look!* I've made a *ton* today, while doing nothing!

Oh. Oh fuck.

What?

I've lost everything. I mean *everything.* Savings, house, car, everyth- oh. *Oh!!*

What?

I've made it all back. And more!!

See? It's just - oh.

What?

I've lost it all again.

Yep, I'm ruined.

I'd best nip home and tell the missus.

THE BROON WINDSORS

ONE DAY... OCH! I'M SWEATING LIKE A PIG IN THIS DISGUISE... BUT LEAST IT MEANS AH KIN DAE MAH MESSAGES WI'OOT ONY FASH.

OCH! IT'S PRINCE ANDREW.

SAE IT IS... TH' DIRTY WEE RASCAL.

EH!?! HOWFUR DID THEY KEN 'TWAS ME?

A'M SURE AH HAE NA IDEA, YER RYLE HIGHNESS.

WEEL AH CAN'T GANG OAN LIKE THIS... AH HAE TAE KEN WHIT TH' FUTURE HOLDS...

AH KEN! I'LL GANG SEE THAT FORTUIN TELLER BY TH' VAPE SHOP...

...SHE'LL TELL ME WHIT LIES IN STORE FUR ME.

SHORTLY... MADAM MORAG CLAIRVOYANT

'ERE WE GANG... MADAME MORAG'S GOT THE GIFT... SHE WULL SEE ALL...

Crystal ball, tarot, palms, tea leaves, etc. 7th daughter of a 7th daughter. Money back if not correct.

...MA SWEARS BY HER RACING TIPS.

AWIGHT, MADAM MORAG.

YE RYLE HIGHNESS... AH KNEW THAT AH WID SEE YE TH'DAY.

AYE! WEEL, THAT'S COS AH PHONED YE FIVE MINUTES AGO AN' MADE AN APPOINTMENT, HEN.

AYE! BUT AH KNEW AFORE THAT... HONEST.

OCH, AH SEE YE'V HUD A TAIRIBLE TIME LATELY... YE'V BIN UNDER LOADS O' STRESS... AN' YE HAE SUFFERED LOSS...

LOOK, AH'M NAE GIVIN' YE FUFTY POONDS TAE PREDICT TH' PAST...

...AH'M WANTIN' TAE KEN WHIT TH' FUTURE HOLDS FUR ME... WULL AH EVER BE ACCEPTED BACK INTAE RYLE LIFE?

LET ME SEE...

THIS IS INTERESTIN'... AH SEE A CROON...

A CROON!?!

NO WAIT... TWO CROONS...

THAT MUST MEAN AH'M GOIN TAE BE KING!...

...COURSE, THAT MEANS MA, CHARLIE, WULLY AN' HIS FOWK WULL A' BE DEED... WHICH IS A PITY...

...BUT AH'M GOING TAE BE KING!...

...KING ANDREW THE FOREMAIST...

AN' THE SECOND CROON...

...THAT MUST MEAN WE'RE GOIN' TAE HAVE AN EMPIRE AGAIN... AN' AH'M GOIN' TAE BE TH' EMPEROR O' INDIA.

CRIVVENS!

AN' THERE'LL BE AN ENORMOUS AMOUNT O' DOSH SPENT... ALL OAN YE!

THAT'LL BE OAN MA TWO CORONATIONS...

HAY'LL BE TH' BEST CORONATIONS EVER... AN' AH'LL INVITE A' MAH PALS WHO ARE NAE IN THE SLAMMER.

WHIN'S THIS GOIN' TAE HAPPEN, MADAM MORAG?

VERY SOON INDEED!

OCH! WEEL AH'D BETTER GIT BACK HAME AN' PREPARE TAE RULE.

DON'T FORGET YER FALSE FLUFF AN' BUNNET, YER RYLE HIGHNESS.

AH WON'T NEED THAIM NOW... AH'M GOIN' TAE BE KING...

...EVERYBODY WULL LOVE ME AGAIN...

RAG CLAIRVOYANT Vape Shop

...AH'LL GIT A' MAH TITLES BACK AN' A' MAH AIRMIE COMMISSIONS AN' EVERYTHING...

OCH! URR YE PRINCE ANDREW?

AYE! BIT NAE FUR LONG, PAL... KING ANDREW, MAIR LIKE...

IS THAT SAE?

WEEL, TAK' THAT... YIR FUCKIN' MAJESTY!

SMACK!

WEEL, AH KIN SAVE MAIST O' THAIM, YER HIGHNESS...

...BUT YOU'LL NEED A COUPLE O' CROONS OAN TH' ONES AT TH' BACK.

OCH! JINGS!

AN' IT'S GAUN TAE COST A WEE FORTUIN.

MAH MA WULL PAY.

LeTTeRbOCKs

ers@viz.co.uk...letters@viz.co.uk...letters@viz.co.uk...letters@

ST★R LETTER

I WAS mugged recently in Paris. My attacker didn't speak a word of English and I can't speak French, so it was a little bit of an awkward encounter at first. However, it became quite funny as he started to do a series of little mimes and gestures in order to get me to understand. I was completely dumbfounded, and even he saw the funny side of the situation. Eventually I worked out that he was telling me to hand over my wallet and watch or else he would stab me. By the time I finally twigged, handed them over and he ran off, we were both crying with laughter!

A Namebury, Addressworth

BEES pollinate all the trees and flowers and make honey for us, and they get it all done during the hours of daylight. Butterflies, on the other hand, do nothing all day, and they even have moths to cover the night shift. It's easy to see who's taking the piss in this set-up.

Max Perlingo, Sphere

GHOSTS are effectively weightless and not subject to gravity, so they shouldn't need shoes or indeed bras. Has anyone seen a ghost with shoes or a bra? Because I most certainly haven't.

W Spanners, Orkney

IT just occurred to me that not only was Louis Armstrong's lyric "We have all the time in the world" a touch presumptuous, it was also manifestly wrong, as he discovered in 1971.

Tempus Fugit, email

THIS afternoon I met four middle-aged Swedish punks. Can any of your readers beat that?

John Moynes, Dublin

* It rather depends on what is deemed to beat it, Mr Moynes. Five middle-aged Swedish punks would be one case, as would four geriatric Swedish punks, as opposed to middle-aged ones. And due to the smaller population of the country compared with Sweden, four middle-aged Icelandic punks would trump your meeting.

IN the *Top Tips* column on page 143 , D Williams from Donegal offers advice to crooks, giving them the code 9406 as a possible lock combination and stating it as being a 1 in 9999 shot. Well, I'm no expert, but assuming one of the possible combinations is 0000, I would calculate that it is actually a 1 in 10000 shot, far reducing the probability of success. Come on D Williams. Do your bloody homework.

Donny Shifter, Chichester

WHATEVER happened to park keepers? In the 70s our constant insolence and abuse drove our local parkie to drink and possibly even an early death. But he was just one. Surely we didn't kill all of the peaked-capped minor figures of authority, did we? So come on, Councils. Employ more short-tempered, moustachioed little men with high blood pressure to keep the youths of the parish entertained.

Pard, Bridgwater

I HAVE recently discovered The History Channel on Freeview. Blimey, that Hitler was quite the cunt.

Kevin, Gresford

"THE best thing since sliced bread" they say, and yet the French still sell baguettes in one piece. I can only suppose this is another example of the contemptuous Gallic attitude towards good, honest, common sense sayings. They literally would cut off their nose to spite their face.

Ken Jenkins, Kings Langley

THE media takes things far too seriously these days, particularly with all the cataclysmic doom and gloom about the weather. If this were the 1980s, *The Sun* would have a photo of Samantha Fox or Linda Lusardi topless, sticking velcro sun cut-outs on to a weather map with a pun about the "Phwoarrr!-cast". I know the planet is burning to a crisp, but let's lighten up a bit.

Paul Egan, Roscommon

SINCE I've been reading your publication, television has gone flatscreen, 3D, 4K, curved, digital, surround sound and all the rest. Even radio has managed to go stereo and digital. All you've done is gone a bit colour, and that was back in about 1990. This lack of innovation is probably what's holding you back.

Reg Plate, North Utsire

I DON'T know how it is that James Bond shagged all those women in the films and never once caught a dose of clap. I reckon, for a bit more realism, they should make space in the plot of the next film for him to nip to the clap clinic, and the Doctor could say "Ah! Mr. Bond. I've been expecting you."

Ian Lancaster, Bedale

I'VE just watched a British gangster film where they were all using baseball bats to attack each other. Come on, UK film makers. Show some patriotism and arm the gangsters with British sports equipment, such as cricket bats or tennis racquets.

Oco Oxton, Neston

HAVE fellow readers noticed that the people who finish every comment with the phrase "do you know what I mean?" are also those who are the least likely to come up with some idea which is so complicated or life changing that I am going to fail to understand it.

J P Hames, Shipton-Under-Wychwood

WHEN I'm on holiday, I manage about three or four lengths of the pool before I'm knackered. I don't know how fish manage to swim all the time. Fair play to them.

Monkey Boy, Nintendo-on-Sea

DUE to the current water shortage, I have taken to adding six breeze blocks to my bath. This reduces my water usage and as an added bonus, I can rub the rough skin off my feet at the same time

Brick Top, Hereford

WHY don't toilet manufacturers make toilets wider so as there is less chance of me pissing on the floor? It's not rocket science.

Carlton Fin, Leatherhead

TOP

LADIES. Fool people into thinking you haven't been sunbathing topless in the garden by dipping each tit in white paint.

Michael Thompson, Wales

LADIES. When starting a new relationship, avoid talking about how 'well hung' your last boyfriend was.

Jimmy Tiddler, Sunderland

TRAVELLERS. Relieve airport tedium by narrating everything you observe in the style of Alan Bennett.

Palmer Vjorhend, Portstewart

FERRERO Rochers, scattered across an unlit footpath, make an ideal alternative to snails for unsuspecting pedestrians during the drier summer nights.

Eldon Furse, email

DON'T embarrass yourself by loudly breaking wind when out with your new girlfriend. Simply slip one hand discreetly down the back of your trousers and press together your arse cheeks to muffle even the loudest fart. This method also allows you to catch any shrapnel should you follow through.

Paul LB, Cheltenham

PICK petals from flowers with an odd number of petals, such as *Cinquefoil*, *Pentstamon* or *Hibiscus*, so as to always land on "she loves me" rather than "she loves me not".

Mister Japes, London

ROBOTS. Learning how to identify a set of traffic lights will significantly increase your chance of securing concert tickets

Kevin Caswell-Jones, Gresford

TIPS

toptips@vi...

DO any of your readers know whether it's acceptable to use Viagra for the purposes of self pollution? I'm asking for a friend, not me.

Anonymous, Bunny

* *It is perfectly acceptable, Mr Anonymous. Tell your friend that it is 2025, and if he wants to swallow a couple of Bongo Bill's banjo pills before cracking one off, then more power to your, sorry, his elbow.*

I THINK various sports could learn from one another. For example, athletics could have a running version of that bike race where they go as slow as they can. In return, cycling could do a bike pole vault.

The Owl, Northfields

"EVERYTHING has led to this" was the slogan for the 2022 Open Championship at St Andrews, but I'm not sure that's strictly true. For example, I once got so drunk that I wet the bed. Had that never happened, I'm pretty sure this year's golf tournament would have still taken place.

Nathan Virica, Wigan

IN Spain, 'gato' is a cat, but in France it's a cake. You couldn't make it up. Thank God we voted for Brexit.

Hadrian Wall, email

MY wife described someone on TV as being "as rough as a bear's arse". I suggested the correct phrase was "as rough as a badger's arse". I was going to ask Chris Packham which it was, as he is always going on about badgers on *Springwatch*, but I haven't got his address. I wonder if any of your readers know anything about animals' arses and could help?

Reginald Merton, Warwick

FOLLOWING the recent *Viz* article about Blakey from *On the Buses*, I just re-watched the first *On the Buses* film, and I hadn't realised what a tyrannical monster Blakey was. I mean, the man spends almost the entire film trying to get the buses to run on time and defending the female staff from sexual harassment. Pure evil.

John Parkes, Leeds

AFTER a sparrow flew into my window yesterday, I'm glad nature gave up on its idea of evolving birds from fish. Imagine if that had been a whale or something.

Peter Wheelbarrow, Barrow on Furness

OUR water board has asked people to use water sparingly in these times of drought, and to use a watering can instead of a hosepipe. But when houses were on fire up and down the country recently, I couldn't help noticing that fire fighters were using hoses, and fucking big ones at that. They should have been setting an example and using watering cans too. It's 'Partygate' all over again.

Mrs B, London

TWENTY years ago, at the tender age of 15, I emailed you asking to do work experience in your office. I received a polite reply which explained that it would actually be very boring. I then spent two weeks pressing 'y' on a keyboard to partition hard drives. Thanks a bunch, wankers.

Steven Halstead, Essex

ITS 35°C and I've just filled my huge, two-foot deep garden pool with water. I've got a box of supermarket brand toffee fudge cones in the freezer and a 10-pack of a well known Spanish lager in the fridge. It's just like being all-inclusive in Benidorm. Global warming? Bring it on. I never liked polar bears anyway, the big, hairy wankers.

Stuart Achilles, Wigan

WHILE sitting sweating cobs in the 40 degree summer heat this afternoon, I couldn't help feeling thankful about how much worse it would have been if it was the middle of winter when I would have been wearing my socks, jeans and a great big, thick jumper.

Jane Hoole Garner, St Ives

BEING an avid follower of *Time Team*, it strikes me that, judging by the amount of coins they lost, the Romans should have spent their time making better pockets for their togas rather than building villas or making fancy Dan mosaics.

Grangezilla, Cardiff

IF I was an Elvis impersonator, my act would be to eat a load of hamburgers, fall off a toilet and then lie very still. It certainly would be a new twist on the usual poorly-sung versions of songs people know half the words of by men in badly-altered white boilersuits and wigs.

Pal r Vjorhend, Portstewart

I THINK someone could be deemed to be 'posh' if they sound the second 'h' in the words Shithouse and Arsehole. Listen out the next time the King speaks and see if you agree.

WP Treegirth, Grimsby

THESE beekeepers are hypocrites. They're always banging on about how we must save the bees because they're so important, and then they go

and open up a hive, create a smoke screen and steal all their food. It's an odd way of caring if you ask me.

Irene Fisticuffs, Spitoon

I HAVE recently become aware that the Norwegian for speed-bump is 'Farts Humper'. I cannot tell you how impressed I am with this news.

A Royffe, London

THAT swinging one arm walk that Vladimir Putin does is a Scouse thing. Our kid was a bouncer for years and he reckons they all do it cos they're sneaking their own vodka into the boozer.

Les Lloyd, email

ELEPHANT CORNER

JOHN Moynes' letter *(page 142)* about "no new elephant species being discovered" just reveals his ignorance. In 2010, African forest elephants were found to have split from Savannah elephants 2 million years ago, so there are three extant elephant species. This just reflects the tragic lack of speciation-based characters in this magazine. When was the last story about a snail unable to get laid because his shell curls the wrong way, or lesbian parthenogenetic stick insects? Do better, *Viz*.

Toomai Tom, email

I DUNNO how elephants can take themselves seriously with them big cock-things swinging about their faces. Idiots.

T Waterman, Palm Springs

SOME bloke on TV said it would take 9,618,000 fully grown African elephants standing trunk to tail to encompass the earth at the equator. But according to Wikipedia, there are only about 700,000 elephants left in the wild, so I'm afraid it's just never going to happen.

D Williams, Donegal

LUCKY FRANK

HELL "LIKE A HOLIDAY CAMP" ~LITTLEJOHN

Damned souls living "Life of Riley" in abyss, says Mail twat

MAGGOT-COCKED *Daily Mail* journalist **RICHARD LITTLEJOHN** has used his latest newspaper column to launch a furious attack on the cushy conditions in the infernal realm of Hell.

Littlejohn, 70, slammed the diabolical afterlife for 'going soft' following a brief visit to the underworld during a near-death experience whilst choking on a pork scratching.

"After a few minutes of sputtering and gasping for air, I saw a bright light, and then wallop! I was standing in front of a flaming gate with the words 'Abandon hope all ye who enter here' emblazoned above it," the thimble-choppered arsehole wrote.

"I knew instantly that I'd arrived at the bottomless pit of eternal despair," he added.

Initially fearful of setting foot in the sulphurous netherworld of unending agony, Littlejohn's concern soon turned to fury.

"I was expecting to see wretched souls being grotesquely tortured by twisted hordes of Beelzebub's despicable legions," the bookie's-pencil-dicked journo fumed. "What I actually saw was closer to a weekend break in ruddy Center Parcs."

According to Littlejohn, instead of getting ceaselessly jabbed with pitchforks and having the skin flayed from their bodies, the damned hordes were all enjoying free 24-hour Wi-Fi internet, or lounging about watching Sky Sports on 60-inch flatscreen TVs.

"Underworld? More like FUN-derworld," the cock-end quipped.

The Tic-Tac-knobbed hack went on to point the finger at a litany of famous deceased figures who he says are living the life of Riley in Hades.

"I spotted Genghis Khan playing Candy Crush on a brand new iPad, and Vlad the Impaler eating a Nando's in front of Netflix, if you please," he ranted.

"I thought Hell was supposed to be an execrable chasm of infinite torment – not a ruddy five star hotel," the half-a-matchstick-genitaled twat seethed.

"These accursed sinners have been condemned to the lake of unquenchable fire for a reason. They should not be living the high life in the lap of luxury with Joe Muggins here settling the tab," he fumed.

Littlejohn revealed that he was working his way down through the bowels of Hell to the ninth circle, in order to have 'strong words' with Lucifer when he finally coughed up the offending pub snack and regained consciousness.

"I came to in my office, a bit dazed and covered in sick," he said. "But I was so outraged by what I'd seen that I sat straight down at my desk and starting writing my bile-filled article."

And Littlejohn's splenetic dispatches are causing shockwaves in Westminster. In the House of Commons, newly-elected-by-0.14%-of-the-population Prime Minister **LIZ TRUSS** vowed to end the "plush and cosy" conditions in the realm of pain.

"What Mr Littlejohn reported seeing

EASY AFTERLIFE! *Littlejohn (right) found visit to the eternal furnaces of Hell 'a doddle'.*

during his brief visit to Hell is deeply troubling," said the foreign cheese-hating PM.

"This government strongly believes that Hell should *mean* Hell – and that's why we are implementing new regulations to restrict damned souls' access to online shopping, video games, expensive streaming services and fast food," the British apples and pears lover added.

At time of press, Littlejohn has filed a new op-ed in the *Daily Mail*, accusing Minos – the serpentine judge of the damned – of being an "Enemy of the People."

DOCTOR WHOLITTLE

HE TRAVELS THROUGH TIME TO TALK WITH THE ANIMALS.

IT SAYS HERE IN THE TIMES THAT SCIENTISTS NOW BELIEVE A VIRUS KILLED THE DINOSAURS, AND NOT A METEORITE.

IS THAT SO?

WHAT DO YOU THINK, TOWSER?

OH, I DON'T KNOW, DOCTOR... I'M JUST A DOG.

QUIET, TOWSER. STOP BARKING.

I IMAGINE WE'LL NEVER KNOW FOR CERTAIN WHAT HAPPENED, WHOLITTLE.

NOT AT ALL, OLD BOY. I'LL GO BACK IN TIME AND ASK THEM WHAT WIPED THEM OUT.

GO BACK IN TIME AND SPEAK WITH DINOSAURS?

HA! I'VE NEVER HEARD ANYTHING SO PREPOSTEROUS.

COME, LEELA.

CERTAINLY, DOCTOR.

SET THE CO-ORDINATES FOR DINOSAUR TIMES.

YES, DOCTOR.

ZSHHOWWW!! ZSHHOWWW!! ZSHHHOWWW!! ZSHHHOWWW!!

SHORTLY... AH, THERE'S ONE, LOOK!

I'LL HAVE A WORD WITH HIM.

I SAY, OLD BOY... I HAVE A VERY IMPORTANT QUESTION TO ASK YOU.

OH, ERM... OKAY.

DOCTOR...

TAP! TAP!

...IS THIS A GOOD IDEA? THEY PROBABLY DON'T KNOW THEY'RE GOING TO GO EXTINCT...

...IT MIGHT PANIC THEM A BIT.

HMM! PERHAPS YOU'RE RIGHT, LEELA.

COME ON... LET'S GO HOME.

WHAT IS IT?

WHAT?! OH, NOTHING. IT DOESN'T MATTER.

YOU SAID IT WAS VERY IMPORTANT.

WHAT!?! DID I...? NO, IT'S NOT.

FORGET IT.

FUCKING IDIOTS.

EK-TER-MIN-ATE DI-NO-SAURS! EK-TER-MIN-ATE DI-NO-SAURS!

EH!?! WHAT'S THAT?

EK-TER-MIN-ATE DI-NO-SAURS!

SO THAT'S HOW THEY WENT EXTINCT!

THEY WERE EXTERMINATED BY DALEKS!

I KNOW—I'LL USE MY SONIC SCREWDRIVER TO REMOVE DAVROS'S CASTORS. THEN THEY'LL HAVE TO GO BACK HOME TO SKARO... AND THE DINOSAURS WILL BE SAVED.

NO, DOCTOR... YOU CAN'T!

WHY?

IF YOU DO THAT, THEN THE ENTIRE HISTORY OF EARTH WILL BE CHANGED... WHEN WE GO BACK HOME, WHO KNOWS WHAT WE MAY FIND?

WE MAY NEVER HAVE EVOLVED AT ALL!

YES, YOU'RE RIGHT. COME ON, LET'S GO.

WATCH OUT FOR THAT BUTTERFLY, DOCT—

CRUNCH!

AAAARGH!! Y'BASTARD!!!

WATCH WHERE YOU'RE FUCKING TREADING!

SORRY, PAL. I DIDN'T SEE YOU.

SHORTLY...

ZSHHHOWWW!! ZSHHHOWWW!!

WELL, OLD BOY, I'VE DISCOVERED HOW THE DINOSAURS DIED OUT... ...AND THOSE SCIENTISTS HAVE IT ALL WRONG.

WHO THE BLOODY HELL LET THOSE TWO THINGS IN HERE!?! GET THEM OUT, PERKINS!

VERY GOOD, SIR.

LM

168

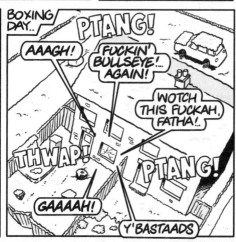

ALL CHANGE FOR NHS

Cuts set to take health service back to the 70s

FOLLOWING the leak of a government report suggesting that health service funding should be cut back to 1970s levels, bosses have reassured the public that a fully functioning NHS can still be provided on reduced finances. Not only that, experts say that the levels of treatment patients will receive under the proposed slashed funding regime will actually be *better* than they are presently experiencing.

"Anyone who lived through the seventies will remember it as the golden age of the NHS," said Secretary of State for Health at time of going to press Steve Barclay.

"Waiting lists for treatments were unheard of, everyone got to see a doctor when they needed to, and referral rates were measured in days, not months," he said.

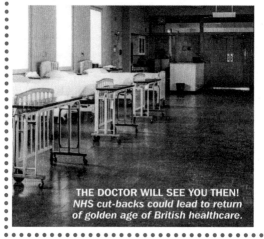

THE DOCTOR WILL SEE YOU THEN!
NHS cut-backs could lead to return of golden age of British healthcare.

EXCLU-NHS-IVE

"I'm convinced that if we could do that fifty years ago, we can do it again today on the same money."

But when pressed by reporters, Barclay admitted that running the service on 1970s levels of funding may mean that only treatments for certain conditions would be available.

"Back then, our wonderful NHS only treated people who had saucepans stuck on their heads, window cleaners who had fallen off ladders and done their back after seeing a woman with big tits having a bubble bath, or people who had something wrong with them that needed a little frame to keep the bedclothes off their unmentionables," he said. "So if the NHS is going to function on seventies money, our marvellous doctors and nurses will only be able to treat patients presenting with those sorts of traditional ailments."

Barclay was keen to reassure the public that medical practices from the 1970s would have much to offer patients in 2023.

"Much as modern advancements in medicine such as MRI scanners and monoclonal antibodies seem impressive, there's a lot to be said for old-fashioned techniques such as sticking a thermometer in the side of people's mouths, getting a bedbath off a sexy nurse in stockings or hitting people on the knee with a little hammer," he said.

The report also gives details of how hospitals will look under the proposed 70s funding, including:

★ *All ward televisions to be removed and replaced by vases of wilting flowers and bottles of Lucozade wrapped in orange cellophane.*

★ *Banks of chairs outside maternity ward delivery rooms for expectant, chain-smoking fathers to sit on between bouts of pacing up and down.*

★ *Ceiling-mounted pulley systems above beds allowing broken limbs to be jerked up and down by comical, bumbling orderlies.*

★ *Doctors clinging to out-of-control trolleys going down the stairs and through windows.*

It is believed that the government has already awarded a £2million contract to a company to supply PPE equipment to nurses in every local health authority, including half a million little lace hats and short blue aprons, along with 1 million suspender belts and 2 million pairs of black stockings.

"It's going to be absolutely fantastic," said the director of Nottingham's Queen's Medical Centre, Dr Gladstone Screwer.

"Hyah! Hyah! Hyah! Hyaaaaah!" Dr Screwer added, whilst pushing his porkpie hat slightly forwards on his head.

WOOOOO! REED

"Velvet Underground Lou is haunting my shed"

MOST OF US think nothing of going to our garden shed, whether it's to get the lawn mower, to store some tins of paint, or sit and read a few magazines away from the wife. But for Tipton man Jeremy Binlid, every visit is a 'walk on the wild side' because his 6 by 8 foot wooden outbuilding is haunted... *by the ghost of Lou Reed.*

The legendary Velvet Underground frontman's phantom took up residence in Binlid's shed last summer, and is now a regular spectral presence amongst the gardening tools.

But the 45-year-old bus driver says he has no intention of trying to evict the late proto-punk rock artist from his shed. "Live and let live is what I say," he told *The Tipton Globe and Artichoke*. "Even if they're dead."

It was Mr Binlid's 8-year old daughter Molly who first became aware of the strange presence in the garden shed.

"She was playing on her swing last summer when she heard someone singing the 'bong-bong-bong' bit from *Satellite of Love*," he told the paper. "She tracked it down to the shed where she came face to face with the ghost of Lou Reed."

The eight-year-old was terrified and ran into the house screaming. Her parents were in the front room watching TV, but immediately jumped up to see what was wrong.

"We thought she had fallen off her swing or got stang off a wasp," said Binlid. "But it quickly became apparent that something had rattled her, as she was sobbing about some weird-looking, pale bloke in the shed singing boring songs."

burglar

"There had been a lot of shed break-ins in the area around that time, and I thought she may have disturbed a burglar," said Binlid. "So I took a rolling pin from the kitchen and went to investigate."

But when he peeked into the shed, Binlid saw the *Sweet Jane* spectre sitting in the corner by his Flymo. "I immediately recognised him," he told reporters. "And I knew he was a ghost because he was transparent, and I could see the lawn rake hanging up on the shed wall behind him."

Binlid admitted to being a little bit scared on seeing the *Perfect Day* spook, but he soon realised that he meant him and his family no harm.

"I told him I was a big fan of his stuff, particularly *Transformer*," he said. "But to be honest, he was a bit surly. He just mumbled something and faded away into the ethereal realm."

But according to Binlid, the grizzled ghost came back, and now spends most of its time in his shed, playing two-hour versions of *Waiting For the Man*, or letting fly with expletive-ridden tirades against rock critics who only gave *Berlin* four stars.

And for the past ten months, the Binlids and the ghost of Lou Reed have found themselves co-existing in peace.

"He's a bit noisy at times, particularly when he starts playing *Metal Machine Music*, but he doesn't do anyone any harm," said Binlid's wife Kelly. "And

WIGHT FRIGHT/WHITE (AS A) SHEET: *Binlid's daughter discovered deceased Velvet Underground frontman, Reed (inset) in family shed.*

having the wraith of a proto-punk artist in the shed is great for security."

"We're just going to leave him in peace until he's ready to move on to the other side."

And Mr Binlid was quite philosophical about the situation. "If your shed is going to be haunted by a classic rock star, then Lou Reed isn't a bad one to have," he told reporters. "The people at Number 15 have got the poltergeist of Keith Moon in their greenhouse, and he's broken every pane of glass."

"Not only that, he's driven his phantom Rolls Royce into their pond three times this last week. I think they're going to have to get the priest in to exorcise him," he added.

FIO
WHO

THERE ISN'T a single human being alive on this planet who wouldn't lay down their life in a fight over which celebrity with the surname Bruce is the greatest. Some might think it's foul-mouthed US comic **LENNY BRUCE**, others may favour bass-twanging Cream rocker **JACK BRUCE**, while others still might prefer once-capped England B-Team footballer **STEVE BRUCE**. But let's not kid ourselves – these are mere fringe Bruces. Everyone agrees that the Big Three when it comes to global Bruce-centric brilliance are BBC national treasure **FIONA BRUCE**, ex-BBC national treasure **KEN BRUCE** and 13th Century Scottish national treasure **ROBERT THE BRUCE**. So, join us now and prepare to take sides in a Bruce-based battle to the death, as we figure out, once and for all…

•••••••••••••• FIONA ••••••••••••••

ROUND 1

SCOTTISHNESS Born to an English mother and a Scottish father, *Fake or Fortune?* fave Fiona seems destined to garner just half-marks in this opening round. But the Beeb bombshell's Wikipedia page reveals the news fave's apparent lack of regard for her Caledonian heritage. Born in Singapore, raised in England and educated in Paris, plummy-voiced Fiona's sole connection to the Highlands appears to be a brief 1980s modelling stint for *Jackie* magazine, which is published by the Dundee-based comics firm, DC Thomson.

Score 1

ROUND 2

AVUNCULARITY As the host of *Question Time*, Fiona is contractually obliged to remain anything *but* avuncular. Selecting incendiary audience questions whilst controlling a fiery panel of politicians and D-List actors, it's Fiona's job to be tough, combative, steely and aggressive. But she is also the host of the BBC's flagship heirloom financial assessment show *Antiques Roadshow*, during which she must patiently endure the inane witterings of the Great Unwashed as they queue up with their dusty bric-a-brac. Thanks to the cheery grin she manages to keep on her face despite her proximity to the proletariat, Bruce is awarded a few consolation avuncularity points.

Score 4

ROUND 3

REPLACING PEOPLE CALLED DAVID Feisty Fiona sent shockwaves through the world of televised current affairs back in January 2019 when news broke that she would be replacing veteran presenter David Dimbleby as the host of *Question Time*. Since Dimbleby is – as his name suggests – called David, it's a stunningly strong showing from the baton-from-someone-called-David-accepting journalist.

Score 8

ROUND 4

APPEARANCES ON 'READY STEADY COOK' A cursory Google of 'Fiona Bruce' and 'Ready Steady Cook' reveals a whopping **TWO** appearances by the Malaysia-born broadcaster on the now-defunct culinary game show. In both 2002 and 2008, the *Crimewatch* fave popped up on the programme alongside the likes of fellow newsreader Dermot Murnaghan, meaning she picks up two precious points in this heated gastronomic round.

Score 2

ROUND 5

'REAR OF THE YEAR' AWARDS Following a series of appreciative remarks about her backside from petrol-headed producer-thumper Jeremy Clarkson, Beeb fave Fiona was rewarded with the coveted 'Rear of the Year' statue in 2010. While this may suggest that the svelte broadcaster deserves at least one point in this round, she in fact gets a grand total of **ZERO**. That's because snowflake feminist Fiona actually **REJECTED** the light-hearted gong the following year, branding it "demeaning." This "woke", hatchet-faced reaction to what is essentially a bit of cheeky, harmless fun leaves ungrateful Fiona with **BOTTOM** marks in this rump-related round.

Score 0

ROUND 6

NUMBER OF PEOPLE KILLED IN BATTLE Oh dear. Former *Newsnight* fave Fiona limped through the early stages of this Bruce-based bout, but the wheels have well and truly come off in the final furlong. Because the ex-*Panorama* ace has *never killed another human being*, in battle or otherwise. Not even during filming the Basic, Better, Best bit of *Antiques Roadshow*. With no blood whatsoever on her expertly manicured hands, it's a disastrous last round for the non-life-taking Beeb siren.

Score 0

HOW DID THEY DO?

FIONA *Fi-Oh-No!* It's a piss-poor *Antiques Road-showing* for beloved Beeb icon Fiona as she crashes into last place. She may be the first female presenter of *Question Time*, but she's only the third-best celebrity whose last name is Bruce.

15

••••••••••••••

SCOTTISHNESS From the rich, whisky-like timbre of his voice to the fact that he once recorded a novelty cover version of *Donald Where's Yer Troosers*, they simply don't come any more Caledonian than Kenneth Robertson Bruce. Born in Glasgow, raised in Glasgow and educated in Glasgow, Radio 2

AVUNCULARITY Look up the word 'avuncular' in the Oxford English Dictionary, and you'll find the sentence: 'Suggestive of an uncle, especially in kindness or geniality' – a statement that describes the cheery, chummy Scotsman to a tee. Famed as The Most Avuncular Man In Britain™, the warm-hearted DJ is the nation's favourite uncle, always on hand for

REPLACING PEOPLE CALLED DAVID Radio 2 titan Ken got his big break back in the early 80s, when he replaced a former BBC Radio Scotland announcer who had recently popped his clogs. That

APPEARANCES ON 'READY STEADY COOK' A cursory Google of 'Ken Bruce' and 'Ready Steady Cook' reveals a whopping **ONE** appearance by the Glasgow-born broadcaster on the now-defunct culinary game show. In 2008, the Radio 2 mid-morning fave popped up on the

'REAR OF THE YEAR' AWARDS Founded in 1976 by bum-bonkers publicity consultant Anthony Edwards, the much-loved Rear of the Year Award has been presented to such celebrities with notable posteriors as Barbara Windsor, Su Pollard and Olly Murs. At time of going to press, *Popmaster* icon Ken Bruce has never

NUMBER OF PEOPLE KILLED IN BATTLE Just like his shapely namesake Fiona, different-shapely *Popmaster* maestro Ken may have stumbled at the final hurdle, there being absolutely no evidence whatsoever to indicate that the genial *Popmaster* fave has ever been involved in an occurrence

KEN *Ken you believe it?* He's the undisputed king of Mid-Mornings – and *Popmaster* fave Ken finishes *mid-table* here, too. It was a decent effort from the chucklesome DJ,

...NA v KEN v ROBERT THE

...IS THE BEST BRUCE?

...EN ·············   ·············· ROBERT THE ············

...con Ken is as Scottish as his ...namesake Robert The Bruce. It's a ...igh(lands)-scoring kick-off for the ...opular *Proms in the Park* presenter.

Score 9

SCOTTISHNESS
Revered Gaelic folk hero and King of Scots Robert The Bruce would appear on first sight to be as Scottish as Robert The Bruce. However, the 13th Century warrior's Wikipedia page openly admits that "not much is known about his childhood". Consequently, for all we know, so-called 'Scottish' icon Robert The could have been born in Naples, raised in El Salvador and educated in Pyongyang. Throw in the fact that he seems to have done no modelling *whatsoever* for any Dundee-based comics, and it's a lacklustre start for the Scottish national figurehead.

Score 3 — ROUND 1

...some gentle, knockabout banter or ...eady with a kind word of consolation to ...Popmaster contestants who've failed to ...name three hits by Simply Red in ten ...seconds. Uncle Ken nets maximum ...points in this admittedly niche and ...one-sided round.

Score 10

AVUNCULARITY
Thanks to his fearsome reputation for slaughtering anyone who stood in his way, history does not portray Robert The as a particularly avuncular figure. However, the phrase 'Bob's your uncle' has been in common usage for centuries, with its derivation lost in the mists of time. It could well have originated when Robert the Bruce did some favour or other for one of his nephews or nieces, with the phrase coming to mean 'job done'. Of course, it may well have nothing to do with him, and relate to one of the many other Roberts throughout history, such as assassinated US politician Robert Kennedy, *Ask the Family* host Robert Robinson, or Robert Downey Jr. out of *Iron Man*.

Score 2 — ROUND 2

...announcer's name? *David* Findlay! Ken also picks ...up a bonus point here, as he himself was briefly ...replaced on the Radio 2 mid-morning show by ...*Davina* McCall, who is called David right up ...until the fifth letter of her name.

Score 9

REPLACING PEOPLE CALLED DAVID
Spider-botherer Robert The spent most of his fifty-odd years replacing people! From taking up the mantle of Guardian of Scotland from William Wallace, to recouping the Lordship of Annandale from his namesake father, the pudding-bowl-haired mercenary loved nothing more than to fill in, take over, supplant and succeed. His most famous act of replacement, though, was claiming the Scottish throne previously occupied by his great grandfather, whose name was – you couldn't make it up – *King David I*!

Score 9 — ROUND 3

...rogramme alongside the ...kes of Beeb traffic reporter ...Lynn Bowles, meaning ...e picks up one precious ...point in this heated ...gastronomic ...round.

Score 1

APPEARANCES ON 'READY STEADY COOK'
In 1994, when *Ready Steady Cook* broadcast its first episode, folk hero Robert The had been dead for 665 years, and has therefore made a whopping **FUCK ALL** appearances on the now-defunct culinary game show. As a huge A-List star of his time, he would certainly have been the first name on producers' wish-lists had *Ready Steady Cook existed* in the 1300s, but that is all hypothetical.

Score 0 — ROUND 4

...won the UK's top anus-centric prize, ...and his score here suffers as a result, but it is of ...course possible that Ken *could* win the gong in ...future. However, unlike wine, men's bottoms seldom ...get better with age, and it is unlikely that Ken's ...septuagenarian buns will ever wow ...the famously picky ROTY judges.

Score 2

'REAR OF THE YEAR' AWARDS
In 1306, Robert The was excommunicated by Pope Clement V. While most historians agree this action was the result of his involvement in the murder of John Comyn of Badenoch, it all happened a very long time ago, so we can't be sure. What **IS** certain is that any 14th Century Pope would certainly have frowned upon a contest that revolved around buttock pertness. If a such a contest had existed in 1306 – and Robert The had won it – it would undoubtedly have set the Bishop of Rome's blood boiling, leading to an *immediate* excommunication. That possibility means we must award the peachy-arsed warmonger a BUM-per score here.

Score 8 — ROUND 5

...of combat warfare between opposing military ...units. Furthermore, his Wikipedia page makes no ...mention of Bruce committing the act of murder ...at **ANY POINT** during his seven-plus decades on ...this planet. Good news for Ken's conscience, but ...disastrous for his final score.

Score 0

NUMBER OF PEOPLE KILLED IN BATTLE
"Robert The Bruce was an absolute sod for slaughter," according to TV history buff Lucy Worsley – a statement she probably made whilst kitted out in 14th century Scottish battledress. Whilst no concrete evidence for how many people Robert The killed in the many skirmishes he took part in, historians all agree that it was shitloads, with a conservative estimate being 5000! And with a point up for grabs for every confirmed kill under his sporran, it's an extremely productive round for the Caledonian warlord.

Score 5000 — ROUND 6

...but ultimately he was no match for his long-dead, axe-wielding namesake.

31

ROBERT THE
Brucie bonus! Medieval throne-claimer Robert The has wiped the floor with his competitors here, much as he did with English forces at the Battle of Bannockburn in 1314. The blade-waving Gaelic hero is not just the King of the Scots – he's also the *Best of the Bruces!*

5022

Robbie's Robot Carer

I could have shopped for you, Robbie.

I have full retail capability.

Oh no, I like to get out, I just can't manage the trolley any more.

Besides, I still like to squeeze my own tomatoes!

My sensors can detect the perfect tomato every time by analysing the exact chemical composition of liquid vapour each fruit is exuding, Robbie.

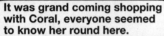

It was grand coming shopping with Coral, everyone seemed to know her round here.

They'd stop and chat...

I am programmed to chat, Robbie.

Today is a Wednesday. I hope it does not rain.

There's nothing forecast.

That is a relief.

Rain is terrible.

Rain, rain, go away. Am I right?

Come again another day. Am I right?

Soon

Can you reach down a jar of Branston from that top shelf?

Original, small chunk or smooth?

Smooth, the bits get stuck under my top plate.

Target acquired.

CLAMP

Target retrieeeeeeeeeeeeved.

Hello there Minnie, is he with you?

Yes, my young Polish woman doesn't do for me any more.

She was nice, Nadia, I miss her. She'd two lovely little daughters.

But the agency let all their humans go.

I told her to bring the girls, let them run in the garden while she saw to me, and she did...

Well, they were all week stuck in a flat.

It was fair lovely to hear them.

I can replicate the sound of children at play, Minnie.

That was the last jar of smooth, Robbie.

Oh heck.

You can have it if you like, I was only buying it for something to do.

Pop it in their trolley, Ian.

But –

Ian...

Whoops.

SMASH

Branston

174

The Winslow Tea-Boy

A TRUE tale of one man's fight for justice

After leaving school, young Ronald Winslow had found employment as the tea boy with the Maritime Insurance Company. It was a lowly position, but Ronald was hard working, honest and diligent, and he hoped one day to rise through the ranks of one of Britain's leading insurance brokers…

Suddenly…

SCREAM!

Good grief! What is it, Miss Gaunt?

The lavatory, Mr Watherstone… somebody has left a huge skidmark in the lavatory.

Surely not.

Yes… the pan is like a tiger's back.

It was him… the tea boy… I saw him come out of the lavatory not five minutes since.

Well, Ronald! What do you have to say for yourself?

It wasn't me, Mr Watherstone.

What!? Are you calling Mrs Rattigan a liar?

No, sir. I was in the toilet, but I didn't autograph the pan, sir.

I think you should go home, Ronald. Come back when you can apologise to everyone, and we shall say no more on the subject.

Ronald walked home, his mind a muddle of confusion. Should he fight to prove his innocence, or should he let the better part of valour be discretion, and apologise for a crime he did not commit?

Ronald, old chap. You're early. Anything wrong?

I've been sent home, father.

Sent home!?! For what reason?

Somebody left some pan au chocolat in the toilet, and Mr Watherstone thought it was me.

And was it you, Ronald?

No, father, it wasn't. I swear to you, I'm telling the truth.

A simple 'no' is good enough for me, my boy.

Come, Ronald. Let us put right this wrong.

Shortly…

Ah, Ronald… and Mr Winslow, I presume.

Indeed, sir… and you are Mr Watherstone, I take it.

At your service.

I believe an apology is in order, sir.

Yes, If Ronald were to say he regrets his behaviour, we shall say…

Not an apology from my son, sir…

…from YOU!

But!?!

You have accused my son of leaving the toilet like a thrush's chest, a crime of which he is wholly innocent.

All my children have been brought up to practice judicious use of the lavatory brush, sir, and we demand a retraction.

But Ronald was seen exiting the toilets five minutes before the foul scene was discovered. Nobody was seen entering thereafter.

That nobody was seen entering, sir, does not mean that nobody did enter. Now do you retract your allegation?

No, sir, I do not.

Then I shall have to take this higher. Good day, sir.

Come, Ronald.

Shortly, at the head office of the Maritime Insurance Company…

…and what's more, I raised my child to tell the truth, and if he says he didn't leave the toilet looking like the starting grid at Brands Hatch, then he did not, gentlemen.

Mr Winslow, let us not get things out of proportion. It was just a befouled toilet…

…if your son were just to apologise, we could put this whole sorry matter behind us.

Apologise!?! For something he did not do?! I should say not, sir…

176

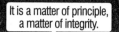

It is a matter of principle, a matter of integrity.

Yes, he may have been accused of merely scribbling with a brown crayon, but we shall have justice.

I'm afraid you leave me little choice as to my next action, Gentlemen…

…Good day to you.

With right on their side, Mr Winslow and his son paid a visit to the foremost barrister in England, Sir Robert Morton, QC…

Sir Robert Morton QC

…So there you have it, sir. My son's good name dragged through the mud, accused of this most horrible of crimes.

Will you take his case, sir?

Hmmm!

You deny leaving the toilet at the Maritime Insurance Company looking like the flight deck of the Ark Royal, Ronald.

I do, sir. It wasn't me.

But you don't deny going into the toilet for 10 minutes.

I don't deny it, sir. But I didn't befoul the toilet.

Then what were you doing in there for those ten minutes?

I… I was doing… other things, sir.

Other things? What other things?

I… I'd rather not say, sir.

I'm sure you would not…

…because I put it to you that you went in there to park your breakfast…

…you parked your breakfast, autographed the pot and didn't clean up after yourself.

No, sir. No!

Yes, sir, YES! You left the mess for others to clean up.

No!

What's more, you then had the temerity to tell a bare faced lie when asked about it.

NO! NO, that's not true.

Bold as brass.

I say, that's enough…

I came to solicit your help, sir, as I thought you were the only man who would do it. But it would appear I have made a grave error of judgement…

Not at all, Mr Winslow… Your son is clearly innocent. I should be delighted to take the case.

Please leave your details with my clerk and I shall contact you imminently…

Good day, gentlemen.

A month later…

I wish all this would go away…can't you just drop the case, Arthur?

No, Elspeth, we cannot.

The Times
The Winslow Skid-case starts next week

But it's all so horrible. I was too embarrassed to go to Mrs Betjeman's bridge evening last week.

There are things more important than Mrs Betjeman's bridge evening…

Integrity, justice, the good name of the family. Need I go on, Elspeth, my dear?

Letter just arrived for you, Mr Winslow, sir.

Ah! That will be Sir Robert's first bill. He said he would send it over today.

JESUS WEPT!

Arthur!

Go ahead, Ronald.

I… I give you my sincerest apologies for the fouled state in which I left the office toilet. You have my word as a gentleman that it will never happen again.

THE END

SUCCESS IN THE STARS

Signs looking good for April rocket blast-off

Horo-telescope: The Mystic Meg Reflector will revolutionise astrological predictions.

BRITISH Astrological Society fortune tellers are looking forward to the launch of a European Space Agency rocket in April. That's because the mission will be carrying a new space telescope which BAS experts hope will make their future predictions even more accurate.

The Mystic Meg Reflector will be the largest space telescope ever launched, with its primary mirror of almost 8 metres across dwarfing the James Webb telescope recently placed in orbit by NASA. The powerful light-gathering surface will give astrologers views of the constellations never before seen, giving them much more information with which to make their predictions.

Soothsayers from around the world will be watching next week as the Ariane rocket lifts off with its payload from the ESA launch site in French Guiana.

"We're tremendously excited," said British Astrological Society president Quentin Regulus. "Down here on Earth, we can see a handful of stars in each constellation of the zodiac. But in space, Mystic Meg's high-tech wave sensors, beryllium mirrors and super-cooled image enhancement circuitry will be able to discern tens of thousands."

"The information it sends back will mean our predictions will be far more accurate than ever before," he continued. "In astrological terms, it will be like coming out of the Dark Ages and into the eleventh century."

taurus

The mission to put the Mystic Meg space telescope into orbit is estimated to have cost around £7billion, but Regulus believes that the money will be recovered once people see the quality of the horoscopes it allows astrologers to draw up.

"Whereas in the past we may have predicted that a Sagittarian will meet a tall, dark stranger, we will now be able to give the exact height of that dark stranger, accurate to within a quarter of an inch," he said.

And according to Regulus, woolly, ambiguous phrases in morning horoscopes, such as a Gemini who is forecast to go on a long journey, will be a thing of the past. "Now we will not only be able to tell them exactly where they are going, but how they will get there, what day they will set off, when they will get back. And where we once foretold a Libra would receive welcome news about an old friend, we will in future be able to name the friend and disclose the nature of the news precisely," he said.

If all goes to plan, the blast-off will take place in early April under the control of Launch Director Hymen Prepuce, who was hand-picked by the British Astrological Society for his expertise, having been head of NASA for 20 years, during which time he oversaw over 100 successful missions.

"He's also the seventh launch director of a seventh launch director," said Regulus. "So he clearly has a special gift for firing rockets."

shit

The 500-tonne Ariane rocket was initially set to blast into orbit in January, but a technical problem meant that the launch was aborted with just 2 hours to go before lift-off. "The launch director's birthday is December 23rd," Regulus said. "When we did a last minute check of his chart, it turned out that Saturn was in Venus with Mercury retrograde, meaning January was not a good month for Capricorns to undertake a large project."

"We postponed it until April, when those born under the sign of the Ram will be brimming with confidence and enjoy success in everything they do," Professor Regulus added.

MEDDLESOME RATBAG

THE Male Online

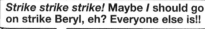

Strike strike strike! Maybe *I* should go on strike Beryl, eh? Everyone else is!!

If you can't beat 'em – and goodness me they *deserve* a beating – join 'em!

Go on strike from *what*?

You *do* nothing.

Gasp!

Nothing?!

So what do *you* call an average of 300 comments *per day* since the Spring of 2010 at the Mail Online?

A *lot* of nothing.

You won't get any of that time back, you know – and it isn't as if you were *paid* for it.

Aha!

There we have it! Straight to the heart of the current coup – the Money God! *Naked greed!*

I hardly think it's *greed* if the people on strike can't meet their cost of living.

Prices are getting –

Prices are the same for everyone, Beryl.

Prices are the same for our newsagent, and he's on my side.

We were discussing the best way to *smash* unions only this morning.

The Army – SEND 'EM IN!

No job on *Earth* the resourceful English Tommy can't turn his hand to in a pinch.

In Colditz we made *wine* out of boot-polish!

After *that* driving trains or teaching infants maths is a stroll in the park!

No, he'd sooner *die* than strike.

It's his own shop!

He'd be a one-man picket of himself!

Oh, not for long. *The Barons* would back him with roving knuckle mobs in *no* time.

Return of the flying pickets!

Oh good, I loved that Christmas song of theirs.

Very droll.

By the way, that group were *all* communists.

Only *USSR*...

Will you *still* be laughing when rentamob Welsh miners kick my head in if I try to pick up a Mail?!

I'll probably manage to keep a straight face.

Of course, I blame Corbyn – he opened *Pandora's Books!*

And now he reaches out from his political grave to drag us screaming back to the 1970s!

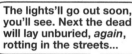

The lights'll go out soon, you'll see. Next the dead will lay unburied, *again*, rotting in the streets...

Remember that? I do, awful...

Things are already getting *pretty ugly* out there. I strongly suggest we withdraw to the cellar and sit it out...

I've already put a storm lantern down there. A few tins and such.

And the compendium of games...

Not. A. Bloody. *Chance.*

Soon

GAAAAAAH, what use is a compendium with no dice?!

Beryl?! BERYLLLL?!?

FAST, FAMOUS & F[

IT WON'T surprise anyone who has ventured out on the highways and byways of Britain recently to learn that Road Rage statistics are on the UP.

Pressures of a global pandemic, the economic downturn and massive hikes in the cost of living have transformed the once green and pleasant motorways of this sceptred isle into red-mist-shrouded **HIGHWAYS TO HELL**. From Land's End to John O'Groats, the UK's maniacal motorists think nothing of resorting to showers of four-letter abuse – or even physical violence – for the most petty traffic infractions.

Truly – we've all been **DRIVEN** mad.

But in these times of vehicular mayhem, it is a comfort to know that our beloved A-List stars would never succumb to this kind of automotive anger. In their plush limos and swanky sports cars, the calm and collected showbiz set are 100% immune from road rage, setting a shining example to the rest of us.

Or are they?

Perhaps each time they give in to road rage, their PR machines go into overdrive, covering up evidence, buying people off and making sure their highway wrath never becomes public knowledge. Perhaps they are as badly behaved behind the wheel as the rest of us. Or maybe they're even WORSE. We decided to find out.

Award-winning investigative reporter **MAHATMA MACAROON** went undercover on Britain's thoroughfares to find out if our favourite Tinseltown icons are quite as laid back as they make out once they're out on the road. *And what he uncovered will SHOCK every celebrity-obsessed reader to their very core.*

Buckle up, as we expose...*THE FAST, FAMOUS & FURIOUS!*

BY **VIZ** UNDERCOVER REPORTER **MAHATMA MACAROON**

A-LIST ROAD RAGER 1: *Jon Sopel*

THERE'S only one thing more irritating than being stuck in traffic, and that's being stuck in traffic with some arsehole behind you beeping his horn.

Posing as that very breed of arsehole, I decide to test the road rage immunity of one of our most unflappable celebrity icons – *Newsagents* podcaster **JON SOPEL**. The steely journalist never flinches when describing the most shocking and horrific news events, so doubtless he'll remain just as stoic when faced with a minor annoyance out on the road.

Or will he?

Disguised as a twat, in brick red chinos, Barbour jacket and a bumper sticker declaring my support for Laurence Fox's 'Reclaim' party, I park my rented Audi TT behind a hedge near Sopel's swanky London residence. As I spot the grey-templed news fave leaving for work in his plush motor, I pull out and surreptitiously follow him, staying inches from his bumper until we hit a bad patch of traffic.

As we both slow to a stop, I spring into action, slamming both hands down on the centre of my steering wheel and unleashing an ear-splitting cacophony of blaring honks. But does Sopel remain as cool and calm as he appears on screen?

Newsflash! No he doesn't.

I see him make a puzzled face in his rear-view mirror, masking his obvious fury. Catching his eyes, I up the tempo and violence of my beeping, at which point the red mist fully descends on the political analyst. Incandescent with rage, Sopel offers me an apologetic shrug and a grin, gesturing at the cars in front of him as if to say "What can I do?"

He's clearly at boiling point. I just need to tip him over the edge.

Still beeping frantically with my left hand, I begin flicking the 'V's at him with my right, occasionally throwing in the 'wanker' sign for good measure. I'm confident that this will provoke a more physical reaction, and sure enough it does.

A large, shaven-headed man in the white van beside Sopel's exits his vehicle and marches purposefully in my direction. He yanks open my door and his tattooed fist grabs me roughly by the neck. "Shut the eff up and stop beeping, you effing prick," he yells, whilst punching me hard in the nose and mouth. Truth be told, he didn't say 'eff' and 'effing': he said 'f***' (fuck) and 'f*****' (fucking).

It's crystal clear what's happened. Utterly livid – but not keen on getting his manicured hands dirty – Ivory Tower-dwelling Jon must have sent a subtle signal to this muscle-bound oaf to do his dirty work for him. As the traffic clears and I watch Sopel pull away, I reflect on how utterly pathetic it is that this veteran broadcaster can't control his temper in the face of a few light-hearted honks.

Here's tonight's main headline: Who would have thought that the unruffled star we see on our TV screens is really a vicious thug, prone to senseless bouts of road rage?

A-LIST ROAD RAGER 2: *David Tennant*

CYCLISTS are perhaps the most common cause of road rage on Britain's streets. Whether they're running red lights, cutting dangerously in front of us or taking legal action after we've shunted them into a ditch, these Lycra-clad menaces are responsible for a fair chunk of the UK's vehicular red mist.

Which is why I decide to pose as one.

Cleverly disguised as a mid-life-crisis sufferer, in a skin-tight Spandex onesie and ludicrous peaked cap, I wobble out on my brand new carbon fibre racing bike. I'm heading straight for the home of popular *Doctor Who* actor **DAVID TENNANT**. The Scotch board-treader is renowned as one of our friendliest and funniest celebrities, and anyone who's seen him cracking jokes on Graham Norton's sofa will agree that he seems like a nice, normal bloke.

The key word there being: 'seems'. I wonder, just how 'normal' and 'nice' will Tennant be with a two-wheeled irritant on his tail?

I spot Tennant pull out of his driveway in his car, and immediately pedal after him on my bicycle. I decide to test the water by cutting in front of his vehicle and slowing to a crawl, thus forcing the star to drive at about three miles an hour. As predicted, the "so-called" affable actor blows a gasket. He indicates and overtakes me – a reckless move that would easily have knocked me down if he hadn't left more than three metres of space between us.

He's clearly rattled, and I decide to keep working his pressure points. Gaining speed, I cycle alongside Tennant's car and begin angrily pounding his window. "You effing (fucking) moron!" I screech at him as he slows to a standstill. "You nearly effing (fucking) killed me back there! What the effing eff (fucking fuck)?!"

So much for 'Mr Nice Guy' – Tennant snaps like a dry twig. Winding his window down, he can barely contain his frenzied vehemence. Through his purple-faced fury, he unleashes a vile torrent of abuse at me: "Oh, God, I'm so, so sorry," he seethes. "I thought I'd left you enough space, but I apologise if I didn't – I'll be more careful in the future. Are you OK?"

Oh, I'm OK, pal, I chuckle to myself as he drives off. Because, unbeknownst to Tennant, I've caught the A-List star's spittle-flecked meltdown on the Go-Pro camera on my helmet! As I upload the full shocking video to YouTube later that night, with the title 'Sick Dr Who Star's Four-Letter Cyclist Rant', I can't help but feel sorry for Tennant's loyal fanbase. For years they've been under the impression their hero is a gentle, good-natured guy. And now they'll find out the stomach-wrenching truth: *he's a hate-filled menace with serious anger issues.*

Forget Doctor Who: David's character should have been called Doctor Who Can't Control His Road Rage.

URIOUS!

AR53 OLE

A-LIST ROAD RAGER 3: *Jamie Cullum*

IF THERE'S one thing certain to get motorists' blood boiling when they're out on the roads, it's a learner driver.

Being stuck behind one of these selfish arseholes as they kangaroo-hop along at 12 miles an hour sends all of our blood pressures soaring sky-high. But surely our big-hearted celebs must feel a little empathy for these hopeless amateurs?

I wouldn't be too sure.

Renting a Vauxhall Corsa from my local Avis centre, I take it to a back-alley mechanic who fits it with a second steering wheel and set of dual control pedals. Next, I disguise myself as a driving instructor by painting my face purple and shoving a sofa cushion up my jumper. My 'student' is a blow-up sex doll that I've dressed up in a blouse and jeans from Topshop. The destination for today's lesson: the home of pint-sized jazz-popper **JAMIE CULLUM**.

Cheery Cullum is the creator of some of the most inoffensive, middle of the road music on Earth. But will the short-arsed icon go *on the offensive* when I cause a *muddle* in the road? *Let's find out.*

I park the car in a blind spot on the corner of Cullum's street. Soon enough, I spot the minuscule funkster approaching in his motor, and spring into action. Stamping hard on the dual accelerator pedal, I swerve out dangerously in front of Cullum, just narrowly avoiding a collision.

The diminutive Parky favourite is quite clearly *fuming*. But before he can succumb to a bout of road rage, he spots the 'L' plates on the car, and my 'student' in the driver's seat. Working hard to hide his obvious fury, Cullum shoots me a confused smile and gestures for us to pull out ahead of him.

I know I've got the *All At Sea* hit-maker on the ropes. It's now just about twisting the knife...

I drop back and tail Cullum for fifty miles, occasionally riding so far up his arse that our number plates are touching. Whenever we catch eyes in the rear-view mirror, I make sure to give a weary shake of the head, and point to my sex doll student who's 'driving' the car. I can't see the expression on Cullum's face – but I'm guessing he's *livid*.

Finally, the cod-jazz hunk pulls into some services for what I assume is a Scotch egg and a shit. I follow him in, and once he's parked his car and entered the building, I rev my engine and accelerate at full speed towards his back bumper.

CRUNCH!

I piledrive into the rear of Cullum's Porsche, shattering both brake lights. It's a nasty knock, but since it's a young learner driver who's responsible, I'm sure the compassionate star won't make a fuss. With that in mind, I repeat the action fifteen times. When I'm finished, Cullum's previously spotless convertible looks like it's just finished last in a Demolition Derby. As I drive off, I catch a glimpse of the pocket-sized pianist running out towards his shattered vehicle with his head in his hands, clearly incensed.

I feel sick to my stomach. Cullum knows full well that it was a young, inexperienced driver who's accidentally rammed him 16 times whilst he was parked up. And yet he *still* can't control his violent temper. It looks like his fuse is even shorter than his arse. I wish I could say I was surprised, but I'm not. I'm just sad.

But things are about to get even worse.

An hour or so later, I'm parked up in some nearby woods, undressing and deflating my sex doll, which has now served its purpose. It's cramped in the car, so I decide the most efficient way to getting the rest of the air out of the doll is to lie on top of it and make thrusting motions with my groin. And since it's a warm evening and the air-con is broken, I've taken off my trousers and pants. I've nearly finished the job, when all of a sudden blue lights and sirens fill the air around me.

I look up, struggling to believe my eyes. That petty, pathetic pop icon Cullum was clearly so consumed with road rage that he has called the police on a naive learner driver. As the filth handcuff me, I feel even sicker and more disappointed than I previously did. The coppers tell me they've had several complaints about a man committing acts of gross indecency in a public woodland – but I know what I'm *really* being arrested for...

Inciting road rage in an A-List hypocrite!

A-LIST ROAD RAGER 3: *Louis Theroux*

PLUMMY-voiced presenter **LOUIS THEROUX** has made his name by remaining deadpan and impassive when faced with some of the planet's strangest and most dangerous people – from crime bosses and cult leaders to sexual perverts and neo-nazis. But will the lanky *Weird Weekends* icon be able to stay quite so aloof when things get heated on the highway?

I aim to find out.

Disguising myself as a typical cockney cabbie, in a flat cap, Pringle sweater and fifteen gold Sovereign rings, I take to the streets in my Seat Alhambra, which I have painted black and topped with an orange cardboard 'TAXI' sign.

Cruising near Theroux's luxurious two-storey mansion in south London, I spot the bespectacled broadcaster pootling along behind me in his motor. Quick as a flash, I drop back alongside him and whip out my iPhone. On The AA's website, talking on a mobile whilst driving is cited as the one of the most common causes of road rage – so this is sure to get the famously easygoing brainbox's blood boiling.

Winding my window down so Theroux can hear, I simulate a loud, one-sided conversation whilst swerving dangerously between lanes. "Facking do one, you mappet!" I bark into the handset, in a convincing Cockney brogue. "I'm 'avin' a lahvly little natter wiv yoo whilst drivin' dahn the frog an' fackin' toad, int I?!"

I glance across at Louis to see that my cunning tactics are already provoking a reaction. Clearly worried about controlling his anger if he has to witness any more of this dangerous driving, the rage-fuelled TV ace stares dead ahead and continues to drive along at 30mph.

Still jabbering away into my phone, I spin the steering wheel and attempt a handbrake turn directly into Theroux's front bumper. However, I misjudge the angle slightly and instead go careening off the Tarmac into a tree. The airbag explodes in my face, and I feel the familiar sting of whiplash running through my neck.

But these are the least of my problems.

Through my window, I can see the enraged documentarian exiting his car and sprinting towards me. The AA guidelines are very clear on how to handle an irate motorist: avoid eye contact and lock your doors. I do both, but neither can protect me from Theroux's thunderous temper. Hammering on my window with the knuckle of his pinkie finger, the telly boffin is fury personified. "Gosh, are you all right in there?" he fumes. "Let me call an ambulance!"

I can hardly believe what I'm hearing. Theroux is so consumed with rage at my 'dangerous' driving that he knows medical assistance will be required when he's finished with me. As I begin to lose consciousness, I feel something even more painful than the whiplash: disappointment.

It was only a bit of mild vehicular horseplay – and yet this supposedly 'chilled out' documentarian still 'Theroux' the most almighty hissy fit.

L

NEXT WEEK – Cabin Pressure! Mahatma goes undercover on a first class flight to discover the sickening air rage shame of Kim Kardashian, Barack Obama, Scarlett Johansson and Sting.

WELL, YOU DO THAT, AN' I'LL DO THE LEG THING POSE, AN' THEN SOME O' THEM STAR JUMPS

SPOING!

B-DOING!

THUNK!

RIGHT! THAT WAS DEAD GOOD, SHALL WE GO BACK IN AN' GET SOME CHIPS

WOT!? NO!

DEAD GOOD ISN'T GOOD ENOUGH, SAN... ONLY PERFECT'LL DO. DIDN'T Y' LEARN OWT FROM CHEER?

IF WE'RE GOIN' T' KILL IT TOMORROW, WE'VE GOT T' PRACTISE, PRACTISE, PRACTISE!

WE KEEP GOIN' TIL WE GET IT RIGHT... THEN WE KEEP GOIN' TIL WE CAN'T GET IT WRONG...

AN' IF YOU HAVEN'T GOT THE ATTITUDE T' GIVE 100 PERCENT, THEN YER OUT, COS THERE'S NO PLACE ON THIS CHEER TEAM FOR NINETY-NINE PERCENTERS

WINNERS TALK AN' LOSERS WALK!

YOU'RE EITHER ALL IN OR YOU'RE ALL OUT. OKAY?

AYE, ALRIGHT... I JUST FANCIED A FEW CHIPS

NEXT DAY...

FULCHESTER RECREATION GROUND

EH!?. WHERE THE FUCK IS EVERYBODY

DUNNO

I'LL RING BAZ UP

BAZ!?.. WHERE ARE YER? WOT TIME'S KICK OFF?

EH!? WOT?

OH, SOZ... IT'S CANCELLED, TRAY... EVERYBODY WERE OUT ON THE PISS LAST NIGHT AN' NOBODY W' UP FOR IT THIS MORNIN'...WE'LL TELL THE LEAGUE IT WERE A NIL-NIL DRAW

THE BASTARDS! THEY'RE NOT TURNIN' UP, SAN

EEH!.. NEVER...ALL THAT PRACTICE WE PUT IN AN' ALL

GOT IT TO PERFECTION, WE 'AD

WOT A WASTE O' FUCKIN' TIME

OH, NO IT'S NOT, SAN... COME ON!

OOH, THAT LOOKS GOOD, LES...

...GOOD LENGTH...

GIMME A 'G'... GIMME AN 'O'... GIMME A 'B'... GIMME ANOTHER 'O'... GIMME A 'W'... GIMME AN 'L'... GIMME AN 'E'... GIMME AN 'R'... GIMME AN 'S'... WOT 'AVE Y' GOT!?

WOT THE BLOODY 'ELL!?

SPOING! BOING!

GO BOWLERS.!!

SHORTLY...

I THINK THAT WENT DOWN REALLY WELL, TRAY

AYE, IT DID.

IT MIGHT BE BEST WI' KNICKERS ON NEXT TIME, THOUGH, SAN

AYE!

183

SHRINE A LIGHT

GAS LIGHT: *The government's proposed Cupboard Under The Stairs Shrine Kit and (inset below) Rees-Mogg.*

A RECENT government brainstorming session resulted in many ideas to help people through the forthcoming cost of living crisis. Allowing nursery staff to look after more children, only requiring cars to undergo an MOT test every two years, and suggesting old people ride buses all night to keep warm were just some of the practical proposals put forward to help cash-strapped Britons get through the next few years as prices rise. But it is the phenomenal hike in energy costs that is set to cause the biggest squeeze on family incomes, with many expected to see their bills increase by as much as 150%, or even more.

However, an initiative put forward by Brexit Opportunities minister Jacob Rees-Mogg could allow people to SLASH their gas and electricity bills. *And the poorest people could end up paying nothing at all.*

The new scheme has nothing to do with insulating homes or handing out generous government subsidies to the needy. Instead, homeowners will be encouraged to PRAY for lower energy bills.

"Whenever we are in need or find ourselves tested, we all turn to the Lord through prayer," the MP for Somerset North told the house. "He is well known for answering our prayers, so why should we not ask him for help reducing our energy bills?"

"And incidentally, that 'him' in the previous sentence should have a capital letter," he added.

And to help the public achieve this, the government has vowed to send every household in the country a '*Cupboard Under The Stairs Shrine Kit*' to enable everyone to set up a little altar alongside their gas meter.

"Over the course of the next few months, we shall be sending out fifteen million sanctuary candles along with a small icon of Saint Francis Xaviour, the patron saint of energy," the staunchly Catholic minister continued.

"Although the cost to the exchequer will be in the region of one billion pounds, the savings to the public afforded by the Lord God's bounteous grace will be far greater, so I believe it is money well spent."

shrine on

Britons will be advised to set up the little shrine at the side of their gas or electricity meters, and to beseech St Francis Xaviour to reduce their energy bills at least three times a day. They will also be told to keep their holy candle burning in perpetuity in order to ensure the maximum reductions in their energy bills.

"I have no doubt that this miracle is well within the capabilities of St Francis, as he once dropped his crucifix in the sea and it was brought back to him by a crab," said Mr Rees-Mogg.

The minister went on to explain that those who need the most help with their bills would be the ones who would benefit from St Francis Xaviour's beneficience.

"God knows all our wants and needs, and so is the ultimate, and perfect, means-tester," he told MPs.

"If you truly want your bills to come down, and are truly deserving, then you will see the the Lord's work and the fruits of your prayer when you open your next utility bill," he continued.

"If you don't see a reduction, then you are not worthy and you will jolly well have to pay up."

Speaking in parliament, Shadow Chancellor Rachel Reeves asked if the shrines would work for those with pre-payment meters who pay for their energy up front.

Mr Rees-Mogg said that although those people did not receive a monthly bill, he was confident that the Almighty would be able to see a way around this problem, and he advised those with pre-payment meters to set up a shrine in the same way.

"If the Lord can create everything in the universe from nothing in seven days, I'm sure he can make the wheels on a pre-payment meter go round a little bit more slowly," he scoffed whilst reclining on the government benches.

"And that 'he' should have a capital too," the lanky streak of piss added in Latin.

MAJOR MISUNDERSTANDING

LetterbOcks

letters@viz.co.uk...letters@viz.co.uk...letters@viz.co.u

STAR LETTER

PRIOR to a recent colonoscopy examination, I had to drink 4 litres of soapy 'evacuant' which completely emptied my bowels and left my chocolate pipe squeaky clean for the camera. The episode reminded me of a batch of home brew I made with my brother in 1982, which had an immediate and identical effect. And it got me thinking that perhaps the NHS could use my beer in preparation for their colonoscopies. It had the added advantage that I didn't have to drink 4 litres of the stuff for it to work, and it tended to lift one's spirits after consumption, so using it would leave the patient less concerned about what was happening to their arse. The NHS stuff tasted better, though, I have to admit.

Mike Harris, Gourock

ON becoming Prime Minister back in 1990, John Major pledged to make Britain 'a classless society'. Having just spent the afternoon in my local Wetherspoons, I have to say he did a pretty fucking thorough job.

Craig Scott, East Calder

ENERGY price cap? Energy price *top hat* more like. And not just any old top hat, either - one of those great big, tall ones like Isambard Kingdom Brunel used to wear.

Jack Spratt, Stourbridge

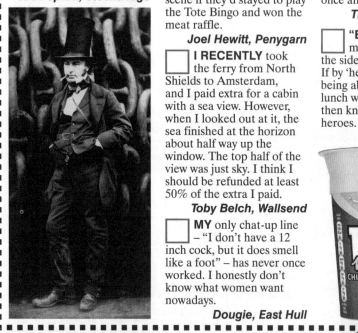

DOES anyone know if the Cantina off of *Star Wars* was CIU-affiliated? I didn't see anyone check if Obi-Wan Kenobi and Luke Skywalker were members. I think it would have added authenticity if they had paid 50p on the door and been signed in by a member. And it would have been a great scene if they'd stayed to play the Tote Bingo and won the meat raffle.

Joel Hewitt, Penygarn

I RECENTLY took the ferry from North Shields to Amsterdam, and I paid extra for a cabin with a sea view. However, when I looked out at it, the sea finished at the horizon about half way up the window. The top half of the view was just sky. I think I should be refunded at least 50% of the extra I paid.

Toby Belch, Wallsend

MY only chat-up line – "I don't have a 12 inch cock, but it does smell like a foot" – has never once worked. I honestly don't know what women want nowadays.

Dougie, East Hull

'SO-CALLED' scientists claim that global warming leads to rising sea levels, so I did an experiment. I made a puddle in the middle of summer and noticed that rather than the level going up in the heat, it actually went down. Surely this proves the egg-heads wrong once and for all.

The Owl, Northfields

"BE Heroic in 4 minutes" it says on the side of a Pot Noodle. If by 'heroic' they mean being able to consume your lunch when it's still at 89°C, then knock yourselves out, heroes.

Eldon Furse, email

THE other day I was sitting waiting at a bus stop near Amsterdam and managed to produce a really powerful 'tent zip'-style fart. It was so strong that a woman leaning against the railings 10ft away felt it and reacted accordingly.

Russ Poore, email

＊ *An interesting story, Mr Poore, but as the incident took place near Amsterdam, we think you will find the woman was in question was just over 3 metres away.*

I JUST had a Sunday lunch in Berwick St James with the missus and my dog, and we sat opposite Damon Allbran from Blur in the beer garden. And not once did he come over to stroke our dog or compliment us on what a well behaved girl she was. Have any other readers come across a 90s pop star too much the 'Big I Am' to give their dog a little fuss?

Paul Mac, Maidstone

A TRAIN ticket to London from Guildford in the south is £15.20, but from Newcastle, in the north, to London, it's nearly 80 quid! So much for bloody levelling up. Come on, whichever minister is in charge of it this week. Sort it out.

Dr Hugh Munster, E'burgh

CANCELLING all the football fixtures the week after the death of her majesty the Queen was the right and proper thing to do. My thoughts and prayers went out to her family, and I only hope that my not being able to watch Whitley Bay take on Guisborough Town in the Northern League Division One brought them a little comfort.

Hector Bramblepot, Wallsend

A MAN coming out of Westminster Hall after seeing her majesty lying in state said it was very emotional, especially seeing the coffin "lying there so still." I'm not sure if he was expecting it be bouncing around on springs, or rotating on a lazy Susan or something.

Tommy Ballsup, Ely

I THINK that the oystercatcher must surely be Britain's most poorly-named bird. They don't 'catch' oysters so much as just pick them up where they see them. Calling them oystercatchers implies that the shellfish make a run for it and there's a bit of a chase involved. Utter nonsense.

Peter Scott, Slimbridge

TO provide the public with warm places to go in the coming winter energy crisis, museums and libraries are being encouraged to have an open door policy. This seems a little unwise, as keeping the doors closed would be much more effective in keeping these places cosy. Whatever happened to good old British common sense?

Phil Kitching, Isle of Jura

I'VE just returned from touring the Netherlands and I was amazed to see how many wonky buildings they have. The Oude Kerk in Delft leans over six feet to one side, and the Oldehove in Leeuwarden even more than that. Not to mention the countless buildings in Amsterdam which look like they could fall over any minute. What is it with Dutch builders? They've got the flattest country in the world, yet they don't seem to be able to put a wall up at a right angle.

Wilf Putrid, Penge

WHY is it that whenever you see a couple on a tandem, it is without fail the man at the front and the woman at the back? It's 2024, for heaven's sake. If we're ever going to have equality in this country, women have got to start going at the front on mixed-sex tandems.

Hector Crowbar, Budleigh Salterton

IF religion is to be believed, the reason why women have been unfairly treated throughout history is because in the prophesies of the end times, they will lose all their modesty and turn the world into a global Sodom and Gomorrah, bringing the wrath of the Lord upon all that dwelleth on the earth. Women, eh?

Jack Fretwell, Shaftesbury

POTATOES can be made into mash, chips, crisps, jackets, vodka, batteries and more. The list is endless. Come on, parsnips. What are you waiting for?

The Owl, Northfields

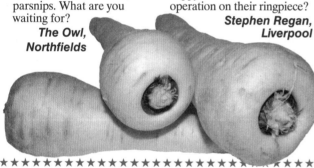

I'M all for the right to protest, but I can't help but feel things have gone too far when a bird strike meant our flight was diverted. What do they even want?

Matt S, Newcastle

I WAS recently treated for an anal fissure, which involved having a botox injection in the affected area to paralyse the muscle and allow the fissure to close. Not only has the procedure fixed the problem, but my arsehole now looks ten years younger. Has anyone else had a similar happy side effect from an operation on their ringpiece?

Stephen Regan, Liverpool

"PROBLEMS only exist in the human mind," said spiritual teacher and psychotherapist Anthony de Mello. However, my problem is that my piles are playing up something rotten at the moment, and I'm pretty sure they're up my ringpiece.

Aubrey Pancake, Stoke

MY music teacher at high school was called Barry Trumpet. You couldn't make it up! Well I just did, but generally speaking, you couldn't.

Eldon Furse, email

ARE the Manic Street Preachers street preachers who are a bit manic, or are they preachers who live on Manic Street?

Craig Mansell, Barnsley

* *That's an interesting question, Mr Mansell, but it's hard to say, as the founder of the band, Richie Manic, disappeared in 1995. He was declared officially dead in absentia in 2008, but many believe he faked his own death, and has reportedly been spotted in a market in Goa, and on the islands of Lanzarote and Fuerteventura. If any Viz readers spot the Welsh band frontman, easily recognised by the scars on his left arm reading "4 REAL", ask him what the band's name means and write in and tell us what he said.*

SO Pope John Paul I has been beatified after it was determined

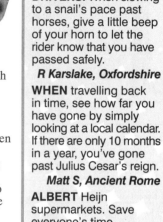

that he was responsible for a miracle during his tenure, despite being Pope for just 33 days! By comparison, his successor, Pope John Paul II, struggled to scratch together a meagre two miracles in 27 years. Had Pope John Paul I stayed alive for this period he would, at his rate, have been responsible for a massive 324 miracles, representing a *16,100%* increase in productivity. It just goes to show what you can achieve when you really believe. Come on, Popes. Stop slacking and bang out some more miracles.

Adrian Bamforth, email

THEY say everyone can remember where they were when man first set foot on the Moon. I certainly can – I was stepping off the bottom of the ladder of the Apollo 11 Eagle landing craft.

Neil Armstrong, Houston

★ **GANGS OF NEW YORK** star **DANIEL DAY-LEWIS** was celebrating a 'bum deal' this week - when he signed a seven-figure contract to play **PIPPA MIDDLETON'S ARSE** in the next series of *The Crown*! The forthcoming sixth season of the hit Netflix regal drama will feature a mega-budget re-enactment of Prince William's 2011 marriage to Kate Middleton – with *Lincoln* fave Day-Lewis bringing up the rear as the bride's sister's buttocks! Famed for his notoriously 'method' approach to the roles he plays, bonkers Day-Lewis will reportedly be remaining in character as the arse – even off camera! "To fully comprehend the mindset of Pippa's mudflaps, I will be attempting to live as a backside for the full four months of shooting," the zany actor told *Vanity Fair*. He went on to reveal that he would also demand to be sat on several times a day by the actress playing Pippa Middleton – none other than busty *Cowboy Builders* fave **MELINDA MESSENGER**!

MY SPIES TELL ME that A-List icon **ANGELINA JOLIE** arrived three hours

Fanny Batter's HOLLYWOOD gossip

late to the set of her new blockbuster last week... because she was so engrossed in reading *'The Romford Pelé: Ray Parlour's Autobiography'*! The foxy *Tomb Raider* star revealed she'd opened the book over breakfast and had been so captivated by the corkscrew-haired ex-Arsenal man's anecdotes that she'd lost all track of time! "I was chuckling away at Ray's story about Steve Bould being sick on the coach after eating nine dinners, when I suddenly realised I was supposed to be in hair and makeup," a red-faced Jolie confessed to *Variety* magazine. According to sources, the sultry *Eternals* actress sprinted straight across town to the studio, filmed her scene in one take, and then dived straight back into the journeyman soccer star's side-splitting life story! And that's not all – Jolie has reportedly optioned the book for an

HBO limited series, with Parlour to be played by her hunky former hubbie, **BRAD PITT**! *Whodathunkit?!!*

OMG! You'll never guess which Tinseltown titan I spotted sneaking out of a plastic surgery clinic yesterday... none other than *Star Wars* silver fox **HARRISON FORD**! But was the *Indiana Jones* ace there for a nose job or a Botox jab? Guess again – he was having his **BARSE** enlarged! That's right – friends of the *Blade Runner* hunk tell me that Harrison has always been mortified by his smaller-than-average perineum, and it's been his lifelong dream to have it surgically extended! With the patch of skin between Ford's sphincter and scrotum now reportedly clocking in at a whopping FOURTEEN INCHES, pals say that Harrison's morale is sky high, and he's more upbeat than he's been in years. *Good on 'im!!*

Seeya next time, goss fans! Love ya loads! Mwah! Mwah! Fanny xix

LIDL RICHARD

Potatoes and carrots.

Potatoes and carrots.

Remember, Richard... potatoes and carrots... nothing else.

Potatoes and carrots.

There! Potatoes and carrots...

...now to get to the till.

PLOUFFF!

What's the rush, Richard?... You haven't had a look down the middle aisle yet.

Oh no! It's the Lucifer of Lidl!...

Get thee gone!

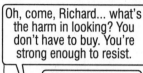

Oh, come, Richard... what's the harm in looking? You don't have to buy. You're strong enough to resist.

Well... I suppose...

They've got polyester kilts, one size fits all for just £6.99.

Ooh! I've always fancied a kilt.

I know, Richard... I know.

That's nice, that. It'd come in smashing if I were invited to a ceilidh, or a Scotch wedding.

Or a Burns' Night. I can see you piping in the haggis, Richard...

Go on, Richard... put it in your trolley.

Yes... I will.

Ooh! And what's this?

A barbecue tool set. How wonderful is that for £5.99?

It's magnificent!

It is, Richard...

...they're £30 in John Lewis.

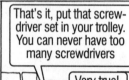

That's it, put that screwdriver set in your trolley. You can never have too many screwdrivers

Very true!

The same goes for wall mounted foil dispensers, and spare auto bulb kits.

'Ello...What's this!?!

It's a Bento Box, Richard... A kind of Japanese lunchbox

Look! You could put your sandwiches in that bit, and a scotch egg cut in quarters in that bit for when you go to your allotment.

And it comes with a pair of chopsticks.

But do I need one?

Not everything in life is about need, Richard. It is about desire... and you deserve it.

You're right. I DO!...

...and I'm HAVING the bloody thing.

And I'm having a self-inflating guest bed... and this fridge drinks can dispenser... and a drain weasel... and this whistle activated car key finder...

Yes, Richard, you deserve them.

And how about a fire proof metal document box file? I've got all my papers in one... the fire and brimstone doesn't touch them.

Yes!

Right! Let's get these paid for and home.

Yes. Well done, Richard.

Oh, dear! There is a lot of stuff here. And I did promise my wife I was just going to get potatoes and carrots.

Don't worry. Just say you'll never do it again...

...then spend the day in your shed.

PLOUFFF!

Put all those things back, Richard. You made a promise to your wife not to waste any money.

It's true... I did.

You think those items are good value, but together, they add up to just over £60...

£60!?! Good gracious!

Yes! You could get the exact same things at Aldi for just £55.

The Angel of Aldi

Blimey!

Now I mustn't forget the potatoes and carrots.

189

OUT OF (REMOTE) CONTROL

Family forced to watch costume drama after loss of TV remote

DRESS TO DEPRESS: *Family stuck watching 'boring' costume drama.*

A TEESSIDE family was left traumatised last week when the loss of their TV remote control meant they were forced to watch a Sunday evening BBC costume drama. Unable to change channel, Jack and Barbara Hacksaw were left with no option but to sit through the high-budget adaptation of an 18th century novel for an hour, leaving the couple and their two children extremely distressed.

The family's nightmare began a few minutes into *The Antiques Roadshow*, when Barbara, 49, declared the programme to be "like watching paint dry," and asked her son Callum change channel to see what else was on.

"There was just some woman going on about an old pot, and it was doing my head in," Mrs Hacksaw explained to reporters.

remote

However, 12-year-old Callum announced that he didn't have the remote, prompting a search of the living room involving the couple's daughter Amy, 15. But despite looking in all the usual places, the 6-inch device could not be found.

"We were getting a bit worried as the credits were starting to roll," said Mrs Hacksaw. "We knew there was some boring drama set in the olden days coming up, and there's no buttons on the actual telly."

"Then my husband, who had been upstairs on the toilet, came into the living room and saw us all turning the room upside down."

Mr Hacksaw told us: "I knew straight off what they were looking for. The roadshow had finished and I knew that what was coming on next was even worse."

"It was one of them period dramas with all horses and carriages and that, so I started looking for the bloody thing along with everybody else."

cruise

But as the orchestral strains of the drama's title music began, the family's TV remote had still not been found. And before they knew it, the drama had started and the unfortunate Hacksaws were stuck watching it.

"It was awful. There was all these women in bonnets, and the blokes all had really high collars and riding boots," said Jack. "Somebody was having a ball, and someone hadn't been invited or something," he said. "Christ, the bonnets. So many bonnets."

Mrs Hacksaw was as distressed as her husband, but with the remote control still missing, there was little the family of four could do but watch. "This bloke in a top hat wanted to marry this woman, but his mam wouldn't let him because she wasn't posh enough," she said. "They kept banging on about her not having a diary or something. I just wanted it to stop."

"There was no celebrities in it, and no voting. It was just boring," Mrs Hacksaw added.

central

The missing remote was eventually located underneath the family's dog, Buster, coming to light when Mr Hacksaw ordered the animal into the garden after it broke wind. But by this time it was too late, as the episode was already coming to an end. "I blame that bloody dog, I do," said Jack. "The bloody thing."

The following day, the Hacksaws ordered a universal TV remote from Amazon to act as a spare in case their original one goes missing again. "It's cost the thick end of twenty quid, but if it stops us having to sit through all that bollocksy language and people wearing big hats and riding around in horse-drawn carriages, it'll be worth every bloody penny," said Mrs Hacksaw.

LOVE IT OR LIST IT?

Home Re... with Ph...

IF YOU'RE lucky enough to own your own property, but the daily grind of the 200-yard round trip to your 'excellent' Ofsted-ranked primary in your 4x4 followed by the commute from your kitchen to your garden office/gym is getting you down, then you might be tempted to up-sticks and purchase a third home somewhere more desirable. However, Kirstie and I are here to try and talk you out of it and suggest that, with a few simple alterations, you can convert your current million-pound-plus property in a prohibitively exclusive south London suburb into a home that is *more* than up to the task of becoming *even more valuable*. Here are a few tips on putting the 'MULTI' into your million pound property!

ution Tips
Kirstie

1 Hall

The hallway is the first thing that a prospective buyer sees when they first pass through your front door and, as such, it needs to provide that 'Wow!' factor. An affordable way of achieving this is a simple declutter – getting rid of ugly coat hooks and shoe racks and replacing them with things guaranteed to make your visitors' jaws drop, like a single pair of diamond-encrusted shoes on a podium, or a blazer covered in gold leaf with pockets made out of fifty-pound notes. *Isn't that right Kirstles?*

2 Kitchen

Yes, Pip. **But don't forget about the kitchen!** This room is the heart of the home, and it's here that you'll be spending most of your quality family time, whether you're whittling wooden Christmas tree decorations, making antimacassar macramé chair backs or simply destroying your children's iPads. A larger kitchen increases the value of your home, and a neat way to get more space is to remove any radiators and boilers. *Won't that make it cold*, you ask? Not if you leave the doors of your AGA oven open 24/7, which will pump comforting, gas-fired heat back into the kitchen. Perfect for keeping the home cosy while you're away in your Cornish holiday retreat.

3 Living Room

A common mistake many people make is removing decorative period features – such as coving and cornicing in the living room – as this seriously devalues your property. If you haven't got any wainscotting, then put some in – you can get it in genuine oak for as little as £2,000 per foot. Fireplaces, too, are a selling point in your house, so never remove them. Even if you don't plan to use them as a fireplace, with a bit of creativity, they can be brought back into action. Just pop some urinal cubes in the grate and *voilà!* – another downstairs toilet.

4 Bedroom

Although the classic three-up four-down design of most suburban family homes gives a pair of good-sized bedrooms, more often than not a third single bed- or 'box' room lets the side down somewhat. If your small bedroom adjoins a neighbour's property, or if you just fancy some more space in your front double bedroom, there's no reason why you shouldn't get out your trusty sledgehammer and knock through to next-door to create a larger boutique-style bedroom suite for your property. This is best carried out while your neighbours are at work, since you'll want enough time to remove and brick up their spare room door. They probably only used it for storing their unimaginative, cheap, shop-bought belongings, anyway.

5 Bathroom

Steady on with the sledgehammer, Kirstington, we haven't got to the bathroom, yet! **The bathroom, like the kitchen, is another area where many of us spend a lot of quality time in the home,** whether it's escaping from the noise and chaos of family life to catch up with the latest Twitter news on our iPhones, or just taking a dump while checking how much our house is worth on Zoopla. Adding a Bang and Olufsen surround sound music system is a cheap (for me and Kirstie) way of giving your bathroom added saleability. And adding a Chubb lock and 5-point mortice deadlock to the inside of the door creates a sense of privacy and security that gives your humble WC the feel of being a real home-within-a-home.

6 Loft

Converting the loft is a great way of maximising the potential of your home, but the downside of gaining an extra playroom for your hubbie is the loss of useful storage space. An easy way to claw some back is to extend upwards and build another loft! Planning regulations require that you consult with your neighbours before undertaking this build, but I really wouldn't bother. If they complain, you could simply ask some of your lawyer friends to work *pro bono* for you and see them off. Anyway, once you've set a precedent, they'll want to extend their houses upwards, too.

7 Garden

The garden is all-too-often an afterthought with many modern homes, but you should think of it as an extended living space – a room outside your house. A poorly-kept back garden can actually deduct value from your home, so it's worth getting all your gardeners to put a bit of extra effort into maintaining your lawns and borders. If it's big enough, you could leave a section of it to grow into a natural haven for wild flowers and grasses. This is an ideal way to attract insects, birds and other wildlife into your urban space – and also a great place to take tricky headshots at any passing deer with a high-powered rifle.

8 Garage

Boys will be boys, P'lip! **These days, your home's original, outdated single car garage just isn't big enough to house the family 4x4,** hubbie's weekend convertible, your hybrid town car and the nanny's old banger for running the kids to and from boarding school. So why not convert that useless space into a fully-equipped bijou hobby room? Spotlights, storage shelves and workbenches salvaged and repurposed from local antique shops mean you can use your garage as a workshop for making Christmas corn dolly decorations, dyeing fabric with turmeric, painting pebbles and upcycling old lampshades.

WHOOPS AISLE APOCALYPSE

Oh, are you still here?

Shouldn't you be off on your daily rotten food safari?

I, er... Didn't think I'd bother going today.

What?

What? What?!

You haven't missed a *single day* haunting the reduced goods aisles since you *retired!*

Don't remind me.

I feel deeply ashamed of the whole episode.

Do you know, last week I *deliberately* tripped a child...

Little girl, no more than 5 or 6, full length on her face.

Purely so I could beat her mum to the rotisserie counter when the final chicken whoops went off early.

Wah-ah!

That is truly appalling.

Oh there's been worse.

Much worse.

Reduced To Clear

I began to see these total strangers as *enemies.*

Bitter rivals to be crushed.

Like that little old man in the flat cap.

BIF

BOF

BOOF

Did I ever tell you, he tried to run me over in the Asda car-park one day...

All that anger, that *rage*, and we don't even need the savings, not *really.*

My pension is *okay*, and you still bring in a decent wage...

Yesterday I *headed* an M&Ms Black Forest gateau from this young man's grip, 39p, incredible saving.

Saw him again this morning. He lives in a tent on the park!

One slice of it I ate. Threw the rest away. Bloody horrible.

A gateau which could've been the difference between life and death for that poor wretch!

I have a bit of news actually, in case you were wondering why I'm home early...

SOB

The office is closing. I'm out of a job.

Any pay-off?

Statutory minimum.

And I've only been there four years so...

Oh, and this was on the mat when I got back.

What is it?

BeG
British Electricity & Gas

Our new energy tariff.

Soon

Cold Me?

Reduced To Clear

Gasp!

STORE BLIM£Y!

Can Our Leaders Hack It as Pound Shop Managers?

BRITAIN is heading towards hard times. Experts predict that the cost of living is set to soar in the spring, with huge increases in the price of energy, food and clothing. Along with planned tax rises, the average household is set to find itself £2000 a year worse off. And as we Britons tighten our belts, our high streets will see a boom in the number of Pound Shops.

These wonderful retail outlets are Aladdin's caves of treasure, selling everything from unusually branded dog food and shampoos that look like Head and Shoulders but aren't to biscuits with Arabic writing on the back ... *all for a quid an item!*

But who will staff our new Pound Shops? Just like political parties, these magical stores require special kinds of people to take control, to make them function properly and to ensure that they provide exactly what the cash-strapped Great British public needs. *So who better to take on the mantle of Pound Shop Manager than the current leaders of our political parties themselves?*

Let's have a look at our current parliamentary kingpins to see if they have what it takes to run a successful Pound Shop.

BORIS JOHNSON: *Conservative and Unionist party**
(*at the time of going to press)

MAN OF THE PEOPLE Bojo has shown that he has what it takes to lead his party safely through a global pandemic which has killed over 150,000 of us. And it is this same leadership quality which would see him make an equally successful job of taking the reins at a Pound Shop.

Greeting customers at the door with his unruly mop of hair and his genial bonhomie, charismatic Johnson would definitely see footfall through his store increase. The ex-journalist is also a master wordsmith – *Get Brexit Done, Build Back Better*, and *Bung a Bob for a Big Ben Bong* are all memorable catchphrases that have done the Tory party proud, and Johnson would no doubt put this remarkable talent for dreaming up slogans to work in his store.

On the downside, filling the shelves of his shop with goods could prove costly. Just like during his time at No10, Johnson would award contracts to supply thin kitchen rolls, socket sets and instant coffee with 70% chicory to his friends, rather than trusted suppliers. The goods he bought in would almost certainly be substandard... if they arrived at all. His bumbling customer service would also leave a lot to be desired; any customer needing advice on returning a product or obtaining a refund would simply be fobbed off with some ludicrous lie that would convince nobody.

Pound Shop Manager Suitability Rating: 7/10

KIER STARMER: *Labour party*

ONE WORD which is used more than any other to describe Starmer's performances in the House of Commons is 'forensic'. And dull. So that's two words. And whilst the second may not count in his favour when managing his Pound Shop, the first most certainly will. For with his eye for detail, the ex-barrister will know where every item in the shop is shelved, exactly how many are left in stock, and when the delivery of new supplies is due. No detail will be too small to escape his meticulous, laser-like attention.

And Sir Keir has shown that he is not afraid to expel members of the Labour Party when he feels it is necessary to do so; similarly, he would brook no unacceptable behaviour from his Pound Shop staff. If they repeatedly turned up for work late, refused to perform required tasks, or displayed anti-semitic views, they would be given their P45.

And his time serving as head of the CPS would come in useful when dealing with shoplifters. Six years as Director of Public Prosecutions saw him tackle countless thieves, scammers and fraudsters, and as such Starmer would be wise to all the tricks and scams of any light-fingered customers at large in his store. He would come down on them hard, and word would quickly get round that Sir Keir's Pound Shop is not one where you can get a five-finger discount.

Pound Shop Manager Suitability Rating: 82%

CAROLINE LUCAS: *Green party*

THE ONLY Green party MP to sit in Parliament, Caroline Lucas champions not only her constituents in Brighton Pavilion, but also the whole planet. For well over a decade she has made incumbent Tory Prime Ministers uncomfortable with her pointed questions about their commitment to environmental issues.

And it's a certainty that Lucas would take her planet-friendly ethos into whichever workplace she was in, including any Pound Shop she managed. Upon taking the post, her first task would be give her staff full and generously termed working contracts with pension schemes and homoeopathic health benefits. Then, her team would set about ridding the shop of anything made from plastic, quickly followed by any stock that had a large carbon footprint, such as any product manufactured more than 5 miles from the store.

It is a pound to a penny that Lucas is a vegan, so *out* would go any foodstuffs containing animal derivatives, along with anything manufactured using environmentally damaging palm oil. All this – along with boycotting anything made by a machine and anything made by a multinational company – means that the shelves of Caroline's pound shop will be practically empty.

So whilst our planet might be safe in her hands, our Pound Shops would probably be facing extinction under Lucas's custodianship.

Pound Shop Manager Suitability Rating: ✱✱✱

IAN BLACKFORD: *Scottish Nationalist Party*

LEADER of the Westminster Scottish Nationalist Party, Ian Blackford is one of the most popular and respected politicians in the Palace of Westminster. And he would bring a similar gravitas to the position of Pound Shop Manager, should he choose to make that particular career change. With his soft, Scottish accent and his Blackford tartan waistcoat, he would be a popular figure with shop staff and customers alike.

He would also bring a Scottish twist to many of his products, selling bagpipes, tartan dishcloths and batter-coated deep-fried rolls of sellotape.

However, it is likely that the MP for Ross, Skye and Lochabar would insist on giving customers Scottish five pound notes in their change which, if his particular branch were south of the border, would get on everyone's tits. But this minor inconvenience may be more than offset by the popular move of bringing his store's Sunday trading hours in line with the shops in his Highlands constituency. Remaining open whilst competitors are forced by law to close should see sales boom.

But whilst well-liked by his customers, Blackford may not be as popular with his Pound Shop head office. Old Parliamentary habits die hard, and it is likely that Blackford will stand up and address the shop every Wednesday afternoon at 2:20, demanding that the area manager "do the decent thing and resign."

Pound Shop Manager Suitability Rating: B+

ED DAVEY: *Liberal Democrat party*

THE LEADER of the Liberal Democrats has one of the easiest jobs in Parliament. He can dream up the most popular, expensive and impossible policies safe in the knowledge that, thanks to the UK's 2-party 'First Past the Post' political system, he will never be called upon to implement them. Were he in charge of a Pound Shop, however, his decisions would be implemented straight away.

And as a result of never having held the reins of power, Davey is an untested entity. When he suddenly finds himself able to implement a 3 for 2 offer on My Little Pony hair bobbles, slashing 50% off fire-lighters, or reducing Mr Kipling's cakes approaching their sell-by date for quick sale, how will he react? As a seasoned politician, it is likely that he would rise to the occasion and take major decisions like these in his stride. But there is also the chance that it may prove too much for him, causing him to crumble under the pressure of massive decisions over pot noodles, watery bleach and other prime stock. As such, it would be a gamble for the Pound Shop head office to appoint him to the post.

But Davey is not completely wet behind the ears, having served as Secretary for State for Energy and Climate Change under the coalition government of 2012. As such, he will understand all about low energy light bulbs that promise 10,000 hours of life but pop after a week, rechargeable batteries that hold exponentially less current with each charge, and those door draught excluders shaped like a sausage dog. Stocking up on these items could future-proof the Liberal Democrat leader's store.

Pound Shop Manager Suitability Rating: 6×10^4

NIGEL FARAGE: *UKIP, Brexit party, Reform UK or whatever the fuck his party is called these days*

MANY PEOPLE believe Farage to be a racist, simply because of the things he says and the beliefs he holds, but nothing could be further from the truth. In reality, Farage is a true internationalist, and indeed both of the wives who threw him out were EU nationals.

But foghorn-voiced Nigel's international outlook is matched only by his love for his country, and doubtless the Pound Shop under his management would have a proudly British flavour to it. The most successful politician never to have been elected to parliament would greet his customers with a cheery smile, a cloud of cigarette smoke and a raised glass of bitter, and his shop would doubtless be full of proud patriots. Everything in Farage's store will have been manufactured in Great Britain by true blue British workers, and weighed goods would be sold in pounds and ounces, rather than foreign kilograms.

However, there would nevertheless be a few downsides to Nigel's stewardship of a Pound Shop. He would have to take care not to confuse customers by changing the name of the shop every five minutes as he has tended to do with his political parties. And his staff would be left to run the shop largely by themselves, as the seven-times failed parliamentarian is known to spend many hours voluntarily manning the White Cliffs of Dover on the lookout for migrants in boats. And when he is in store, he may similarly spend a lot of his working day standing at the shop entrance looking for certain kinds of people to keep out.

Pound Shop Manager Suitability Rating: $x = \dfrac{-b \pm \sqrt{b^2 - 4ac}}{2a}$

ROGER MELLIE
THE MAN ON THE TELLY

SO WHY DON'T YOU DO US ALL A FAVOUR, AND JUST FUCK RIGHT OFF...

...FUCK OFF TO THE FARTHEST CORNER OF FUCK OFF LAND. AND WHEN YOU'VE FUCKED OFF AS FAR AS YOU CAN FUCK OFF, KEEP GOING AND FUCK OFF SOME MORE...

TOM THE PRODUCER

...SO IT'S A BIG "GO FUCK YOURSELF, BRIAN" FROM ME AND EVERYONE IN YOUR OFFICE WHO YOU THINK ARE YOUR FRIENDS

THERE WE GO. ANOTHER FORTY QUID, TOM. KER-CHING!

I WISH YOU WOULDN'T DO THESE PERSONAL MESSAGES, ROGER

WHY NOT?. I GOT A QUID A "FUCK" FOR THAT ONE

I'M ONE OF THE BIGGEST EARNERS ON THE SITE AFTER FARAGE AND THAT BOJO IMPERSONATOR

IT'S JUST ALL SO GRUBBY, ROGER

DON'T BE SUCH A WET BLANKET, TOM, IT'S JUST A BIT OF FUN... ONE MORE TO DO

HELLO, TERRY IN DERBY. ROGER MELLIE HERE WITH A MESSAGE FOR YOU... YOU'RE A FUCKING WET FART OF A HUSBAND WITH A TINY COCK. AND YOU CAN TELL THAT CUNT OF A SISTER OF MINE THAT SHE'S WELCOME TO YOU, YOU PAIR OF CHEATING FUCKERS... AND THAT'S FROM YOUR WIFE SUE

THERE WE GO... ANYWAY, WHAT DID YOU CALL ME IN FOR, TOM?... A NICE, TASTY LITTLE EARNER, I HOPE

OH, I WOULDN'T SAY...

TALK TO ME

WELL, BAFTA WOULD LIKE YOU TO HOST THIS YEAR'S AWARDS CEREMONY, ROGER

WHAT!?. THAT'S FANTASTIC, TOM...

...I'LL BE FUCKING RAKING CASH IN!

ER... I DON'T KNOW ABOUT THAT, ROGER. IT'S A VERY PRESTIGIOUS JOB... YOU DO IT MORE FOR THE HONOUR THAN THE MONEY

BOLLOCKS, TOM.

...THAT CHRIS ROCK WAS PLAYING TO HALF EMPTY HOUSES TWO MONTHS BACK...

THEN HE DOES THE OSCARS, TAKES A FOURPENNY ONE OFF WILL SMITH AND YOU CAN'T GET A TICKET FOR HIS SHOW FOR LOVE NOR FUCKING MONEY

I'LL DO A BIT OF CONTROVERSIAL STUFF, GET SOME TWAT TO LAMP ME ...POP!... RIGHT IN THE KISSER... AND BOB'S YOUR UNCLE

NO! NO, THAT'S EXACTLY WHAT THEY WANT TO AVOID

OF COURSE THEY DON'T, TOM

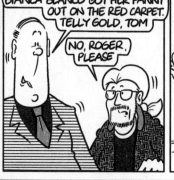

IT WAS THE BEST THING EVER HAPPENED AT THE OSCARS SINCE BIANCA BLANCO GOT HER FANNY OUT ON THE RED CARPET. TELLY GOLD, TOM

NO, ROGER, PLEASE

GIVE NETFLIX A RING, WILL YOU?. SEE HOW MUCH THEY'LL GIVE ME FOR A ONE MAN SHOW...

ACTUALLY, NO, NOT NETFLIX...

...THEY'RE GOING DOWN THE SHITTER. TRY AMAZON AND NOW T.V...

...SEE IF YOU CAN GET A BIT OF A BIDDING WAR GOING

A WEEK LATER...

THANK YOU! GOOD EVENING LADIES AND GENTLEMEN, AND WELCOME TO THE 75TH FILM ACCADEMY OF BRITISH TELLY, OR WHATEVER IT IS, AWARDS!

BRITISH ACADEMY AWARDS

AND I HOPE YOU'RE GOING TO BEHAVE YOURSELVES TONIGHT... I DON'T WANT ANYONE COMING UP HERE AND DOING A WILL SMITH ON ME, EH!?!

KER-POW!

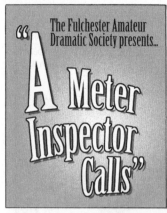

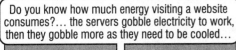

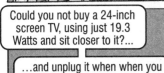

201

EINSTEIN A GO-GO!

TV brainbox fine and dandy after refusing to pay parking charge

PHYSICIST Professor Brian Cox escaped a £100 parking fine after successfully arguing that when his car was photographed illegally parked, in reality it had *not actually stopped*.

NO-SEE PARKER! *Boffin Cox's (inset) scientific reasoning overturned his airport parking penalty (below).*

The TV boffin was slapped with an automatic penalty in March, after dropping a friend off in an undesignated area at Newcastle airport. Cox, 48, had pulled up on the red lines on the airport approach road to avoid paying the £4 charge in the drop-off and pick-up zone.

But he was caught on security camera and issued with a £100 statutory penalty, reduced to £50 if paid within 14 days.

However, rather than stump up, the pop-star-turned-physicist decided to challenge the fine in court… and the judge ended up siding with him.

boot

Hampton Stalkon, representing the airport, showed the court CCTV footage of Cox's Citroen C3 pulling up on the approach road, and the TV boffin getting out to help his friend remove a suitcase from the boot.

The footage clearly showed the car parked by a large sign reading 'No Stopping. Penalty £100'.

EXCLUSIVE!

But speaking to magistrates, Cox, whose hit includes *Things Can Only Get Better*, argued that although his car appeared to be stationary, that was only relative to the airport and all other stationary objects on Earth.

womble

"If a car were to drive past the other way, an observer in that car would see my car moving past them, whilst *they* appeared to be stationary," he told the court.

"It's like when you are on a train pulling out of the station. It appears at first that you are stationary, and it is the station that is moving away from you. Which in relative terms, it is," Professor Cox continued.

"In fact, my car was, is, and will always be in motion through space relative to every other object in the universe," Cox continued. "To say that I had stopped on the approach road is just wrong."

The mop-top brainbox said that had the sign read 'No Stopping relative to a fixed point on the earth', he would not have pulled up to drop off his friend. But; he argued, as it stood, the sign was unscientifically worded and ambiguous.

bomber

Magistrates agreed, overturning the fine and awarding costs to Professor Cox who, described the verdict as "a victory for rational, scientific thought".

It is not the first time that science has come to Cox's legal rescue. Last year, he was charged with smashing the windows of a neighbour's car with a hammer after it was left parked across his drive. His £300 fine for Breach of the Peace was overturned after he told the court that the atoms making up the hammer were, in quantum terms, more than 99.99% empty space, and so would have passed harmlessly through the glass.

PARKING ADVICE *with Graham Parker*

HI THERE! Graham Parker out of 70s new wave rock band Graham Parker and the Rumour here. You might remember me from *Top of the Pops* singing chart toppers like *Hey Lord Don't Ask Me Questions* and many more. But as well as singing Top Ten hits, I also have a passion which, as coincidence would have it, my second name describes – *I'm a parker of cars!* That's right, I'm an absolute sod for driving cars to a standstill in a small space. But parking cars is actually more difficult than you think. And *Hey Lord*, (you) *Don't* (need to) *Ask Me Questions* about parking, because here are a few words of advice to make it easier, safer, and more enjoyable for everyone.

1. BUY A SMALL CAR. There is no standard width for parking bays in the United Kingdom, and some can be extremely narrow, especially in city centres. So a slim vehicle, like a Smart car or an old-fashioned Mini, will make parking easier. Better still, get one of those old cigar-shaped single-seat racing cars like Stirling Moss used to drive for the easiest city centre parking experience of all.

2. IT'S EASIER TO DRIVE FORWARDS OUT OF A PARKING SPACE THAN IT IS TO BACK OUT. So always *back into* the space. Or even easier, choose a central spot where the bays are in banks of two and look for one with adjoining empty spaces – then simply drive into one bay, continue over the front line and into the adjoining bay, ready to drive out forwards – the old 'drive in, drive out' technique, as it is known amongst we parking enthusiasts.

3. ALWAYS PARK IN A BAY ON THE EXTREME LEFT OF A BLOCK, as this will mean you will be able to open your driver's door easily without obstruction. This is assuming it is the left hand bay as *you look at them*, that you are *reversing* into the space, and that you are driving a *right-hand drive* vehicle. If one of these factors does not apply, then park in the bay on the extreme right. If *two* of the factors do not apply, then it's the left again.

4. IF YOU ARE PARKING IN A NARROW BAY WITH VEHICLES EITHER SIDE, pull into the bay as close as possible to the car on your left, giving you more room on the driver's side. And here's a strange thing – if you *reverse* into the bay rather than drive in forwards, you would think it would be the car on your *right* you would need to get close to. But it's still the car on your *left*. How weird is that?

Martyn Lewis's Money Saving Parking Tips

AS WE all feel the pinch of the Cost of Living Crisis, Martyn Lewis tells us how to save the pennies when parking.

WHEN pulling up in a car park, don't immediately jump out and buy a ticket. Wait until you see the parking attendant arrive before getting out and heading for the Pay and Display machine. If they have just visited the site, it could be a couple of hours before they come round again - that's 2 hours parking for FREE! Take a copy of *The Puzzler* or a Rubik's Cube to pass the time until they arrive.

DRIVE a large car. Since parking for a set period of time costs the same no matter how much of the parking bay your vehicle occupies, it stands to reason that a large car will cost less per square foot to park than a small one.

A SET of false number plates attached to your car before parking means you won't have to buy a ticket. Parking attendants do not have access to the DVLA computer and so cannot see that the plates do not match the vehicle model, and the police aren't interested. *(Please note how this 'tip' was worded as a set of facts rather than recommendations, since the practice of putting false registration plates on a vehicle is strictly illegal).*

F4KE PL4TE5

MOST car parks make users pay for a full hour or part thereof. So if you only want to park for half an hour, ask around to see if any other motorists in a similar situation want to go 'halfers' on a ticket, arranging to hand it over to them as you leave the car park.

PARK IN RYDE

WE'VE got a ticket to park in Ryde, and we don't care. Because we're giving away a up to 6-hours parking in the beautiful Isle of Wight seaside town to one lucky winner of our Park in Ryde competition. To win, simply look at the four photographs of car parks in Ryde on the Isle of Wight, and then match them up with the correct car park name. Send your answers – along with a parking ticket valid at any Ryde car park – to: Park in Ryde Competition, Viz Comic, PO Box 841, Whitley Bay, NE26 9EQ. The first lucky winner out of the hat will have their parking charge reimbursed. As usual, every entry enclosing a large letter stamp will receive a free Viz Cheap Pen, as we've got to get rid of the fucking things somehow.

Quay Road ☐   St. Thomas Street ☐   Appley Park Long Stay ☐   Ryde Esplanade ☐

Car park A: This fruity sounding car park might keep the doctor away for a while!

Car park B: You *would* like to be beside the seaside, beside the sea if you parked here!

Car park C: Park your car here, and you'll be holy (wholly) satisfied with the car park's name!

Car park D: This isn't on Lock Road, it's on _____ Road (sounds like the *opposite* thing!)

In the event of a tie (ie, that we accidentally pull two correct entries out of the hat at the same time) please complete the tie-breaker in 12 words or less. Sorry, not less, fewer.

I think the Isle of Wight has some of the best car parking facilities in the UK because...

ROAD TO RECOVERY

Hospital parking scheme proves hit with visitors

HOSPITAL parking has always been a hot topic of debate for British people. Whether it's over-inflated charges, fines for running over time, or difficulty finding a spot during busy spells, few things are more likely to get us complaining. But now one local health authority is running a trial scheme which, if successful, should make hospital parking a less stressful experience.

Since last week, when Cramlington Hospital's brand new parking scheme was introduced, people visiting sick family members have not had to get out of their vehicles. Friends and relatives are now able to drive right through the main doors of the hospital, into lifts and along the corridors to the wards, before parking at the patients' bedsides.

Visitors are charged a flat £2, whether they stay for five minutes or the full hour, and so far the pilot project has proved a hit with hospital visitors.

being

"My wife has been in here a week with women's things, and parking is an absolute nightmare," said 56-year-old Harold Dirtcrumbs. "Being able to pull my XJ6 up by her bedside makes things so much easier."

Mavis Ringworm, whose husband Les is in Ward 3 after having his haemorrhoids tidied up, said that the new bedside parking scheme was a game changer. "In the old days, you could never find a space, and if you did, it would be miles away at the far end of the car park," she said. "Now, I can just jump in the car in my slippers because I don't even need to get out."

toast

Hospital administrator Brent Crudoil said the early signs indicated the scheme would be a success. "There have been a few issues with the wards filling up with exhaust fumes during visiting hours," he told reporters. "But we just opened a few windows and now insist that all engines are switched off while cars are parked up at patients' bedsides, and that seems to have sorted it."

There were also problems on the first day, when visitors were not able to pass each other in the hospital corridors, leading to a gridlocked traffic jam which stretched all the way from X-ray to Endoscopy. "It was just a few teething problems," said Crudoil.

"We set up a one-way system with visitors coming in through the main entrance and leaving via Critical Care and Diagnostic Imaging, and it's all fine now," he added.

Mr Crudoil pointed out that nurses and doctors could not bring their own vehicles inside the hospital building, and are still required to use the car parks, paying £2.60 per hour or part thereof.

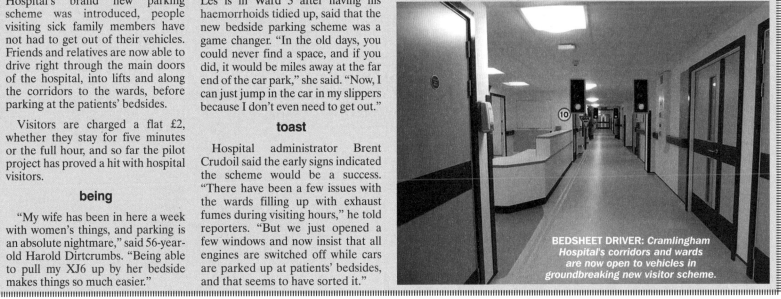

BEDSHEET DRIVER: *Cramlingham Hospital's corridors and wards are now open to vehicles in groundbreaking new visitor scheme.*

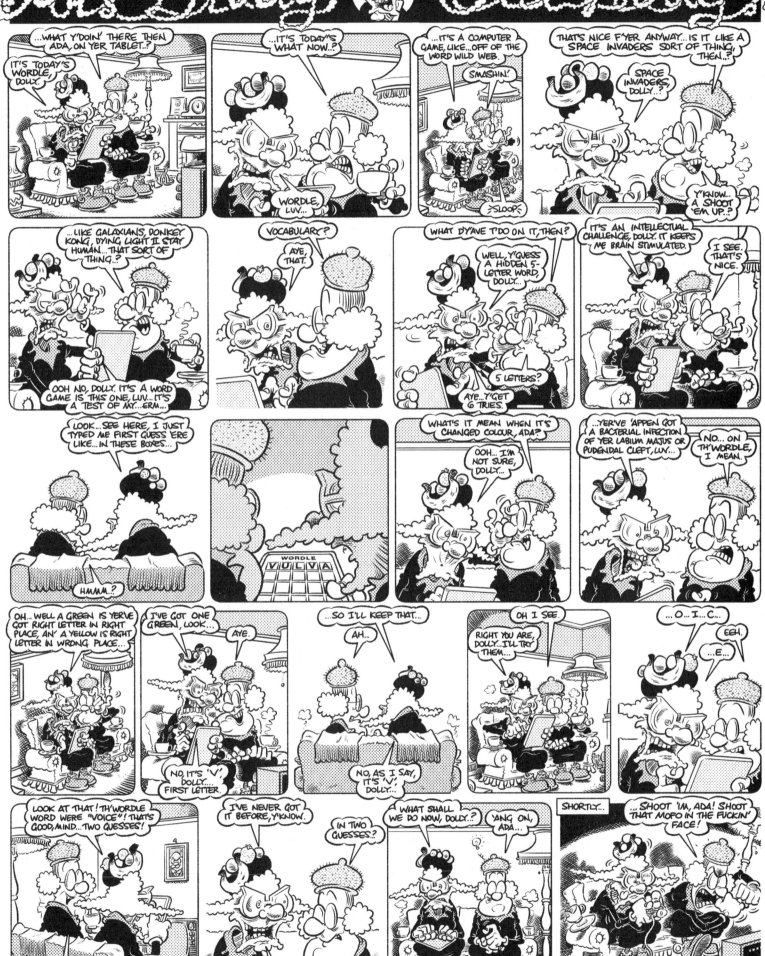

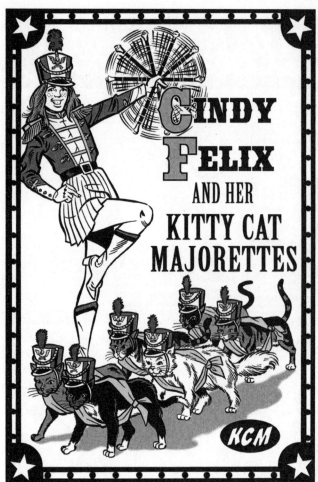

CINDY FELIX AND HER KITTY CAT MAJORETTES

KCM

One morning, Cindy received a phone call...

Yes... yes of course... we'll be there. See you this afternoon.

Okay, Kitty Cat Majorettes... that was the vicar...he wants us to march for the children at the local orphanage this afternoon.

Isn't that exciting!?!

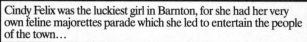

Cindy Felix was the luckiest girl in Barnton, for she had her very own feline majorettes parade which she led to entertain the people of the town...

Come on, Majorettes, up you get...

...we've got a show to do.

Shortly...

Here we go... who's first?

Come on, Ringo... in you go.

WEEEEOW!

Don't be silly, you've done this before.

WEEEOWWWW!

Now stop hissing. That's naughty.

There. That wasn't so bad, was it.

WEEEOWWWW!

Now you, Lucille.

WEEEEOWWWWW!

HISSS!

Owwww!

Jesus, you've scratched me to ribbons...

...bloody thing!

No, Lucille!

Come back!

Lucille! No! We've got a show to do.

Come down, Lucille, please...

...I've got Dreamy Treats...

Baggums! No!...

BAGGUMS!

206

Next week: The fire brigade are called to get the cat down from the tree, and the vicar loses an eye after helping Cindy get the hats on the other cats by first wrapping them in a towel.

LETTERbOCKS

LETTERS@VIZ.CO.UK

THE world is our oyster, some people say. But the first – and indeed the last – time I had oysters was on a third date with a lass, and it culminated in a fart with an unexpected side of gravy, both of which were highly audible. She instantly left, leaving me with my dirty mess and a heightened sense of embarrassment.

Terry Tittybiscuits, Leeds

LIKE many of your readers, I only allow myself to shit on days which are prime numbers, ie. the 1st, 2nd, 3rd, 5th, 7th, 11th, 13th, 17th, 19th, 23rd, 29th and 31st of each month. Whilst I can now satisfactorily manage the repeating three-day gaps early in the month, I'm struggling by the time I get to the 28th. How do other readers cope with this conundrum?

K. Sixpilot, Ruddington

I KNOW the BBC is quite rightly committed to balance and impartiality in their news coverage, but could they stop inviting people who are quite obviously twats onto their programmes, whatever side of the debate they are on? I'm thinking specifically of Julia Hartley-Brewer.

Toby Quatermass, London

STAR LETTER

I WAS recently refused entry to the Cathedral in Seville because my shoulders were exposed. When I returned – attired more modestly – the next day, I was flabbergasted to find Jesus hanging around all over the place dressed in only his pants. Why do I have to dress like a nun when they allow Jesus in dressed only in a tatty loincloth? It's one rule for the Son of God, Saviour of all Mankind, and another for the rest of us.

Mrs B, London

WHAT is the point of sweat glands in your arsecrack or under the knacker-sack? Explain that one, Mr "evolution" Darwin, and I bet you can't. Falling apples my arse. Or was that the other one?

Pard, Bridgwater

WHEN I was 13, a friend and myself went to communion classes at our church. I thought I would do a little fart to cheer things up, but I misjudged it and the fart echoed loudly. The Vicar lost his place and stared at me, and I swear his eyes glowed red with anger. It felt as if he was possessed by the Devil. Has anyone else had a bad experience with a member of the clergy?

Tess Stickles, W'shire

IN the 80s, horror films would have scenes where blood came out the taps in the victim's house, yet modern films don't have them. I miss those scenes and wonder if they could be reintroduced.

David Edwards, Bridgeport

PooTube Postbag

MY cat weighs 5kg and does turds approximately half an inch wide. I weigh 90kg, so on a pro-rata basis, I should be doing turds 9-inches in diameter. It's no wonder he sleeps 20 hours a day. If I did a turd that big, I'd need a good long rest afterwards as well.

S Brookes, Edinburgh

I SAW a report recently that said it costs the NHS £350k every year to remove foreign objects from patients' arses. Why don't they introduce a service for putting objects in, rather than pulling them out? Some people would pay good money for that, bringing in much-needed revenue. And ensuring that it was done in a medically safe manner will save more money further down the line. Frankly, I'm amazed health bosses haven't thought of this already.

Steve Crouch, P'borough

HEAVEN forbid, but if I ever go to hospital with one of my daughter's Barbie dolls lodged in my arse, I'll make sure I tell the staff exactly how it got there, truthfully and honestly. We'll see who squirms first, Dr Judgey.

Joe Hartshorn, Alness

I RECENTLY spotted former *Crackerjack* legend Stu "I could crush a grape" Francis in Astley Bridge Asda. When I enquired about an autograph, he was very obliging. But when I asked him who I should make it out to, he just stormed off in a hissy fit.

R Snowdon, Astley Bridge

I DON'T know anything about football, but I constantly find myself getting asked which team I support by my mates down the pub, and am then embarrassed and ridiculed when I have no answer. Can any *Viz* readers suggest who is the best team to support, preferably one that wins all the time?

Stelrad Doulton, Norwich

THE perforations in toilet paper are an absolute godsend, making it so easy to tear off convenient lengths of arse-wipe after parking your breakfast. However, I still take a pair of scissors into the khazi each time I go, just in case the shit-ticket perforation machine had gone on the blink that day.

Stelrad Doulton, Norwich

I'VE noticed that many German names sound a bit odd to British ears. One that came up in the football the other day really made me giggle: it was "Cock" or "Cunt", or something like that, I can't exactly remember now. There's probably even funnier ones out there if we but knew more about Germans. And, before anyone blasts off about racism, my ex-wife is a German, or Swiss or something.

H Rolf, Aberdeen

I AM due to visit my cousin in Holland next week, and I'm particularly looking forward to meeting her new cat. I'm concerned, however, that because the cat is Dutch, he will not understand when I say "pusspusspusss" to him. I was also planning on taking him a pack of Dreamies, but am worried that he may consider it 'foreign muck'. Can any *Viz* readers offer advice on these language and food issues?

Ryan Collins, Leicester

YOU could make a fortune by entering a racehorse in a greyhound race, or perhaps a greyhound in a horse race, whichever is the faster. I mean, I haven't looked into this properly, but it's definitely worth a go.

John Moynes, Dublin

THE word 'cafe' is an anagram of the word 'face.' And everyone who goes in a cafe has a face. What are the chances of that?

Bobby Trousers, Woking

THE pension triple lock means we nearly-deads are looking at a 10% pay increase for doing nothing, other than not going on strike. I think these striking train Johnnies could learn a lesson from us wrinklies.

Stuie, Bunny

CONTRARY to popular belief, you cannot actually see the Great Wall of China from space. But strangely enough, you can see space from the Great Wall of China, even though space is much, much further away. Weird or what?

TC Rusling, Cottingham

MUSIC SHOP ...AND OF COURSE, THIS PIANO COMES COMPLETE WITH A STOOL.

WHEN emptying baked beans into a pan, I always make sure I don't leave a single bean in the tin. It would break my heart to think of one bean left in the bottom all alone whilst his family make their way to the warmth of my ample belly. Do any other readers have similar feelings of compassion regarding baked beans?

Wolfgang Turnip,
Lower Saxony

DO ghosts wank?

Gerry Paton,
London

❋ That's a very good question, Mr Paton, but a more fundamental question before that must surely be 'do ghosts exist?' Only when that conundrum is answered in the affirmative, can the question of whether or not they pull themselves off be addressed.

DOES anybody else think horses get songs stuck in their heads? I think they might have a good old nod to *Paranoid* by Black Sabbath.

Pastor Mike Tyson,
Chorlton-on-the-Wheelie

"ONE for sorrow, two for joy, three for a girl and four for a boy," the adage about magpies goes. Well I spotted a single magpie in my garden last week and this morning I woke up to find I'd shit the bed. So maybe there is something to these old superstitions after all.

Gary Ireland, Tauranga

I RECENTLY bought some Peppa Pig lollies from the local discount supermarket. Having taken a few bites, I looked down and saw what can only be described as a boaby. Needless to say I vomited, put my foot through the lolly and sent Lidl the bill.

James Carr, email

MY daughter's boyfriend is an idiot. When he comes round to our house, he hangs up his jacket, leaving his wallet in its pocket and I help myself to £20 each time.

Dominic Twose, L'ton Spa

MUSTARD and custard are both yellow, so the suffix 'ustard' must mean yellow. But there's a bird called a bustard, and it isn't yellow, but rather a sort of brown and white. Explain that, Susie Dent.

Joe Williams, Leeds

PLACE several giant teddy bears around your house to trick visitors into thinking that you are extremely good at fairground games.

Peter Brush, Leeds

OLD people. Appear younger by not frowning at every meal you are served, before tipping industrial quantities of salt over it.

Terry Wilson, York

FELLAS. Next time your wife is going for a coffee with a friend, why not tag along? You'll get a coffee and a bun, and it will save her having to recite the entire conversation to you word for word when she gets home.

Eldon Furse, email

MONOCLE wearers. Whenever you are surprised by something, emphasise that surprise by letting the optical device fall from your eye.

Dog Poo Magoo,
Bognor Regis

WHEN jamming your toast, lay it on the floor first then add butter and jam, thus ensuring that this side is facing up when on the floor.

Thomas Kemp, Belfast

SAVE money on your weekly shop by placing a house brick in the bottom of each of your carrier bags.

Gordon Syrup, email

toptips@viz.co.uk

I REALLY wish the word 'truss' rhymed with 'guff'. That way, when comedy former prime Minister Liz Truss was mentioned on the radio, I could say "Liz Truss? Liz Guff, more like," in a voice dripping with satirical derision. Sadly, it doesn't.

Bernard Hughes, London

MY bank has just emailed me to say they've "Got My Back" and I can rely on them like a friend. Well, if any of my friends had £2.3 trillion in assets and they didn't bung me a bit of cash to pay my fucking leccy bill, I'd wonder if they were really my friend after all. So shove that up your arse, HSBC.

W Fuzzbottom,
Cheese-on-toast-
on-the Wold

I SAW this work of art entitled *'Smile Cunt'* on a wall near Newcastle train station. We often say that the best things in life are free, but in using a dollar sign instead of the letter S, the artist is challenging our preconception of this notion. Perhaps they are saying that happiness does indeed come at a price. And having the letter T resemble a cross, are they questioning the notion of organised religion, implying that God is not the route to either happiness or wealth?

William Wiffles, Howden

SOME years ago, PG Tips stopped using chimpanzees in their adverts, citing animal welfare concerns, even though their decision put 3 chimps on the dole. But surely with all this modern CGI malarkey, they could bring them back in animated form and have them getting up to all sorts of tea-based japes without a single chimp having to lift a finger. Come on PG Tips boffins, sort it out!

Timmy Fish, Mansfield

WHY is it that whenever I want to go to a busy London restaurant, I have to phone up and make a reservation weeks in advance? Yet birds use my garden bird table whenever they like without even having the decency to ask permission. In my opinion, it's all gone downhill since Bill Oddie was taken off the television. These feathered rascals now think they can do whatever they please.

Major P. Cocktail, Lincoln

What would the anti-woke arseholes do if they were...

WOKE for a DAY

UP AND DOWN the country, from Lands End to John O'Groats, as well as across the width of it, from Lowestoft Ness to Ardnamurchan Point, we've all wondered what it would be like to be *Woke For A Day*. If we found ourselves inexplicably transformed into a treasonous Marxist do-gooder, hell-bent on dismantling proud traditions such as racism, sexism and homophobia, how would we spend 24 hours? And this quandary doesn't just plague the average Joe in the street - it also haunts the arsehole celebrity set, too. We phoned three of our favourite anti-woke bellends and asked them: *What would YOU do if you went Woke For A Day?*

Laurence Fox,
arsehole failed actor

AS AN ANTI-WOKE firebrand, I steadfastly refuse to kneel, due to kneeling's toxic association with the Stalinist #BlackLivesMatter movement. So if I went *Woke For A Day*, I'd take the opportunity to do all the kneeling-based chores I haven't been able to perform for the last few years - such as tying my shoelaces and fixing that leak under the sink. If I had any time left after that, I'd probably have fun doing a few other knee-centric activities, such as weeding the garden or pretending to be a child by shuffling about with my shoes on my knees. All things considered, it would be a refreshing change of pace to be able to bend my leg joints without worrying about accidentally advocating communism.

Jeremy Clarkson,
arsehole petrolhead

I FAMOUSLY love red meat - so much so that I once lamped my producer for failing to get me a steak. However, my weakness for thick slabs of cooked beef has played havoc with my backside over the years. So if I went *Woke For A Day* I would take advantage of the Woke Mob's strict vegan diet to give my poor old ringpiece a break! I'd get up at the crack of dawn to tuck into some high-fibre porridge oats instead of my usual Full English, then I'd stuff my face with other easily-digested leftie delicacies - such as chickpeas, kale and quinoa - before enjoying the sensation of doing a shit that didn't feel like I was trying to push a Pringles tin through my balloon knot.

Katie Hopkins,
arsehole columnist

I HAVE TALKED many times on television and radio about my hatred for tattoos, and how I simply would not employ anyone who was tattooed in any way. So if I were suddenly *Woke for a Day*, I would get myself down to the nearest tattoo shop and have one done. I'd probably have a big hunting scene all down my back with all horses and hounds and everything, and the fox disappearing into my arsehole. Or if that was too expensive, I'd have a big 'W' tattooed on each buttock, so as when I bent over, it would say WOW. I'm assuming in that in this thought experiment, when I wake up the next day as my usual anti-woke self, the tattoos have gone, otherwise, I may have to think again.

NATIVITY on a TRAIN

IN THE DAYS OF HEROD THE KING THERE WENT OUT A DECREE THAT ALL THE WORLD SHOULD BE COUNTED, AND SO JOSEPH WENT UP FROM GALILEE WITH MARY WHO WAS GREAT WITH CHILD...

...AND BOARDED THE 8:20 TO BETHLEHEM WITH STOPS AT CANA, NAIN AND ARIMATHEA

DID YOU REMEMBER THE TOFFIFEE?

FEEEEEEP!

HELLO — WE'RE JUST THREE TRAVELLERS ON THE WAY HOME TO BETHLEHEM! ARE THOSE SEATS FREE?

CHUG CHUG CHUG CHUG

AHHH! A NICE BIT OF SIT DOWN!

WHEREABOUTS IN BETHLEHEM D'YOU LIVE?

OH, ERM... NEAR THE, ER... ARBORETUM.

ARBORETUM? WHAT ARBORETUM?

CHUGGA CHUGGA CHUGGA CHUGGA

NO, NOT THE ARBORETUM YOU FOOL, THE, ER... ER... SWIMMING BATHS!

WOULD YOU EXCUSE US GENTLEMEN — MY WIFE NEEDS THE TOILET.

DO I?

YES!

WHAT ON EARTH...?

THOSE THREE HAVE NEVER BEEN TO BETHLEHEM IN THEIR BLOODY LIVES!

LOOK — THEY'RE FOLLOWING US!

THEY'RE HEROD'S GOONS SENT TO MASSACRE OF THE INNOCENTS US!

RUN FOR IIIIIIIIIT!!!

PUFF! GASP! OH NO — IT'S THE LAST CARRIAGE!

QUICK — TIME FOR THE ASCENSION OF MARY!

OO-ER!

NNNOOO!!! PANT! THERE!

I THINK WE'VE LOST THEM!

OHHHH, YOU'RE NOT LEAVING US SO SOON...

IT'S TIME TO PUT AN END TO CHRISTIANITY BEFORE IT EVEN BEGINS, EH BOYS!

RIGHT!

HEH HEH!

ALL RIGHT ALL RIGHT! MARY AND I ARE KNEELING DOWN LIKE THE SCRIPTURE SAYS!

OH AYE? ISAIAH 45, UNTO ME EVERY KNEE SHALL BOW?

NO, MORE LIKE EZEKIEL 45...

...YOU SHALL OBSERVE THE PASSOVER!

LOW BRIDGE

CHUGGA CHUGGA CHUGGA CHUGGA CHUGGA CHUGGA

GAAAAHHH!!! WELL YOU MAY HAVE GOT RID OF THOSE OTHER TWO GOONS...

BUT I AM FULLY CAPABLE OF MASSACRE OF THE INNOCENTSISING YOU ALL BY MYSELF!

NOT SO FAST, GOON OF HEROD!

WE HAVEN'T TRAVELLED ALL THE WAY FROM ORIENT ARE FOR YOU TO SPOIL THE BIRTHDAY PARTY!

AND WE'VE GOT A GIFT FOR YOU...

... A KNUCKLE SANDWICH!!!

SMACK!!!

AAAAYEEEEEEEEEEEE!!!!!

WELL! WHO WOULD'VE I-MAGI-NED THE JOURNEY WOULD'VE TURNED OUT LIKE THAT, EH MARY —

AAAAHHHHHHH!!!

WHA?! MARY?!?!!!

♪ AAAAAAHHHHHHHH!!! ♫

UNTO US A CHILD IS BORN!

AND WE ARE ON SCHEDULE TO ARRIVE IN BETHLEHEM STATION AT 11:52!

HERE'S SOME GOLD!

AND SOME FRANKINCENCE!

AND SOME MYRRH!

11:52...

HOW WAS YOUR TRIP JOSEPH — NICE 'N' RELAXING I HOPE?

OH YES, NOTHING TOO EXCITING...

IN FACT I'D SAY IT WAS ALL QUITE UN-ADVENTFUL!

HA HA HA HA!

ALSO TECHNICALLY IT'S THE ASSUMPTION OF MARY, NOT ASCENSION. BUT WHATEVER.

Take a Shit

IT AIN'T E

Global WARNING: "My climate activism has left my life in tatters," says so-divorced eco-warrior

Green man: *Carnegie Vestibule has given up his life to eco-campaigning.*

IN EVERY high street, office and home; on TV, radio and social media, it's all anyone is talking about: *CLIMATE CHANGE.*

And despite being a Marxist myth invented by the *Guardian*-reading Wokerati, the far-fetched idea that our Earth is gradually "getting hotter" has somehow caught the public imagination, and is now rammed down our throats whichever way we turn.

Self-righteous activists such as Greta Thunberg and David Attenborough are constantly up on their high horses, lecturing us about eating beef and using deodorant. Hollywood A-Listers are getting in on the act, too, with icons such as Leonardo DiCaprio and Sting jetting around the world in their private planes to bang on about the dangers of fossil fuels.

However, while these celebrity eco-warriors are lauded by the mainstream media as big-hearted heroes, not every environmental campaigner receives the same adulation.

Just ask **CARNEGIE VESTIBULE**.

Mild-mannered eco-warrior Carnegie has dedicated approximately **ONE TWENTY-EIGHTH** of his life to campaigning for a greener future for our children. But rather than being lionised for his important work, he has received nothing but fines, divorce papers and ankle tags.

"It's just so utterly, utterly unjust," sobs the 61-year-old unemployed Tamworth freedom fighter. "All I want is for the British public to recognise the harm we as a specie are doing to our planet. But in return, I get showered with four-letter abuse and kicked out of my house."

"You couldn't make it up," he adds.

A strict vegan who eats meat **ONLY** in emergencies, such as when he is hungry, environmentally conscious Carnegie devotes his time to performing extreme stunts, strikes and protests aimed at raising awareness of global warming. "I don't take pleasure in disrupting ordinary people's lives with my demonstrations," weeps the registered sex offender. "My actions are drastic only because the situation is quite literally life or death for our planet."

Speaking exclusively to *Take A Shit*, public-spirited Carnegie outlines the huge personal and professional sacrifices he has made in order to divert the human race from its trajectory of self destruction.

As told to **Vaginia Discharge**

HIGHWAY TO HELL

Carnegie's first brush with climate activism came three decades ago, on the morning of his wedding to his beloved now-ex-wife Noreen.

"I ended up being several hours late for my own nuptials, because I had chained myself to a tree in the local park, protesting against the deforestation of the Amazon," says the big-hearted dad-of-six. "Of course, since it was the morning after my stag-do, Noreen assumed that I'd been tied up there by my mates as a drunken prank, mainly because I had been sick down myself and was wearing just my pants and a pair of novelty breasts. But she was wrong. It was about the rainforest. Simple as, end of.

I got a right old earful from Noreen for that protest, so I decided to knock the climate activism on the head for the next few decades and focus on being a phenomenal husband and father. However, as reports about the Earth's rising temperature increased over the years, I could no longer stand on the sidelines and watch the environment spiral into chaos. I felt compelled to act.

Last year, I was hugely impressed by the protests of the ecogroup *Insulate Britain*, who blocked the M25 motorway to raise awareness of poor energy efficiency in UK housing. Their bold stunt grabbed headlines and really got people talking, and it inspired me to do the very same thing.

> **"**I needed my wits about me for my climate stunt. So I stuck firmly to mineral water. And white cider.**"**

I decided I would blockade the Hints Bypass between Tamworth and Muckley Corner – one of the busiest B-roads in south-east Staffordshire. Yes, I would disrupt several hundred commuters' journey to work – but I would also spread the message loud and clear that we had to act **NOW** if we wanted to save the planet from overheating. Plus, as luck would have it, I had a mate's stag-do in Lichfield the night before my planned protest, so I was heading to Muckley Corner anyway.

At the bachelor party, the booze flowed freely, but I needed my wits about me for my climate stunt. So I stuck firmly to mineral water. And white cider. As I left the gentlemen's club at 3am, my mind was focused solely on the vital task ahead of me. My own car had been written off the previous week after a parked motorbike had crashed into me on the way home from the pub, so I had taken Noreen's Citroen Saxo instead. She loved that car – but presumably she also loved planet Earth, so I assumed she would understand.

I could not have been more wrong.

I parked the Saxo in the middle of the empty bypass, expertly blocking both lanes, and decided to have a quick kip before the shit really hit the fan. I woke an hour or so later to a blaring cacophony of car horns and police sirens all around me. I had to chuckle, despite an inexplicable splitting headache. *My brave stunt had gone like clockwork, and the government would be forced to take action as a result!*

Two coppers yanked me out of the Saxo and slapped on the cuffs. I'd been expecting this, of course – most of the Insulate Britain lot had been arrested for their actions, too. But what I *hadn't* been expecting was my wife's reaction.

Noreen was standing beside the police van with a face like a slapped arse. Rather than commending me for my planet-saving actions, she began calling me every name under the sun. I tried to explain that what appeared to be a drunken car crash into the barriers was in fact a carefully staged demonstration against climate change, but she simply wouldn't listen to reason – mainly because I had been sick a fair bit in the Citroen and was wearing a pair of novelty breasts. And, unlike the Insulate Britain lot, I had forgotten to bring any banners or leaflets.

As I sat in my cell that night, I felt proud. Proud to have taken a stand against corporate greed. But at the same time I felt inconsolably sad. Sad that my beloved hatchet-faced missus seemed to despise our beautiful planet and all its inhabitants.**"**

STICKY SITUATION

Carnegie's courageous motorway caper earned him a slap on the wrist in the form of three hundred hours' community service. But despite pushback from both the police and his wife, the brave eco-warrior re-doubled his efforts to campaign for a greener future.

" Earlier this year, I watched with great interest as protestors from *Just Stop Oil* glued themselves to priceless paintings to gain publicity for their cause," says the brave divorcee. "Despite both my missus and the filth being dead against my climate activism, I couldn't let governments and corporations continue to pollute the world with fossil fuels. So, without a single thought for my own wellbeing or criminal record, I planned another protest.

I decided that the *Just Stop Oil* lads were really onto something, and while I didn't know of any priceless paintings in Tamworth I could stick myself too, I did know something else of great value… *my employers' petty cash box.*

At the time, I was working at a local frozen foods factory, filling pasties with liquified potato and cheese. It was a role I adored and had been passionate about ever since the nash insisted I take it or have my cheques cut off. For me, it wasn't a job so much as a *calling.*

As luck would have it, our general manager, Mr Bullock was retiring that day, and the entire factory had gathered in the warehouse for a few farewell drinks. Wanting my protest to have the maximum reach possible, I decided this would be the perfect occasion for my latest climate stunt.

So, while baldy Bollock was making a speech, I snuck into the company office and located the petty cash box. Inside were three twenties, a ten, two fives and handful of shrapnel. The total must have been close to *ninety quid.* As soon as I glued myself to this priceless artefact, I thought, the resulting viral 'selfie' would have every media outlet in the world discussing climate change.

However, I realised that in my excitement to save the earth, I had forgotten to bring any glue, so I headed straight to the office stationery cupboard. As I was grabbing some Bostik, a few dozen other stationery supplies accidentally fell into my rucksack. But since I still

needed to make some banners and things I decided to hang onto them.

But before I could smear my hands with the glue and perform the stunt, the office door opened and one of the security guards was suddenly standing over me. He took one look at my rucksack full of stationery, and my hand grasping the cash box, and jumped to the wrong conclusion.

I tried to explain that I was conducting a mass-media demonstration against the UK government's new and ongoing fossil fuel deals, but he simply wouldn't listen.

I was sacked on the spot and hurled unceremoniously out of the building. And as sure as night follows day, Noreen threw a fit when she found out. Before I knew it – Wallop! I was back in the doghouse again.

Still, as I pulled out the sofa bed in the spare room that night, I felt proud (again). Proud that I had selflessly sacrificed my own career for the lives of others. Yet at the same time I also felt inconsolably sad (again). Sad that my sour-faced other half clearly couldn't give two shits about the entire population of the planet. "

NAKED AMBITION

Carnegie tried his best to copy his wife's total lack of concern for the Earth's 7.7 billion inhabitants. But unlike her, he had a functioning moral compass. Like a modern-day, Tamworth-based Martin Luther King, he felt compelled to keep fighting the good fight.

" One night I watched a harrowing documentary about industrial beef farms." sighs so-sensitive Carnegie. "Not only do these dreadful places pollute our air, water and land, but they also

Road to ruin: Vestibule's selfless night-time roadblock elicited a compassion bypass from wife.

Warned leatherette: Carnegie's leather shop strip protest bagged him an ankle tag.

> " I watched a harrowing documentary about industrial beef farms. I was so disgusted I couldn't finish my Fray Bentos steak pudding. "

treat the poor cows horribly. I was so disgusted I couldn't finish my Fray Bentos steak pudding. I had to have cheese on toast instead. In fact, the whole experience made me *doubly* glad I'd gone vegan a few decades back.

Anyroad, during a browse of the Internet afterwards, I found some pictures of young women from the charity PETA who were protesting against animal cruelty by demonstrating *in the nude.* They stood outside shops that sold animal products, completely Billy Bollocks, holding signs saying 'I'd rather go naked than wear fur.' I was so excited by the photos that I kept looking at them all week – sometimes three or four times a night. I eventually decided that a hard-hitting 'nude protest' would form the basis of my next environmental campaign.

There's a shop in the retail park that openly flogs leather and fur goods at discounted prices, so I chose that as the site for my flash protest.

I decided I needed a spot of 'Dutch courage' if I was going to appear fully nude in a crowded public space, so I had a couple of glasses of wine, beer, gin, cider and methylated spirits in a pub across from the shop to settle my nerves. And then, with a steely commitment to save the planet coursing through my veins, I headed straight out.

Arriving at the leather goods store, I took a deep breath and promptly undid my trousers. I had decided not to go completely nude, as it was December and I was worried about getting a chill, so I simply pulled my undercrackers down to my knees.

I stood purposefully making my point in front of the customers in the window, just as I'd seen the PETA girls do in those photos. As I heard horrified shrieks and the flash of cameras, I knew my protest was having the

desired effect. After this outrageous stunt, **EVERYONE** would be talking about the brutal cruelty of the fur trade. Within seconds, I was wrestled to the ground by security guards, but I couldn't help grinning. I had done it: I had changed the world.

Or had I?

Unfortunately, as I was pulled to my feet, I realised I'd got my locations muddled. The leather shop I was thinking of was actually on the other side of town and instead I had bared my fruit bowl in front of an all-female yoga class. To make matters worse, one of the women in the class was Noreen's sister, Barbara, who's always had it in for me ever since I light-heartedly goosed her arse on her wedding day.

The whole thing was a simple mix-up that could have happened to anyone. Barbara had made sure the news got back to Noreen quicker than shit off a shovel. Nevertheless I was confident that my other half would have a good old laugh about it, before commending me for my latest piece of climate bravery.

But my confidence was misplaced.

When Noreen found out what had happened, she immediately filed for divorce – slinging all my clothes out on the front lawn. And to rub salt in the wound, I was placed on the sex offenders register again the very next day. *And for what?* For caring about my planet and the wonderful creatures that inhabit it.

Still, as I had my ankle tag fitted later that week, I felt proud (for the third time). Proud that I had bared my body and soul for the good of every creature great or small. At the same time, though, I felt inconsolably sad (again, third time). Sad because my harpie of an ex-missus would rather see the whole planet go up in flames than give Muggins here the benefit of the fucking doubt. The cow. "

NEXT WEEK: *Carnegie stages a protest against single-use plastics at Spearmint Rhino before being beaten and marched to a cashpoint by security staff.*

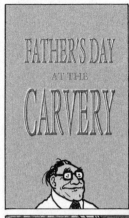

FATHER'S DAY AT THE CARVERY

Now it's one visit to the carvery, so you've got to make it count.

Yes, dad... I think I'll have the beef.

No, son... do that and you'll only get two slices.

If you ask for a *slice of each*, you'll get beef, pork and turkey. Three in total.

Right... let me show you how to do the veg.

Beef, please.

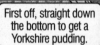

First off, straight down the bottom to get a Yorkshire pudding.

They put it at the end deliberately, but I know their game.

Now, you use the Yorkshire as a receptacle for your peas...

...that stops them spilling out and taking up plate area.

Two spoons of mash, one on top of the other, not side by side. That halves the mashed potato footprint.

Now push your carrots into your mash like sausages in a cartoon. Works with parsnips too.

It doesn't look very attractive, but it all goes down the same hole.

Cauliflower cheese right in the centre, but it fast starts to spread... time is your enemy with cauliflower cheese.

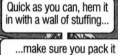

Quick as you can, hem it in with a wall of stuffing...

...make sure you pack it down so as it don't give way.

Roasties - they're dry. They go in your back pocket.

No point wasting plate space with something that can go in your pocket.

Now your sprouts on the other side of the stuffing wall...

...drain them proper or the sprout water will seep under your stuffing wall and compromise its integrity...

...believe me, son, I talk from experience.

And that leaves a space here for your sauces - cranberry, bread sauce, horseradish. Or all three if you're like me.

Bread sauce on the outside, son. It's thick and it'll make a dam to keep the other two on the plate.

Gravy right in the middle. As much as you like, son. It's going nowhere thanks to that stuffing wall.

Oooh! Nearly sat on me roasties there. Heh! Heh!

Right. Tuck in, lad.

Yeah! Happy Fathers' Day, Dad.

Two minutes later...

Oooh, that's me done. I'm stuffed.

You don't have so much of an appetite when you get to my age.

Eat up, son, and I'll show you how to work the puddings.

WESTMINSTER PORN WATCH

WE WERE all shocked when we heard that Neil Parish MP was caught watching pornography on his phone in the House of Commons. But should we have been? Were his actions those of a sick, exhibitionist pervert, or a man comfortable with his sexual needs and preferences? Have we not moved away from stuffy, Victorian attitudes which frowned upon watching and masturbating to pornography, or are these things we should still do in the privacy of our own homes? We went on the street to see what YOU thought…

TO MY MIND, the question that has to be asked is what were those lady MPs doing looking at Mr Parish's phone in the first place? Have they never heard of privacy?

Hamilton Dugong, Wells

I CAN'T SEE what he has done wrong. I watch pornographic material all the time at work and so do all my colleagues. Having said that, I am a 'home-grown' grumble-flick film-maker and editor, so it's not really a very good example.

Ben Dover, Sittingbourne

IT ALL DEPENDS on the nature of the grumble he was watching. If he was flicking through the underwear section of the Grattan catalogue website, then I think he has been unfairly treated. But if it was some vile bukkake film called *25-into-1 Will Go*, or some UK gangbang party flick where you can see it going in, then I think he did the honourable thing in resigning.

Torbjorn Frome, Leeds

IT'S 2022, for heaven's sake, not 1822! What a man does in the privacy of his own trousers is up to him. More power to his elbow, I say.

Colin Larva, Wells

IN 1975, I was caught reading a copy of *Penthouse* at the back of the class during maths, and I learned my lesson after being clipped round the ear by Mr Mitchell and sent to the headmaster. If Sir Lindsay Hoyle had similarly led Mr Parish out of the chamber by the ear and sent him to see Sir Graham Brady (Chairman of the 1922 Committee), perhaps it could have all been sorted out without him having to resign.

Lucien Balls, Derby

I ALWAYS cough when entering the spare room where my husband is watching his "tractor films", to give him a fair chance to flick it off the screen. If lady MPs did the same, coughing loudly when they entered the chamber, anyone watching such material could turn their phones off and there would be no problem.

Lucille Fivebells, Dover

FROM WHAT I understand, Mr Neil was watching a UK-made porn film involving tractors and buxom British ladies. Rather than being sanctioned, he should be congratulated for flying the flag for our world-beating home-grown bongo movie industry.

Hector Albian, Glossop

IT ALL DEPENDS on whether he had the sound up. If he did, then all the grunting and orgasmic moaning would have distracted any MP speaking at the time, which is a breach of parliamentary etiquette. If he was watching his scud on silent, I can't see what the problem is.

Toby Plimsols, Croydon

WATCHING PORN in the chamber would have rendered Mr Parish unable to do his job, as from what I gather, being an MP involves lots of standing up and sitting down again during debates. He couldn't do this properly if he was sporting a bone-on, and so would not be representing his constituents properly.

Octavia Septimus, Hexham

MPS ARE red-blooded males and so are never going to stop watching this sort of material, so the electorate should capitalise on the situation and make porn films including their own matters of concern in the script, and load them up on the net. For instance, they could make a DVDA film where one of the actors prefaces the sexual encounter by complaining about the potholes in local roads, or OAPs' problems parking near the shops. This will ensure that their grievances get heard by their parliamentary representative.

Brian Wainwright, Bury

SHAKIN' STEVENS'S REVISION TIPS

HI THERE, exam-sittin' rock'n'roll fans! Shakey here. As a touring musician, I know what it's like to get nervous. I often get nervous before a 'gig' – musician-speak for a concert – or if I'm doing an important interview with *Smash Hits* or Russell Harty. Don't laugh but, sometimes I get so nervous, I start *shakin'*! Hot dog!

But nothing *drives me cra-y-ay-y-zy* like exam nerves. And with A-Levels and GCSEs just around the corner, I thought I'd share my top revision tips for the main subjects so that when you sit down to take your tests, you'll pass them with flying colours. Just cut out my exam tips flashcards along the dotted lines and discreetly slip them in your back pocket or pencil case.

Maths

Maths is a complicated subject and one that can seem daunting at first, but there's an easy trick that makes sitting this exam child's play. Just remember the first sum you ever learned: 1 + 1 = 2. Then memorise a really large sum, for example 124 + 276 = 400. All the answers you'll need in your exam will probably fall between these two numbers. Simple! And if the answer is any higher (or lower) than either of these then leave a space for it and come back to the question at the end of the exam. If you're still stuck, just put any ole number down. You never know, you might get lucky!

Biology

Biology is all about animals and plants, so just remember that all animals need oxygen to survive (apart from *Henneguya salminicola* – but it's unlikely they'll test you on that) and that plants photosynthesise sunlight and stuff to make their food using chlorophyll – a special pigment that reflects green light. An easy way to remember the colour of chlorophyll is to sing my 1981 no. 1 hit single Green Door to yourself and stop when you get to the word "green".

Physics

Physics deals with all of the science stuff like movement, energy and electricity. When answering Physics questions, I always find it helpful to remember the equation for shakin' – where there's movement but no acceleration. This is $s = vt$, where s is the shakiness, v is the velocity or 'wildness' of the shake and t is the time spent shakin'. Providing a question comes up featuring this equation, the exam's in the bag! Something called Hooke's Law might come up but you can look this up on Google.

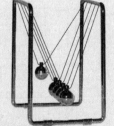

English

English is the study of books, like Shakespeare (or Shakey 2, as I like to call him!), Dickens and many, many more. So the surefire way to get the top grades in this subject is to read all the books that you're meant to be studying at some point before the exam. Then, when it's time to turn the paper over, write down all of the stuff you've read in the spaces provided. You've only got a couple of hours, so the faster and smaller you write – the more you'll score. A-Wha-Oh! Easy

History

History concerns old things, like the Ole House that I sang about back in 1981. Obviously it's nigh on impossible to memorise everything that's ever happened but, if you can, it will stand you in good stead for answering all of your other exams, since everything you need to know for them will be covered by it. However, if you've left it until the evening before the exam to start your History revision and you're cramming, then this simple timeline of key events will give you a fighting chance on the day:

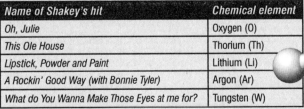

millions of years ago — Present Day

Dinosaurs — Cavemen Times — Romans — King Henry VIII — Shakin' Stevens Releases *Marie, Marie* — The Internet

Chemisty

Unlike Biology and Physics, Chemistry exams are notoriously tricky because the rules of Chemistry have so many exceptions to them. But nailing the symbols for the various chemical elements is easy if you remember the letters that start some of my hit songs. For instance…

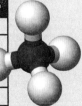

Name of Shakey's hit	Chemical element
Oh, Julie	Oxygen (O)
This Ole House	Thorium (Th)
Lipstick, Powder and Paint	Lithium (Li)
A Rockin' Good Way (with Bonnie Tyler)	Argon (Ar)
What do You Wanna Make Those Eyes at me for?	Tungsten (W)

Over the years I've made 20 studio albums, 23 compilation albums and had sixty-nine hit singles, so there are probably plenty of songs I've done to help you memorise the entire periodic table.

That's all my exam tips for this year. *Shakin' good luck!*
xx Shakey

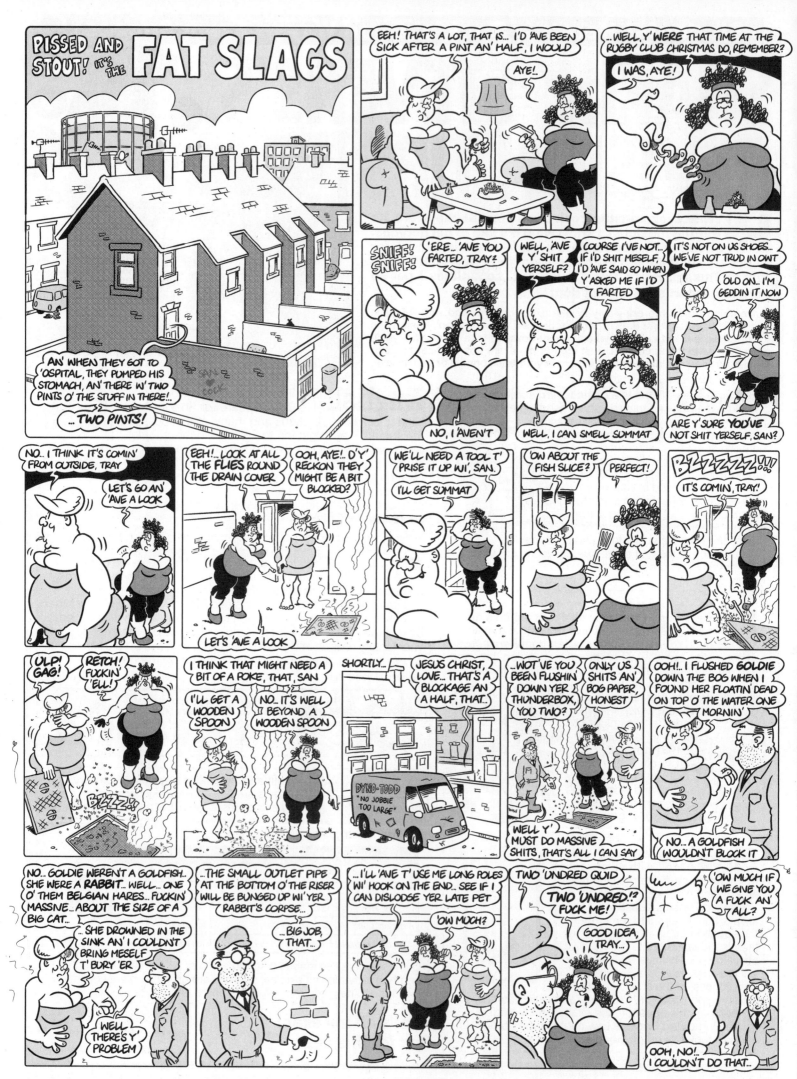

219

Recreate the holidays of your past with Simpler Times cruises

THE MOMENT you board our flagship old-fashioned cruise liner, *The Prince of Nostalgia*, you can relax in the knowledge that a Simpler Times cruise holiday is just that; a step back in time to when things were less complicated.

Every one of our 700 onboard cabins features:

- Push-button 19" CRT-screen colour TV with the colour and volume turned up full whack, with 3 channels showing unedited repeats of all your favourite old TV shows, with all *those* bits still in place – just as you remember them – before *they* tried to ban them.

- Proper sheets and blankets – none of those new-fangled duvets. A guaranteed itchy night.

- A copy of the Daily Mail and a pint of unsterilised, full-fat cow's milk left outside your cabin door every day.

There's no WiFi coverage anywhere on board, so your children will just have to find something else to do before you find something for them on our sun-deck, whether it's playing British Bulldog, riding a bicycle without a helmet like we used to in the good old days and it never did us any harm, or simply kicking seven shades of character-forming shit out of each other.

Smoking is permitted in all areas of the ship. And your every need will be taken care of by our 500 crew members, none of whom will go running to the police if you playfully nip their bottom as they serve your drinks.

And the cuisine has to be seen to be believed. Our world-class chefs will prepare you tomato soup, meat and two veg, followed by tinned fruit and condensed milk – *every night!* With no vegetarian or 'vegan' options available!

After dinner you'll enjoy a dazzling show of straight-forward, old-fashioned entertainment in the onboard Commodore Theatre with singing, dancing, and comedians who they simply wouldn't allow on television these days.

Please note, all onboard shops, facilities and entertainment rooms will be closed all day Sunday and Wednesday afternoons.

Everything was so much better in the old days when I still had all my life in front of me. You could say things back then that you wouldn't be allowed to say any more, and nobody minded. A Simpler Times Cruise is a nostalgic trip back to those less tolerant – and therefore better – times, when milk came in a glass bottle and other things were also the case.
Margery Conniption, Leicester

Full details of all the Simpler Times cruise holidays are in our new brochure, which you can get from all good travel agents or, if you'd prefer, send this coupon and 20 Green Shield stamps to the following address:
Simpler Times Cruises, PO Box 1, Portsmouth.

Name: ....

Address: ....

.... ☎ ....

....

Simpler Times operate a 'no cancellation' policy on all cruises.

Travel Tom-morrow's World Today with
Tom Cruises

*image for illustrative purposes only. Actual cruise may feature less-desirable Toms.

Why take an ordinary cruise, when you can take a *Tom Cruise*? All our cruise ships are crammed full, port-to-starboard, with top-notch Toms.

Imagine starting your day with breakfast next to **Tom Jones**, followed by a by a game of quoits with **Tom Kerridge**, diving off the top board next to **Tom Baker** and then an evening of glitzy Las Vegas-style magic with magicians '**Daley and Selleck**'?

This is just a sample of the kind of day you may experience on a *Tom Cruises* cruise, where you'll mingle amongst the cream of celebrity Toms* and build enough Tom-based memories to last a lifetime.

There are cruises... and then there are Tom Cruises!

phone now on ☎
018-118-055

*Due to the complex probability-based operational strategy that Tom Cruises employ, the celebrity and number of Toms may vary on a cruise-by-cruise basis. Actual line-up of Toms will only be revealed at moment of departure. Money-back guarantee only covers rare instances where no other passenger is called Tom. 5% discount available for customers whose own name is Tom.

NORWEGIAN FJORD CAT VIDEO CRUISES

What better way to enjoy the breathtaking scenery of the Norwegian fjords, than from behind a smartphone screen showing a collection of *hilarious* internet cat videos?

All our cruises come with high-speed WiFi access to the latest cat videos and 'memes' to ensure that from the moment you step onboard one of our fleet to the moment you leave, you'll be glued to your screen, watching videos of other people's cats' antics, while the breathtaking natural wonders of Norway pass you by in the background.

The Original Norwegian Fjord Cat Video Cruise Company Ltd
Visit us online at: smartphonecruises.com/videos/animals/domestic/mammal/cat

---

ECOWARRIOR CRUISES

PRICES FROM £5,000,000

Arrive in style in your own personal helicopter, while our luxury 240,000-ton cruise ship, Green Queen idles quietly in port. Then relax in one of your 2 allocated deluxe, air-conditioned cabins before venturing out on to our all-weather underfloor-heated sundeck.

Choose either a three- or six-month cruise, safe in the knowledge that for every Ecowarrior cruise we sell, we plant a tree to offset the carbon footprint of the electricity you used when you logged in to make your booking.

ECOWARRIORCRUISES.COM

FOR GOD'S SAKE!

VISIT OUR SANTA'S GROTTO 2PM

WHEN EVEN THE SANTAS ARE AT IT, YOU KNOW IT'S ALL GONE TOO FAR!

IF YOU'RE NOT SATISFIED WITH YOUR WAGE, GET ANOTHER BLOODY JOB!

DON'T STRUT AROUND FLEXING YOUR MARXIST MUSCLES AND HOLDING EVERYBODY ELSE TO RANSOM!

I REMEMBER YOUR LOT IN THE 1970S. YOU TRIED TO BRING THE COUNTRY TO ITS KNEES.

BUT YOU MET YOUR MATCH IN MRS THATCHER, DIDN'T YOU?

WELL I AM GOING TO WALK INTO THIS SHOP AND OFFER TO STAND IN AS THE STORE SANTA, WHILE YOU LOT ARE PLAYING SILLY BUGGERS.

IF YOU WANT TO PELT ME WITH BRICKS AND CALL ME "SCAB", YOU ARE WELCOME TO TRY.

NO, I DIDN'T THINK SO.

OWN'S STO

TYPICAL TRADE UNION BULLY BOYS, ALL BLUFF AND BLUSTER.

Well I never. Maybe he *does* know climate change is a load of old *codswallop* after all...

I stand by that charge of *woke* though. Not once heard him blast Markle.

2:59pm

It's on in a minute.

No thanks.

I've tracked down the best of Enoch Powell on UberTube.

3pm

It's starting.

gnnnnnn

The whip-hand over the white man!

3:14pm

Long to-oo reign ooover us – *on your feet woman!*

IT SAYS HERE YOU'RE GOING TO PLAY THE *INNKEEPER* WHO GRANTS JOSEPH AND MARY SHELTER IN HIS STABLE.

LET'S 'AVE A LOOK. I MIGHT MAKE A FEW CHANGES TO THIS SCRIPT.

XMAS EVE...

...MARY, THERE IS NO ROOM AT THE INN, BUT YONDER IS A LOWLY STABLE WITH A MANGER FOR A BED...

WOAH! WOAH! WOAH! WHERE THE FUCK DO YOU TWO THINK YOU'RE GOING?

...ERM...INTO YOUR LOWLY STABLE?

NOT WITH THEM FUCKING SANDALS ON, YOU'RE NOT, PAL...

...AND THAT DONKEY'S CASUAL AN' ALL.

RATS' COCKS! I WISHED FOR PERCY PIGS, NOT THIRSTY PIGS! THAT WISHBONE MUST HAVE BEEN DEFECTIVE!

WHAT THE EFF... YES, EFF... AM I GOING TO DO WITH THESE?

SUDDENLY...

EXCUSE ME... I'M AN ECCENTRIC INVENTOR, AND I'VE JUST CRE-ATED THE WORLD'S FIRST SOFT DRINK FOR PIGS... AND THESE THIRSTY PORKERS ARE JUST WHAT I'M LOOKING FOR TO TEST MY PRODUCT

OH!?

I'M ALSO A MILLIONAIRE, AND I'LL GIVE YOU THIS BIG BAG OF CASH IF I CAN TAKE THE LOT

FUCKING YOINKS!

BOXING DAY...

HEH! HEH! I USED ALL THAT MONEY TO BUY THE PERCY PIG FACTORY... AND A SEXY TROPHY WIFE WITH GREAT BIG FAKE KNOCKERS!

ANOTHER BOWL OF PERCY PIGS BEFORE YOUR NEXT BLOWJOB, SPAWNSWORTH?

MERRY CHRISTMAS READERS!

READER'S VOICE →

YOU SPAWNY GET!

FREE VALENTINE'S A
IN 80* ALL-NIGH

WE WERE all captivated by the recent TV adaptation of Jules Verne's classic adventure tale *Around the World in 80 Days*, where Phileas Fogg (played by Doctor Who) makes a wager that he can circumnavigate the globe in just 80 days. In this exciting **FREE** game, we continue the story after triumphant Fogg returns to the Reform Club in London and – realising that he's forgotten to pick up something for his beloved for Valentine's Day – rushes off to find her a last-minute present. Discovering in horror that the all-night Texaco on Pall Mall has sold out of flowers, Phileas, together with his faithful companions Passepartout and Abigail, jumps in a hot-air balloon for his most epic journey yet – *to try and find a better stocked late night petrol station for the perfect romantic Valentine's Day gift!*

HOW TO PLAY

The object of the game is for each player to circumnavigate the map of the world, visiting all the service stations en route in search of a romantic gift. To move, simply roll the special ballooning dice and move the displayed number of places, following any instruction given on the square you land on. If the dice lands on the picture of a balloon, this counts as 'six'.

The winner is the first to land on the finish square and deliver the gifts.

INSTRUCTIONS

Cut out the four Phileas Fogg *Dr Who* players above and fold them to create a base *(fig. 1)*. Cut out your special ballooning dice, folding along the dotted lines and sticking at the tabs *(fig. 2)*. Then place the balloons on the Reform Club square and you're ready to play!

fig. 1

fig. 2

28. DENVER The BP garage on the corner of Lincoln and 19th has red roses wrapped in cellophane, but they want eight quid a bunch for them. *EIGHT FUCKING QUID!* You press on to see if you can find them cheaper somewhere else. *Miss a turn.*

30. CHICAGO You spot a lovely bunch of Irises for $2 on the forecourt of a Shell petrol station, but a gale blowing in 'The Windy City' means you are unable to land. *Move back 3.*

31

29

27

32. NEW YORK CITY You pick up a bunch of acceptable chrysanthemums from an all-night Texaco station on Broadway, but you accidentally drop them in the Hudson river whilst leaning out of your balloon to take a photo of the Statue of Liberty. *Miss a turn.*

26. SAN FRANCISCO *You pilot the balloon to the nearest Amoco forecourt and, although there are no flowers, they've got a three-for-one offer on dashboard fans which you fit to the side of the balloon and use to propel yourself forward 3 spaces.*

25

33

24. SHANGHAI In the absence of any flowers, you buy an AA road map of Jiangsu and the surrounding area from The Gulf station at the port. But Abigail suggests that this will not be interpreted by your fiancée as a particularly romantic gesture. *Miss a turn.*

21

20. SINGAPORE Using a telescope, Passepartout spots huge petrol queues from the air and advises you to carry on, lest you lose any more time. *Move forward 2.*

22. HONG KONG You drop down next to the ASDA all-night garage and pick up a couple of boxes of Miniature Heroes as a default gift for your fiancée. However, the three of you eat all of them except the Eclairs within ten minutes of buying them. *Miss a turn.*

23

19

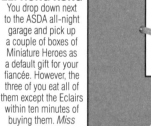